Radiant Health, Inner Wealth

A Fun, Comprehensive Toolkit for Ultimate Wellness, Including Over 240 Scrumptious Recipes!

QUINTESSENCE C. CHALLIS

QUINTESSENTIAL HEALTH PUBLISHING
P.O. BOX 1784
PAGOSA SPRINGS, CO 81147
WWW.RADIANTHEALTH-INNERWEALTH.COM

TO ORDER BOOKS OR FOR MORE INFORMATION,
PLEASE VISIT:

WWW.RADIANTHEALTH-INNERWEALTH.COM

Food photographs by Michelle McCluggage and Olga Vasiljeva

The information in this book is based on the personal experience of the author, and that of her clients. It is not intended as a substitute for medical advice. Please consult a knowledgeable health-care practitioner if you have any specific health issues or concerns, and before beginning this or any other health program.

Published by Quintessential Health Publishing
P.O. Box 1784
Pagosa Springs, CO 81147
www.radianthealth-innerwealth.com

Printed in the United States of America
Second edition 2009 (first edition published in 2008)

Design by Quintessence Challis
Food photograph front cover: Thai Tofu & Tropical Fruit Salad (by Michelle McCluggage)
Food photographs back cover: Luscious Lemon Bars with Ginger Shortbread Crust, Rosemary Herb Pizza Crust, and Three Citrus Asparagus
(Cover photo of author by Jeff Laydon; hair styling by Reta Jarvie)

ISBN# 978-0-615-25439-5

TO ORDER ONE OR MORE BOOKS OR FOR MORE INFORMATION,

PLEASE VISIT:

WWW.RADIANTHEALTH-INNERWEALTH.COM

In Gratitude

I am greatly aware that there are many people who have made this book possible. First of all, I would like to thank my mother, Kathryn Barnes, who was my first natural foods teacher. She taught me how to bake bread, create an organic garden, compost, and use whole foods. She has also been just about my biggest supporter as a cook and writer. Thanks also to my uncle, Mark Challis, for being a role model of lifelong vegetarianism (and excellent health). My grandma, Patricia Challis, also deserves many thanks for helping me through college, where I began to study holistic health and nutrition. I thank her also for being my farmer's market buddy, and for all of her love and support as well.

I would also like to thank Dale M. Fuller (Bulleh Shah) for first suggesting I write this book over ten years ago, and for his wonderful support in so many ways. Thanks also to N. Ross for her encouragement and support in countless ways.

Thanks so much to Sheila Barrows, an expert editor, for her gift of editing several of the chapters in this book. I can't imagine what I would have done without her help! Also, thanks to Barbara Kennedy for so eloquently sharing her experience of overcoming allergies. Thanks also to Christina Knoell, C. Booth, and Natalie Carpenter for their kind assistance to a computer-challenged writer!

I also owe a debt of gratitude to the wonderful recipe testers. Because of their feedback, this book is so much better than it would have been otherwise. Many thanks to Jeananne Libbert, Peg Graham, Christina Knoell, Lizz Baldwin, Chuck Watkins, Erica Hunter, Amy Hoffer, Allison Nordahl, Tiffany Theden, Tess Cysz, Holly Reed, Amy Biar, and Michelle McCluggage.

And finally, extra special thanks are due to Michelle McCluggage and Olga Vasiljeva for their beautiful photographs in this second edition. It was a genuinely thrilling pleasure to replace almost every one of my photos with theirs!

Thanks so much. I love you guys!

Table of Contents

Introduction

What if you could live a life of perfect radiant health while still loving every bite of food you put into your mouth? What if you could enjoy a continuous state of inner wealth (tranquility, joy, fulfillment, and harmony) just by incorporating a few easy habits into your daily life? The basic message I wish to share is that you *can* have it all! We are beings of immense potential and are capable of all of this and more.

This book contains a variety of tools that you can use to create radiant health and inner wealth for yourself. However, since everyone is different, you may wish to look at these suggestions and recipes as if they were a buffet. Some of you will want to use this book solely as a nutrition guide and/or cookbook. Others may find the toolkit of suggestions in chapter two to be exactly what you were looking for. I suggest that you take and enjoy the things that speak to you and merely set aside the things that don't.

If you do decide that you're interested in going for the whole package (radiant health *and* inner wealth), then right on! The good life truly is more achievable than most of us realize. For example, there are really only five main concepts throughout this book and they all begin with the letter *E*. The five *E*s are as follows: eat reasonably, eat less, exercise regularly, emphasize the good stuff, and elevate your consciousness.

How exactly do these five *E*s work? Well, to start with, eating reasonably means that we are eating in balance and making conscious, sensible choices. For example, it's fine to eat a delicious "green" or "blue" dessert from this book after a light and healthy dinner, but not three pieces of cholesterol-laden pie after a huge meal! It means listening to that wise inner voice within us that is never wrong.

By eating less, I mean that we should be eating *just* enough to satisfy our physical hunger, as this is a huge part of claiming our natural state of radiant health. Tuning into the hunger and fullness gauge (on page 13) is a great way to start. Exercising regularly is rather self-explanatory, although the section in chapter two may help you find renewed enthusiasm and inspiration in that department.

Emphasizing the good stuff means that we are prioritizing things like vegetables, beans, and whole grains in our diets. The color-coded recipe system in this book (as explained on page 45) will make it easy for you to prioritize the most health-supporting foods. Simply by emphasizing the good stuff, our taste buds naturally adjust so that we crave (and enjoy) truly healthy foods. Plus, when we eat the most nutritious foods first, we automatically have less room for everything else.

Finally, elevating your consciousness means making a daily effort not only toward creating a healthier body but also toward realizing greater and greater wellness *within*. Elevating your consciousness is about changing the way you think so that you can align with your highest self and live in a state of inner wealth. Many of the tools in chapter two (such as meditation, visualization, and affirmations) can assist you with this process so that you can enjoy a beautiful life on *all* levels!

However you choose to use this book, I want to thank you very much for reading it! I wish you fulfillment and many blessings on your path to greater health and inner wealth.

Chapter One: Holistic Health and Optimal Nutrition

What exactly *is* holistic health? Simply put, it refers to a persons state of health on multiple levels—physical, emotional, mental, and spiritual. When you are living in a holistically healthy way, you are taking care of your physical body by eating consciously and exercising. You are also fulfilling your emotional and spiritual needs in a way that feels right for you. People who neglect their inner selves and focus only on how their bodies look cannot be said to reflect holistic health. Finally, it means knowing that our experiences and states of well-being come not only from what we eat but how we choose to think.

For myself, holistic health means being at the weight I feel best at, rather than what media images promote. It means that I am feeling balanced by taking care of my spiritual, emotional, and physical needs. It means I'm in a general state of thinking positively about myself and my life, and choosing to feel gratitude for every experience.

Many people may be thinking, "That all sounds fine and fancy, but I live in the real world. I have kids, a job, and loads of responsibilities. How can I possibly find the time to take care of all my needs?" Believe me, I understand. A few years ago, I was a single mom, working a fifty-hour a week job and spending another twenty hours a week building our house. I can't say that I remained totally focused on my holistic needs during that time, because I didn't. However, I did find some small ways to still care for myself. I started taking walks and meditating during my lunch breaks (the only time I had to myself in those days). I kept fruits and veggies in the fridge at work so that I could eat well on the run. I had to make the best of the time I did have, since I knew how important it was to retain some sense of balance. As any mother knows, there is not much left to give to our children when we ourselves are feeling depleted. We can all share much more with all of those in our lives when we first take loving care of ourselves.

Holistic health means refining our daily habits that create our circumstances. It means choosing life-giving foods to nourish our bodies and using the tools in this book to nourish our inner selves. We are the sum total of the choices we make, so let's make them count! Why not? We are, without a doubt, worth it.

Common Questions Addressed

Despite the emphasis in this book on holistic health, I still firmly believe that *what* we eat matters greatly, so the question arises: "What makes up a truly healthy diet?"

There is so much controversy and difference of opinion on this subject that it is hard to define exactly. However, we do know that despite our affluence, Americans are some of the unhealthiest people in the world. Obesity is an epidemic, and much of our society thinks of medications as a normal part of life. True, we do not generally suffer from diseases due to lack of hygiene and scarcity of food. But we do suffer greatly from the excesses we consume, including excesses of food in general, processed foods, and animal products.

Is it part of nature's perfect plan to become sick and unhealthy with age? My answer is very simple. We are intelligently and lovingly made, and we are intended to live a life of good health and well-being. The more often we choose a higher way of eating and living, the more we will align with our *natural* state of radiant health.

> ## "THIS IS STARTING TO SOUND LIKE ONE OF THOSE VEGAN BOOKS, AND I COULD NEVER BE A VEGAN. WHAT DO YOU HAVE TO SAY FOR YOURSELF, YOUNG LADY?"

Yes, I admit it. I firmly believe (and have experienced) that the benefits of giving up animal foods are enormous. Our health improves, our bodies look better, and a whole new world of delicious cuisine opens up. I can honestly say that I have enjoyed food far more as a vegan than I ever did as a meat eater (or as an ovo-lacto vegetarian). It only takes practice and patience to adjust our palates and lifestyles. However, I am also realistic enough to know that not everyone is destined to eat a vegan diet. People are different and have different circumstances. Therefore, I recommend keeping an open mind and trying things out for yourself. This is *not* an all-or-nothing proposition! The more you live a healthy lifestyle (and eliminate foods and habits that no longer serve you), the more benefits you will enjoy. Just go at your own pace and have fun!

> ## "ISN'T FISH A HEALTH FOOD?"

Many people are turning to fish these days as a result of all of the hype over Omega-3 fatty acids. True, these essential fats are important nutrients that every body needs. However, they are also found in many plant sources such as ground flax, walnuts, algae, and ground hemp seed (to name just a few).

In addition, plant-based sources of Omega-3s are also considered much safer. For example, although salmon has been considered a top source of this nutrient, even the most prominent physicians have questioned its safety levels. Dr. Mehmet Oz, the well-respected doctor who frequents the Oprah Winfrey show, has come up with a great solution. He suggests that we instead turn to the source (what the salmon themselves eat) to avoid issues of over-fishing and rising mercury levels. Salmon eat spirulena algae, which has valuable DHA Omega-3s, says Dr. Oz. "You can grow algae pretty easily, and it's a much more efficient way of getting it (than from the salmon)."[1]

Another highly respected physician who is extremely well studied in the area of nutrition is best-selling author, Dr. John McDougall. He states that fish is high in fat and cholesterol, highly contaminated with environmental chemicals, and therefore not a health food by any means. As with all animal products, fish contains cholesterol, excess protein, and absolutely no fiber.[2]

> ## "WHAT ABOUT THE FOUR FOOD GROUPS?"

Although this is perhaps less significant to those who grew up with the food pyramid, in the past, many (including me) took the four food groups as a fact. I was shocked when I found out, many years later, that this colorfully presented "scientific fact" was actually an advertising tool presented by the National Dairy Council, along with other industrial interest businesses.[3] When I began to find out that so much of what I had been taught about nutrition was actually advertisement, it was a revelation. I began studying genuine scientific information and was amazed to find out what truly represented a proper diet. Needless to say, it wasn't the stuff that advertising budgets were made of. Money plays a huge part in our society, and often the people who have lots of it have the most highly visible products. Those without the grand capital (such as the fruit and vegetable industries, the kale people, me...) are not pushing their products on such a grand scale.

> ## "HOW WILL I GET ENOUGH CALCIUM IF I DON'T EAT DAIRY PRODUCTS? WHY WOULD ALL OF THOSE CELEBRITIES SPORT A MILK MOUSTACHE IF IT DIDN'T REFLECT THE TRUTH?"

It's interesting to note that the societies who have the highest rates of osteoporosis are those who consume the most animal products. In societies that consume little or no dairy products, this disease (wrongly linked to inadequate calcium intake) is practically unheard of. Dr. John McDougall states, "Osteoporosis is not a disease that results from too little calcium, but rather primarily from too much animal protein animal food derived acids that rob the body of calcium and structural materials, and thus weaken bones."[4] In other words, the less animal protein we consume, the less calcium we need. The Dairy Council is one of the largest businesses in the United States, with quite the budget for advertising. Again, before you take something as a fact, make sure it is not funded by a special interest business.

It should also be noted that many plant foods contain loads of calcium. Sesame, tofu, kale, and other greens are just a few examples of foods that contain very high levels of calcium. Plus, this kind can be properly absorbed, unlike dairy products that can rob the body of calcium (because of their high levels of animal protein) while they supply it.

Finally, consider this: If you believe that we live in an intelligently designed universe, how would cow's milk originally have been intended? Perhaps to feed a *baby* cow? Mother's milk is as natural as it gets, and contains the ideal amount of nutrients, fat, calories, and protein for the nursing mother's growing child. Milk is absolutely the perfect food, but it is intended for the baby of *that mother's* species. Cow's milk is perfect for baby cows, just as human mother's milk is perfect for human babies.

"HOW WILL I GET ENOUGH IRON IF I EAT A PREDOMINANTLY VEGAN DIET?"

I hear this question very often. In my own life, I went from being borderline anemic (as an ovo-lacto vegetarian) to having high levels of iron when I gave up dairy products eighteen years ago. This makes perfect sense when we note that meat is high in iron while dairy products contain absolutely no iron. Therefore, it's common for people to experience a drop in iron levels when they give up meat and begin eating lots of dairy. However, when the iron-free dairy foods are dropped, it becomes very easy to get plenty of iron. Plant-based foods are naturally iron rich—especially beans, greens, tofu, sesame seeds, and pumpkin seeds (to name a few). In fact, the only supplement I'd even *consider* on a healthy vegan diet is vitamin B-12, and even that is stored in the body for long periods of time. However, taking an occasional B-12 supplement is a good safety precaution for *anyone*, whether long-time vegan or all-time meat eater.

"DON'T I NEED TO COMBINE FOODS TO ENSURE I AM GETTING ENOUGH PROTEIN?"

The best-selling book "Diet For a Small Planet" popularized this idea in 1971. People then began talking about how vegetarianism *could* be safe, as long as you combined your proteins and starches. However, after further research, the author (Frances Moore Lappé) bravely printed a retraction in her 1981 version of the book, stating that plant foods do *not* need to be combined! Unfortunately, many people still hang on to the original notion today, despite the fact that plant foods contain sufficient proteins for a healthy, adequate human diet. In fact, all plant foods contain protein—even celery and huckleberries.

On a personal note, after almost twenty years of being a vegetarian, I have never once intentionally combined proteins. And this has never caused me even an ounce of trouble (unless you count that one time in '97 when I was fighting off street gangs with nothing but a plate of beans).

"HOW WILL I GET ENOUGH PROTEIN IN GENERAL WITHOUT EATING ANY ANIMAL FOODS?"

The question we really should be asking is: "How can I make sure I don't eat too much protein, since excess proteins are so detrimental to my health?" Sad, but so true. People in our culture eat *waaaay* too much protein! Excess proteins can seriously damage our health, resulting in calcium loss, kidney damage, and liver damage.[5]

The World Health Organization has recommended that we get 5 percent of our calories from protein. *Five percent*! Even strawberries contain eight percent protein. Of course, if you are a pregnant woman, they do recommend you increase that amount to a whopping 6 percent. Our highest protein needs are during infancy, since babies grow and develop at warp speed. How much protein is in mother's milk? About 5 to 6.3 percent.[6]

As you can see, Americans are not in trouble because of insufficient protein intake, but rather because of an excessive protein overload. Once we reduce our protein intake (which happens naturally on a healthy plant-based diet), our bodies respond with greater health. Additionally, it should be mentioned that plant-based proteins are much more easily assimilated than those from animals, and therefore they are far less damaging when eaten in excess. However, if you were suffering from a disease due to excessive protein intake, the first thing to do would be to eliminate animal proteins. Next, emphasizing fruits, vegetables, and whole grains (with a moderate amount of concentrated vegetable proteins such as beans, nuts, and other legumes) would help your body restore itself to proper health.

Foods to Reduce or Eliminate

Unfortunately, many of the "foods" we should be avoiding are some of the most common ingredients in American cuisine these days! However, please don't let that intimidate you. When we begin transitioning to a natural, plant-based diet with an emphasis on fresh, whole foods, it becomes surprisingly easy to avoid these unhealthy items. Plus, the more we eliminate these foods from our diets, the less we crave them. Our bodies and taste buds readjust to healthy, whole foods and we learn that we *can* love food that loves us back! I have listed the unhealthy items in order here, with those at the top being the ones I recommend eliminating first. However, since everyone is different, lasting change will only happen if you use this list in a way that works for you. Only you know your strengths and weaknesses, and which "foods" you have the most attachments to. If you can't (or don't wish to) eliminate some of these now, just reduce them as much as possible. Every little bit counts. Do your best, and the rest will happen naturally!

•*MSG*: Monosodium glutamate is an ideal way to flavor your foods inexpensively. Unfortunately, you may have headaches and damage to your health as a result. Do yourself a favor and avoid foods that contain this toxin.

•*Meat and meat products*: Meat contains excess protein, absolutely no fiber, high levels of cholesterol (even chicken and fish), and an unappealing buffet of additional toxins. If you still have a "meat tooth," you may wish to try using meat analogues while you are working to eliminate meat from your diet. Almost any craving you have for meat can be replaced with a vegetarian substitute.

•*Aspartame*: This artificial sweetener found in diet sodas (amongst way too many other processed foods) has been linked to many side effects such as inability to concentrate, dizziness, and headaches. Oh, the diet soda stories I could tell...

•*Hydrogenated oils*: Originally developed as a cheaper alternative to candle wax, this stuff works like magic to increase the shelf life of processed foods. However, it's so toxic that some studies have shown that there are no acceptable levels for consuming this trans-fat. Some countries have even banned this product completely! Run far. Far far away.

•*Artificial colors, artificial flavors, and preservatives*: Learning to read labels and shopping in the natural foods aisle should help you make a habit of avoiding these bright and shiny (and completely unnecessary) detriments to your health.

•<u>*Dairy products (especially non-organic dairy and eggs)*</u>**:** As with meat, there are many delicious nondairy versions of our favorite items. Sour cream, butter, cream cheese, and more can all be easily be replaced with healthier animal-free versions.

•<u>*Unhealthy soy products*</u> that are marketed as health foods include soy oil (often cleverly marketed as "vegetable oil"), TVP (textured vegetable/soy protein), and isolated soy protein.[7] It is my belief that soy's recent bad rap is due to some of these products. Do you remember when soy was first discovered several years ago as being associated with all kinds of wonderful benefits? Next thing we knew, everything had to have soy in it! *"Wow, soy is so good for us, why don't we add it to everything? We can even alter its natural structure and isolate the soy proteins to make it easier and cheaper to mass produce!"* Well, after a while, we began to hear stories about how soy wasn't good for us after all, and many people began to develop soy allergies and aversions.

My contention is this: Soy, like any other natural plant food, is good for us. It is good for us when we eat it in moderation (versus having to eat soy-based *everything*) and in its natural state. Admittedly, I do call for dairy replacements in a handful of my recipes. However, I do not recommend making staples out of these processed foods by any means. But as I try to keep an eye on balance, they make acceptable substitutes from time to time as they are still free from animal products and are non-hydrogenated.

•<u>*Refined flours and grains (white rice, white flour, etc.)*</u>**:** These products contain very little fiber and are stripped of many of the nutrients (and dignity) that they contained in their whole state. Because of this, it is also easier to overeat when consuming refined foods as our bodies must eat more of them to feel full and properly nourished. Be aware that on many products, white flour is often referred to as "wheat flour." Look for labels that read *whole* wheat or 100% whole grain.

20 Superfoods to Emphasize for a Lifetime of Radiant Health!

These are the vitalizing foods that should be *emphasized* in our diets. Eat more of these. If that last bit about the "bad" foods stressed you out, here is something that may help: Instead of putting your energy into avoiding unhealthy foods, simply begin to focus on eating more of these vitalizing foods every day. By doing this, your body will quickly become healthier and more tuned to eating fresh, wholesome foods. You will *naturally* stop craving junk, and your taste buds will cooperate. Anyway, what is the point of having taste buds that are out of tune? Once you are rolling with foods that are both delectable *and* nourishing, a whole new world will open up, of eating the most delicious dishes while fulfilling your health wishes! (must…stop….rhyming…)

1. All vegetables are superfoods! However, if you are really looking for specifics, here are some of the most nutrient dense veggies: carrots, broccoli, cabbage, beets, kale (and other dark leafy greens), Brussels sprouts, and parsley. Have you ever noticed that the most nutrient-rich veggies are also the most densely colored ones?

2. Shiitake mushrooms: Shiitakes increase immune system function, are strengthening, and contain many B-vitamins. Not to mention the fun you can have mispronouncing their name.

3. Sprouts: When <u>anything</u> is sprouted, its nutritional levels become exponentially higher. Like, *crazy* high.

4. Chili peppers: A great source of vitamins C and A, chili peppers are medicinal, cleansing, and vitalizing. They are also linked to an increase in metabolism. Yeah!

5. Fresh ginger: Ginger is cleansing and aids digestion. It is also great for treating colds and motion sickness (and for boosting the immune system in general).

6. Fresh garlic: Great for increasing immune system function, garlic is also detoxifying and antibacterial. And delicious in everything. *Every*thing.

7. Fresh lemon: This lovely fruit is alkalinizing, cleansing, and detoxifying.

8. Nuts and seeds: These are rich in essential fats, Omega-3s, and many other nutrients. However, I do not recommend making them the *bulk* of your diet, as they are also very high in fat.

9. Kale: A highly strengthening vegetable, this superfood is high in iron, immune-boosting properties, calcium, and chlorophyll. Consider kale as evidence that we live in a benign universe.

10. Miso: This traditional Japanese paste is anti-carcinogenic, a digestive aid, and highly detoxifying. It is also just the thing to speed up recovery from any illness. Miso=love.

11. Sea vegetables (seaweed): "Ounce for ounce, seaweed is higher in vitamins and minerals than any other class of food," writes Rebecca Wood in her book, *The New Whole Foods Encyclopedia*.[8] She also states that it counteracts obesity and calls it a "beauty aid."

12. Berries: All fruits are superfoods, but berries are a standout. They are exceptionally high in fiber, bioflavonoids, and vitamins, while still managing to be low in calories.

13. Beans: I learned of their value firsthand when I lost forty pounds nine years ago. They are very high in fiber (and low in fat and calories), yet extremely filling. They are also high in phytonutrients, protein, vitamins, and minerals. I personally make it my mission to eat some form of these goody two-shoes every single day.

14. Quinoa: Pronounced keen-wah, this whole grain is energy giving and contains more calcium than cow's milk. It is also high in iron, protein, and vitamins.

15. Fiber rich foods: The most fiber rich foods include vegetables, fruits, beans, and whole grains. What exactly is so great about fiber? Dr. Oz states that it helps maintain a healthy, functioning system by moving "things through your system—including toxins—very quickly. Bile, when it gets absorbed through the bowel, turns into cholesterol. So when you take a lot of fiber in your diet you suck the bile out of you, and your cholesterol drops automatically. It also gets rid of sugar… and is a great tool if you want to lose weight because it makes you feel full."[9]

16. Fermented soy foods: These include such foods as tempeh, miso, and natto. When a food is fermented, it becomes one of your digestive system's best friends.

17. Barley: High in fiber and low in fat, this whole grain is easy to sprout and very nourishing.

18. Although not actually a food, purified water is essential to good health. It will keep your digestive system happy, your skin glowing, and your bowels moving. Moving on...

19. Fresh herbs such as basil and mint not only add a delicious element to our foods, they also contain loads of concentrated vitamins and minerals.

20. Amaranth: Amaranth is *freakishly* nutritious, strengthening, and vitalizing. It is "higher than milk in protein and calcium,"[10] states Rebecca Wood. It can be popped like popcorn or cooked and served as a savory grain dish or sweet breakfast cereal.

Why Organics?

The first time I considered switching to organic foods was in 1995. I even remember the exact moment! I was standing in my grandmother's kitchen preparing us each a glass of fresh carrot-apple juice using her juicer. I made the first batch with some non-organic produce and then proceeded to make the next batch with some organic produce I'd purchased on a whim. The color difference was shocking! When compared to the brilliant orange of the second glass, the first glass was remarkably pale in color. Naturally, the taste difference was pronounced as well. I had never been aware of such a "personal" difference before that and began to study up on organic foods. Needless to say, I have never gone back! To me, eating slightly more expensive organic foods is worth it. I consider them *my* brand of health insurance.

REFRESHING RESEARCH

Last year, the local health food store was passing out flyers on an organic foods study. At first, I figured it was the same kind of thing I had heard many times before—more reasons why conventional produce is so bad for us. But I was pleasantly surprised when I read the article. It was actually a *positive* motivation for once! Researchers at Rutgers University had purchased both non-organic and organic versions of the same fruits and vegetables at a supermarket. They then analyzed them to see how their nutritional profiles compared. The findings were absolutely amazing! Not only were the organic foods higher in minerals, but they were so by *huge percentages*! Here are just a few examples of their findings: [11]

•*Lettuce take this for example:* Inorganic lettuce was found to contain 16.0 millequivalents per 100 grams dry weight (mpg) of calcium while the organic contained 71.0 mpg. Inorganic lettuce contained 9 trace elements parts per million dry matter (tep) of iron while the organic version contained a whopping 516 tep!

•*Tomatoes:* While the inorganic tomatoes registered at 1 tep for iron, the organic tomatoes came in at 1938.0 tep of iron! Crazy stuff.

•*Spinach:* Our fine friend potassium is present in non-organic spinach in the amount of 84.6 mpg. In organic spinach, potassium registers at 237.0 mpg. Known for its high iron content, spinach (when grown conventionally) registers at 19 tep for iron. However, organic spinach came in at 1,584 tep! No, that's not a misprint. Kind of makes you want to eat organic to get the most out of your veggies, doesn't it?

TRANSITIONING TO ORGANIC FOODS

If switching to an exclusively organic diet overnight sounds intimidating, you may wish to begin by phasing out the foods that are the most contaminated. Plus, the following information also comes in handy when all of the produce on your shopping list isn't available organically.

Foods that should only be eaten if organic (most contaminated when non-organic): [12]
Apples, bell peppers, celery, cherries, grapes, nectarines, peaches, pears, potatoes, spinach, strawberries, green beans, tomatoes, lettuces, citrus zest, Mexican cantaloupe, and apricots. Notice a trend here that includes many thin-skinned fruits and veggies.

Foods that are the least contaminated when non-organic: [13]
Asparagus, avocados, broccoli, sweet corn, kiwi, mango, onions, papayas, pineapples, sweet peas, blueberries, Brussels sprouts, cabbage, eggplant, oranges, grapefruits, okra, plums, radishes, bananas, and watermelon. Notice that several of these "safer" non-organic items are tropical fruits.

WHAT'S *NOT* PRESENT IN ORGANIC FOODS?

If something is certified organic, you can be confident that it does <u>not</u> contain any of the following: GMOs (genetically modified organisms), herbicides and pesticides, sewage sludge, antibiotics, and ionizing radiation.[14]

CRACKING THE CODES

Here is a helpful tool for you to use at the grocery store when all of the employees are in the back.

•Conventional, non-organic produce usually has a four-digit number, beginning with the number four. *Example*: #4583
•Organic produce usually has a five-digit number, beginning with a nine. *Example*: #98645
•Genetically modified produce will typically begin with the number eight and have five numbers. *Example*: #87506

My Experiences with a Vegan Diet

When I remember my childhood, many things come to mind. A loving family, vacations, water slides, bologna sandwiches, diet sodas, and ice cream. I also cannot help but remember my endless cases of strep throat. In fact, I had strep throat so many times while I was growing up that I eventually developed an immunity to every antibiotic imaginable!

Now, I have no interest in boring you with excessive details, so let's skip ahead, oh, about ten years. During my freshman year in college, I unconsciously took my first step toward vegetarianism. I still remember the moment when I was standing in my dorm room, scanning over the foods on my shelf. I was trying to decide on a lunch item when the thought came to me, seemingly out of nowhere: "Why don't I give up red meat?" Since everything in my cupboard that contained red meat seemed unnecessary and I'd never really liked beef or pork that much anyway, I gave it a try. Aside from one isolated moment of weakness (involving, yes, Taco Bell), it was cake.

The following year, I began taking a philosophy class called "The Ethics of Animal Rights and the Environment." As time went by, I began to feel like a hypocrite. I could no longer rationalize eating the flesh of chickens and fish, no matter how much my palate seemed to like the tastes I was accustomed to. The students in the class who argued the case of eating meat used rationalizations like "it tastes good" and "what if plants scream too" but that just didn't fly with me. So, I decided to try giving up chicken and fish for two weeks. A month later, I realized that I had gone well over the two weeks and hadn't missed a thing. It probably helped that I was also falling in love with many of the new culinary avenues I had never known about before. I was also pleasantly surprised to find that my energy levels were so much better. As an omnivore, I had generally felt so tired after lunch that I could hardly stay awake during my next class. As a vegetarian, that feeling had left me completely. I was beginning to feel energized by food rather than depleted.

Several months later, I moved in with a vegan friend—someone I viewed as the picture of health. I was intrigued by her diet and began to really study scientific research on nutrition. I was surprised to find that eating plant-based foods represented a nutritionally complete and supremely nourishing diet. So I took the plunge and tried it. I relapsed with Cool Ranch Doritos (a big hit in 1991). I tried it again. In a month, I ate the Doritos again and found that somehow their flavor was no longer appealing.

Even more profound than the changes I experienced when I gave up meat were the changes I noticed when I gave up *all* animal products. My frequent colds went away. My strep throat saga ended once and for all, never to return (my last case began about four months before becoming vegan). Very noticeably, my acne cleared up as well. I had been very self-conscious about my skin ever since adolescence and had given up on finding a solution—despite all of the skin care products I tried and dermatologists I visited. However, to my utter surprise (and deep relief), my skin miraculously cleared up completely only weeks after switching to a plant-based diet.

Another interesting change I experienced was that my iron levels went up significantly. As an ovo-lacto vegetarian (one who consumes eggs and dairy), I was borderline anemic. This is because I had replaced meats (which are rich in iron) with dairy foods (which have no iron). However, after a short time on a vegan diet, I was pleased to find that my iron levels were at the high end of the normal range. Additionally, although I have never taken calcium supplements or vitamins since becoming vegan, I also noticed that my nails were becoming much stronger. I had always had brittle nails previously, so I was very happy to experience this change! Needless to say, with all of the positive health benefits I was experiencing, I was quite motivated to stick with my new plant-based diet.

In 2002, I became pregnant. Although my midwives always pronounced my health to be excellent, I still worried that I should be taking prenatal vitamins. However, whenever I discussed this with my husband, he would say: "Who eats healthier than you? You don't need them!" So I agreed to give the ultimate "natural pregnancy" a try. I passed on the prenatals and instead just continued to eat a healthy vegan diet. I listened to my body (and that little being growing inside of me) and ate the foods I was craving. For me, that meant a ridiculous amount of raspberries, lots of salads, and a newfound fondness for anasazi beans. Nine months later, I was blessed with a healthy baby girl. She nursed for the first two years of her life (yes, I consider that to be vegan!) and then began eating exclusively plant-based foods. Although she has always been a picky eater (like I was as a child—can you say "instant karma?"), she does eat a variety of fruits, vegetables, and whole foods. Now, for anyone who is concerned about raising children on a vegan diet, I have to mention that my daughter (who just turned six) is the picture of health. Despite the fact that she doesn't take vitamins (and I don't even go out of my way to make sure she gets all of her nutrients), she is unusually strong, energetic, healthy, and physically active. In fact, she recently completed a very challenging ten-mile hike—and then wanted to go for a run that same night! Incidentally, I say all of this not to brag, but in hopes that my positive experiences will reassure anyone who is concerned about the adequacy of a plant-based diet.

A New Take on Allergies

Food allergies are everywhere—wheat, corn, soy, you name it. Why are so many people having trouble with certain foods these days? I don't pretend to be an expert on the subject, having been fortunate enough not to experience allergies firsthand. However, it does seem interesting that this epidemic coincides with an increase in genetically modified foods and an overconsumption of foods (such as corn and wheat) in their *non-organic* and *refined* state. For example, a humble soybean is generally benign in its natural state when eaten in moderation. However, after soy protein isolate began showing up in everything, people started complaining of soy allergies. Another example, wheat, causes problems for many people. But I have to wonder whether if everyone were eating only whole, unrefined, organic wheat (and doing so in moderation and balance), would the same problem exist?

On another note, allergies can also be a powerful way for our bodies to give us important messages. As with any *dis*-ease, allergies can manifest when there is something out of balance in our lives, or when there is something that we need to pay attention to. Perhaps we received subtle signs before the allergies showed up, but didn't pay much attention to them. Unfortunately, sometimes we humans need to be shaken up a bit before we resort to actually learning the lesson that is being offered!

I recently asked a good friend of mine, Barbara Kennedy, to share her personal experience with allergies. She has been an inspiration for many who suffer from allergies, as she went from being someone who was allergic to *everything* to someone completely freed from the hindrance of allergies! I also wanted to share her story as a testament of what we humans are capable of. We are beautiful, powerful beings, and often our "problems" in life are there to guide us toward a deeper healing, which is available when we become *open*. Here is what she was kind enough to share:

> In 1990 I noticed that my face had persistent breakouts and I was suffering from migraine headaches almost every other day. I tried everything until finally resorting to having my blood tested for 300 possible allergens.
>
> When the results came back, I was floored! There were a number of "good" foods (oats, berries, green beans, cinnamon, avocados, cucumbers, etc.) that were causing allergic reactions. My symptoms cleared up when I eliminated those foods, and I continued to avoid them until 2007. This was when I discovered a chiropractor who practices the NAET technique of clearing allergies. NAET (Nambudripad's Allergy Elimination Technique) diagnoses with muscle testing, curing the allergies using techniques to rebalance your energy. For me, it only took four treatments before I was eating anything I wanted again! The joy of tasting blueberries and strawberries again after thirteen years was indescribable.
>
> After a year, a problem with an avocado reappeared (and was quickly solved through another NAET treatment), and I asked my chiropractor about why this may have happened. He suggested that eating too much of a food, or deep emotional connections to a food could cause reactions. I reflected on what he said, and the revelations were fascinating. Eating is very emotional and we use foods to enhance joy or stuff away sadness. Sometimes we just can't "stomach things." I have learned to reflect on my life and the associations I have with the foods that I couldn't stomach for so long. It has been a wonderful, healing journey and being able to eat whatever I want again has been an emotionally freeing experience. [15]

Another friend of mine (we'll call him Paul) also had an interesting experience with allergies. As a physical therapist, he had always been a very health conscious person. However, a few years back he began to develop persistent digestive difficulties. After many failed attempts at figuring out the cause of his troubles using conventional methods, he finally went to a holistic practitioner. This practitioner led Paul into a very relaxed state, and then asked him to visualize what the pain in his stomach looked like. After a while, Paul began to see something that completely surprised him. What he was seeing was a cow! Paul, being of open mind and heart, tried to understand what this meant as he knew there was a reason he was experiencing this in his life at that time. When he listened deeply, Paul realized that the cow was telling him: "You are hurting yourself when you put me in your body—don't do this anymore. It is not necessary and it hurts me too." As Paul continued with this exercise, he found that the same message was being offered by chickens, pigs, and fish. For some time after, Paul was a vegetarian.

Several months later, I spoke with him on the phone. He was having all kinds of digestive problems again. I asked him to tell me about it. He replied that he had developed allergies to numerous plant-based foods such as soy, legumes, wheat, corn, nuts, and certain vegetables. When I asked him how his vegetarian diet was going, he replied that he was no longer able to be a vegetarian because his allergies prevented it. After all, not being able to eat those important vegetarian staples made it very difficult to avoid meat. When he asked for my opinion, I responded with a question. "Are you sure you want to know what I think?" He assured me that he did. "Do you remember your session with that holistic practitioner?" I asked. Surprisingly, he had completely forgotten! I then suggested that perhaps Paul was subconsciously creating allergies for himself because he was having a hard time avoiding meat. By being "allergic" to vegetarianism, it had become convenient for him to forget about his epiphany and revert to the familiarity of a meat-based diet. To my surprise, Paul immediately agreed with me. After he became clear once more about what he needed to do, he decided to eliminate meat from his diet and try eating those foods he had thought he was allergic to. To this day, Paul no longer has food allergies or digestive issues.

On a final note, I am sharing these stories not to convince you to try NAET therapy or become a vegetarian, but to give you the confidence to look beyond what your circumstances appear to be on the surface. Our experiences are here for a reason. If we choose to look at them with an open, inquisitive mind and heart, we will be surprised and rewarded with the beautiful higher level of living that awaits us!

Free Yourself from Numbers!

Why have we become so dependent on numbers to tell us what to eat? We keep ourselves distracted counting calories and fat grams, hoping to solve the mystery of what we should be eating. Yet, studies have shown that people who count calories and use other forms of rigid dieting rules often overeat and even binge when alone.[16]

Perhaps the solution is so simple that we, as part of such a busy society, haven't given it the time of day. What if we just *listened* to our bodies? What if we just took a little more time to pay attention to our inner wisdom? We are perfectly designed and capable of so much, but all too often we forget to trust ourselves. Sometimes we even feel afraid to hear the messages being offered, as we think we might lose something in the process. However, if an inner message really reflects the truth, it will come forth in a loving way and it will feel right to us. In reality, we do not need to be afraid of anything. Ever. We can naturally thrive as healthy human beings…while still enjoying our diet! Once we get into the habit of listening to our bodies (and inner wisdom), everything else will fall into place.

"We're born with the capabilities ... to tend toward foods that our bodies need and to stop eating when we're full," says Karin Kratina, a nutritionist in Gainesville, Florida who specializes in weight and eating disorders. "But events conspire throughout our lives to encourage us to ignore our bodies' signals. As children, we eat in response to internal cues. As adults, we eat in response to the clock, the latest diet, social cues, or uncomfortable emotions."[17]

Another way to lessen the need for external rules is to simply eat fresh, whole foods. Our bodies naturally become satisfied more quickly when they receive the nourishment they need. Dr. Oz, the well respected physician who frequents the Oprah Winfrey show, noted an interesting study. In England, a group of volunteers went on a diet similar to that of an ape. Each person consumed eleven pounds of raw fruits, vegetables, and nuts every day for the length of the study. Despite the fact that only twelve days had passed, the results were amazing. Their cholesterol and blood pressure had dropped significantly, and they had each lost about ten pounds!

"When you eat this kind of food, you're sending a very clear message to your brain," Dr. Oz says. "You're taking calories and nutrients. What we normally do in America is we give calories to people without nutrition. … The natural colors are gone, and so your brain sits back there and says, 'Am I still hungry or not?'"[18]

Best-selling author Michael Pollan has simplified some of these concepts very well: "Eat food. Not too much. Mostly plants."[19] He also mentions a Japanese principle called "Hara Hachi Bu" which instructs people to eat until they only feel eighty percent full. "If you do that," he says, "you will actually reduce your caloric intake quite a bit."

I have incorporated this principle into a hunger and fullness gauge, which many clients (and I) have used with great success. Just the simple act of paying attention to this scale can elevate you from your current state of health (and/or weight) to what you ideally want for yourself.

THE HUNGER AND FULLNESS GAUGE:

1. You are so hungry that you feel ravenous! You might have trouble concentrating and you may even feel weak. Headaches, stomach pains, crankiness, and dizziness are also possible at this level because of excessive hunger. If you allow yourself to get to this point, you will be much more likely to make unconscious choices about what you eat, as well as *how much* to eat. You are just too darn hungry to think straight!

2. You are hungry, but are not experiencing the negative side effects of the first level.

3. You have eaten just enough to satisfy your hunger. Your taste buds and habits may entice you to eat more, but your body would feel fine without more food. You feel light, nourished, and physically satisfied. Try to gravitate toward this ideal level as much as you possibly can.

4. You have eaten past the point of simply satisfying your physical hunger. You still feel fine for the most part, but are a little full. You didn't need to eat quite as much as you did.

5. You have eaten so much that you feel very unpleasantly full. You may have binged, or you may have even started eating when you weren't hungry. Any eating at this stage is a form of self-sabotage and abuse. However, you **can** heal this habit, no matter how long you have been in this cycle!

One way to begin using this gauge is simply to check in with your body several times a day. Each time, try to identify which level you are at. Next, become very familiar with how you feel, physically and emotionally, at each level you find yourself at. Move away from levels one and five as much as you can. If you are at level one or two, eat something! If you are at level three (or higher) and you are tempted to eat more, take a little time to reflect. Perhaps you can learn something new and empowering in the process.

You may find it particularly helpful to pay special attention to how you feel at level three. Try to bring more awareness to that healthy place, as what we focus on is what expands. If we focus on where we *do* want to be (instead of where we *don't* want to be), we will find ourselves there more and more consistently! By listening to the profound wisdom we have within ourselves, we absolutely can let go of the external rules we have depended on for so long. The results? Radiant health and newfound freedom!

Why ask why?

Why am I overweight? Why can't I seem to make changes? Why am I avoiding the habits that will benefit me? Why do I have persistent illnesses? Why can't I stop eating deep fried chocolate bunnies? You may answer that genetics, your hectic schedule, an unsupportive family, or a lack of finances prevent you from achieving your goals. That's understandable. It is truly the absolute norm in our society to blame external factors for our circumstances.

However, I submit that there is only one answer to all of these questions. If there were no definite reason *why* we were subconsciously sabotaging ourselves, we wouldn't be doing it. Hurting ourselves is needless otherwise. There is just no **real** payoff for us to be imbalanced or to use food improperly. There has to be a reason—no matter how many times we have rationalized otherwise—and it will become clear when we take the time to listen.

A great example of this comes from my own life. At the age of twenty-two, I was fit and thin, and I was just beginning my quest for higher consciousness through meditation. I spent the next seven years delving into my new interest for spirituality…and steadily growing in body weight as well! By the time I was twenty-nine years old, I had reached my highest weight ever of 165 pounds. After one day, becoming ridiculously winded climbing the flight of stairs to my apartment, I knew it was time for a change. I began to exercise and eat less, and finally lost forty pounds after several months of committed change. Oddly, it was only *after* I lost the weight that I realized why I had gained it in the first place. I had somehow developed a wrong concept that as a spiritually minded person, I could no longer be physically attractive. I especially could not be in a romantic relationship if I was on a quest for enlightenment, and being thin made that kind of relationship a lot more likely. Gaining weight had been an unconscious defense mechanism to "protect" me from those potential distractions. Luckily, I was able to find balance and realize that I could be thin and simultaneously spiritually minded. I could be in a relationship and not lose sight of what was truly important to me. In fact, I eventually learned that being in a relationship could actually *help* my spiritual development, as other people act as mirrors for us if we are willing to reflect on our experiences.

I am reminded of another example from several years ago. A client of mine (we'll call him Eric) had lost about thirty pounds and really wanted to lose another fifteen to reach his goal. For some reason, his weight had reached a plateau that he couldn't seem to overcome. He asked me about this and proceeded to share some other details about his life. When Eric began to tell me about his wife, it became clear to me that he was subconsciously sabotaging himself for one reason. His wife had a long history of insecurity and jealousy issues. She was deeply afraid that if her husband became much thinner, he would be attractive to more women. Because of her insecurities, she was not comfortable with this. Eric finally realized that he had been unconsciously accommodating his wife by allowing her fears to prevent him from reaching his goal.

Geneen Roth is a writer for Prevention Magazine and author of several books on the subject of emotional connections to food. She narrates an event in her own life when she binged (after having been "clean" for over five years). It happened after she had spent the day with a dying friend. She was tired and really wanted to go home and "process," but had promised to meet a friend at a party. By not taking the needed time to herself, she instead "went unconscious" by opting to overeat at the party. Although this was only a one-time event for her, it is a great example of how we use food inappropriately as way of avoiding the real issue. It is not about *enjoying* the food at all. "When you binge, you are using your drug of choice to deny, swallow, or escape your feelings" she says. Geneen also tells her students that kindness and curiosity after a binge are very important. Her wise words are: "Notice yourself. Be kind. Be tender. Be curious. You'll be surprised at what happens. (Trust me—it'll be good.)" [20]

NOTES:

[1] www.oprah.com; "Dr. Oz's Ultimate Aging Checklist" from the show "Dr. Oz Reveals the Ultimate Checklist for Great Aging" originally aired 2/05/08

[2] The McDougall Newsletter, February 2003—Fish is Not a Health Food

[3] *The McDougall Plan*, author Dr. John McDougall, page 2

[4] Dr. John McDougall, "Free McDougall Program: Your health is not determined by heredity."

[5] *The McDougall Plan*, author Dr. John McDougall, page 102

[6] The McDougall Newsletter, January 2004—Protein Overload

[7] *The New Whole Foods Encyclopedia*, by Rebecca Wood

[8] *The New Whole Foods Encyclopedia*, by Rebecca Wood, page 306

[9] www.oprah.com; (from the show "The Truth About Food with Dr. Oz and Bob Greene") originally aired on September 17, 2007

[10] *The New Whole Foods Encyclopedia*, by Rebecca Wood, page 9

[11] Firman E. Baer Report, Rutgers University Study

[12] Environmental Working Group Study (ewg.org)

[13] Excerpts from *Your Organic Kitchen*, by Jesse Ziff Cool and Environmental Working Group Study (Washington D.C.)

[14] The National Organic Program, www.ams.usda.gov/nop, 1/07

[15] Barbara Kennedy, e-mail to author on February 5, 2008

[16] Delicious Living Magazine, June 1,2007, article by Lisa Turner

[17] Delicious Living Magazine, June 1,2007, article by Lisa Turner

[18] www.oprah.com; Investigating Food Myths with Dr. Oz (from the show "The Truth About Food with Dr. Oz and Bob Greene") originally aired on September 17, 2007

[19] www.npr.org "Cut the Nutri-Hype. Eat Real Food," with Michael Pollan, author of *In Defense of Food* and *The Omnivore's Dilemma*

[20] Prevention Magazine, "Why am I eating like this?" article by Geneen Roth, May 2006

Chapter Two: Aligning with Your Radiant Life

Now that we have discussed nutrition (along with other aspects of physical health), it is time to turn our attention to what else constitutes radiant health and inner wealth. Although it is very important to eat a nutritious diet and exercise regularly, it is equally important to nourish our inner state of being. What good is a healthy body if the consciousness within that body is not in a positive state? In this chapter, I have shared some of the things that have worked miracles in my own life. Some can be applied to physical health as well, and some can simply be used to uplift our state of consciousness and energy. Please don't feel overwhelmed by the multitude of suggestions here. I recommend that you decide which of these tools work for you in your life right now and begin there. Start with a small, doable goal and build on it. Be gentle with yourself. Some change does happen overnight, but big changes can take persistence and patience. As you do a little more here and a little more there to create harmony in your own body and being, you will continually surprise yourself with positive change!

BEGIN WITH CLARITY, OPENNESS, AND EMPOWERMENT

Waiting for you is a life of harmony, joy, radiant health, and fulfillment. Yes, you. No matter what your life appears to be in this moment, you *can* align with your highest life simply by making doable, consistent changes on a regular basis. It is as if the Universe is constantly raining goodness upon us, but unfortunately we are not open to it. When our "cup" (or state of receptivity) is facing downward, we cannot receive the abundance that is being showered upon us. However, you *can* turn your cup upright and live a beautiful life of radiant health and inner wealth. If you choose to use the tools in this book, they will help you to become receptive and in alignment with this higher state of being. Additionally, if you adopt an attitude of clarity, openness, and empowerment before you begin, your transition will be easy and natural.

To begin with, it helps to become very clear about you truly want. Invite the quality of clarity to come to you and then be open to it. Ask yourself what you are wanting to gain from using these tools. Is it better health, more loving relationships, spiritual evolution, a state of inner peace, or simply more joy in your life? It never hurts to write down your intentions, as it will help you stay on track as you use these tools to create what you desire.

The quality of being open can also assist you greatly as you use these tools. It relieves the need to push or force things to happen. Of course, you still need to put forth the effort to make positive changes, but being open creates a space of receptivity within you that makes the process much easier. By being open, you allow yourself to receive all of the goodness the Universe is waiting to offer you. If you are *open* to aligning with a higher way of being and a better way of living, you will automatically attract everything that you need in order to make it a reality for you.

Finally, it is very beneficial to adopt an attitude of empowerment. Unfortunately, many of us were raised to believe that we are victims of our lives and are not in control. However, you really are so much more powerful than you realize. You **do** have the ability to change your life in any way that you desire. Just by applying *some* of the tools in this book (such as dietary suggestions and healthy recipes, visualization, prioritization, exercise, gratitude, meditation, self-love, balance, affirmations/mantras, and daily reviews), you will begin to notice something very extraordinary. Your inner being and outer life will <u>both</u> shift into a much higher state. And you will like it.

Your Toolkit for Greatness...

HERE IS THE PART WHERE I STOP FOOLING AROUND AND ACTUALLY <u>GIVE</u> YOU THE TOOLS SO YOU CAN START BEING EVEN MORE FABULOUS!

VISUALIZE TO ACTUALIZE

This tool has purposely been listed first as it can help you implement all of the others. Visualization is actually one of the most powerful tools we human beings possess. Each one of us has the ability to create an image in our mind and then use our will to manifest it as reality. In fact, everything that we see outside of ourselves was once a thought or an image. Indeed, we are beautiful, powerful beings that have the ability to create anything we choose. Although it does take work, patience, and perseverance, it is *always* possible—no matter what our current health or other circumstances may be.

There are several ways you can use the tool of visualization. The one most people are familiar with is using visualization techniques to manifest external goals. While there is absolutely nothing wrong with this, you can also use the power of visualization to create a state of radiant health and *inner* wealth for yourself. Additionally, visualizing will help you align your habits and behaviors with those of your highest self. More effective than will power, visualization will motivate you from within. For example, I used to teach a meditation class in which everyone made a weekly commitment to themselves. One woman was really struggling with this as she kept "failing" the assignment she had given herself, which was to meditate for ten minutes each morning. Finally, after two weeks, I asked her to give up on her commitment to meditate. I suggested she instead commit to simply *visualizing* herself meditate. The next week, she returned to class with a very pleased look on her face. I asked her how her new assignment went. She replied that after only three days of visualizing, she had automatically and effortlessly started meditating for *thirty* minutes each morning! Another example comes from my own inner experience. In my late teens, I began having bouts of depression. Luckily, I had a friend who recommended I begin using visualization techniques. So, I began to imagine myself in a state of bliss, dancing around my college campus without a care in the world. I still remember the moment when I was walking to class several weeks later and realized I was happily skipping and dancing along the sidewalk! I started to laugh out loud and must have looked like a complete lunatic to anyone passing by. However, I didn't care. It worked, and I was swiftly on my way to complete freedom from depression.

A final visualization I will share here is one that I have used to keep myself in a state of "happy discipline." Years ago when I was in the process of losing forty pounds, I began to realize the simple truth that unhealthy choices are just unnecessary and don't contain real pleasure. I became conscious of the fact that I would lose nothing and gain everything by being disciplined and making positive choices. To reinforce this new understanding, I began to visualize the image of a huge garden with a fence around it. This garden was beautiful and contained everything I could possibly want, including any foods I enjoyed. There was no need to go outside of the fence, as that area represented eating things in an unbalanced way (past the point of their pleasure) as well as being overly full. Going outside of the garden basically meant choosing self-abuse over real enjoyment. So, I continued to visualize myself being content and happy within the garden. I truly believe that this visualization is why it became so much easier for me to stick with healthier ways of eating.

Suggestion for practice: It is helpful to begin by becoming very clear about what it is that you *really* want to create. Whether it is a radiantly healthy body, a peaceful state of mind, or a new job, write it down. It is also important to make sure that everything you write down represents what you truly desire. The old adage of "be careful what you wish for, because you just might get it" is really quite true. If you visualize your desires enough and put forth the effort to make them a reality, they **will** manifest. Therefore, it is important to listen to your inner wisdom and make sure your goals are in alignment with what you really want deep down. Next, it is helpful to make a manifestation poster. Once you have defined what it is that you truly want to create, you can put images that reflect your desires on a poster. Write out affirmations beside them as well, using a positive statement in the present tense. For example, let's say that one of your desires is to develop a meditation practice. You could put a picture of yourself (or a picture from a magazine that looks vaguely like you) in a meditative state on the poster. Next to the picture, you could write something like "I am deeply grateful for my daily morning meditation practice as it brings me joy, clarity, and peace." As often as possible, look at your poster and let those beautiful images and affirmations begin to resonate within you. More and more, begin to imagine that you are *already* your highest self, living your ideal life. The more you envision what you want to be and have, the more you align with the forces that are waiting make your desires a reality for you.

ROCKS = RADIANCE!

"There is *always* time for what is really important." I noticed this phrase on a post-it note at a friend's house, amidst the busiest time of my life. I remember thinking that it was a gift, reminding me that I could *always* choose balance no matter what was going on externally in my life. Thanks, Sally!

Another friend, Anna, shared a visual aid with me that she uses with her students. She sets a glass jar, several rocks, and some sand on a table. The rocks represent the most valuable things we can do with our time. They symbolize things like focused work, meditation, exercise, and anything else that makes our lives better. The sand represents the little things that we do every day to fritter our time away, such as watching television or talking on the phone. Sand is the "fluff" of our lives.

In the demonstration, Anna first pours the sand into the glass jar. Next, the rocks get placed in the jar. However, when the sand is placed in the jar first, only *some* of the rocks fit. In the next demonstration, she places all of the rocks into the jar first. Then, the sand gets poured into the jar. You guessed it! This time, all of the sand easily finds its way into the jar.

This visual aid is so powerful because it so simply reflects the truth of our daily lives. When we make sure to do first things first, we can still fill in the gaps with plenty of "fluff" if we choose. I can tell you for a fact, that just this one simple act of prioritizing will make a huge difference in the quality of your life. Plus, by taking good care of yourself, you will have more to offer others. You will function at a higher, more efficient level because you have made conscious choices with your time.

Suggestion for practice: Take a moment and think of at least three things you would like to find more time for in your life. These three things should all be something that will enrich your life and benefit you in some way, such as visualization, meditation, exercise, or even a special work (or play!) project. Next, reflect on your schedule and find a way to budget some special time every day to prioritize these things in your daily life.

Another way to begin is to take a "time out." Don't worry—this doesn't involve sitting in a chair for five minutes until you apologize! Each day, there is a "first fluff" time. The first time we get a chance to watch television, talk on the phone, let our mind drift, or read a magazine. Don't worry, you can still do these things if you so choose! However, take just a moment before you engage in that activity to sit quietly and reflect. Is there anything else that would benefit you to do first? For example, could you take five minutes to do a visualization exercise *before* you make that phone call? Just take a "time out" and see what happens!

WORK IT! IT'S WORTH IT!

You've heard this way too many times, as have I: "Exercise is an important part of a healthy lifestyle." However, it's a cliché for a reason! Regular exercise keeps us fit, strong, and healthy and helps us to stay in balance. Here are just a few of its other benefits:

♥*Exercise builds muscle, and muscle burns more calories than fat. Therefore, just by exercising, our bodies become more muscular, thus creating a steady boost in metabolism.*

♥*Exercise is a great way to energize ourselves and overcome fatigue.*

♥*Exercise aids our bodies in circulation and digestive functions. It also decreases blood pressure, blood sugars, and triglycerides.*

♥*The act of exercise burns calories and therefore makes it much easier to lose weight and/or maintain a proper body weight.*

♥*Exercise releases endorphins, which helps us feel better and maintain a more positive outlook.*

Since exercise is so beneficial, what could possibly be stopping us from making it a part of our lifestyle? Actually, this is a really important question to ask ourselves. Finding out the answer(s) will help us determine what our perceived obstacles are, so that we can overcome them.

Ask yourself what it would take for you to *really* stick with a regular exercise routine. Be honest with yourself, and pay close attention to your thoughts. Maybe you are the type of person who needs a gym membership to stay motivated. If so, perhaps you could find a way to make that happen. After all, your health is worth it! If you are the kind of person who would rather exercise at home, perhaps there are fitness routines you could do right in your living room, such as yoga, Tae Bo, or dance. Perhaps you are thinking that you just don't *like* to exercise, or find it boring. Well, now is your opportunity to turn that around! Because, to realistically work in the long term, your exercise routine must be able to hold your interest. And this is far more likely if you are doing something you enjoy.

For me, making exercise fun was one of the reasons I was finally able to stick with it on a regular basis. I expanded my horizons to include not only walking, but also hiking, swimming, cross country skiing, dancing, biking, weight lifting, Tae Bo, pilates, and yoga. I also enjoy having a weekly goal to achieve. For example, I might set a goal of 280 minutes of exercise per week, giving me an average of 40 minutes daily. Of course, everyone is different. Your number will need to reflect your current state of health, your goals, and what is *realistic* for you to achieve. If you know you can only commit to 10 minutes a day, then, by all means, start with that! Every little bit really does add up. The more you exercise (even if it is just a wee little bit), the stronger you will become. The most important thing is to be loving and patient with yourself, and to set realistic goals that will keep you motivated and encouraged. You are laying a foundation that you can build on more and more with time.

Suggestion for practice: Make a list of several things you enjoy doing that constitute exercise (mostly rated G). Next, set a very reasonable exercise goal for the next week and/or month. Define how much you would like to exercise each week or each day. Make this something you feel very confident you can stick with and incorporate the enjoyable exercises on your list. Just be patient, persistent, and remember to trust yourself. You really can do this!

UNCONDITIONAL GRATITUDE IS THE ATTITUDE!

There is something almost mysterious about the quality of gratitude. Being genuinely thankful can create miracles and dramatic shifts in energy. It is, simply put, one of the easiest ways to transform our lives. We have all heard the question: "Is your glass half full or half empty?" When we strive to see our glass as half full at all times, we somehow attract the pitcher of abundance which is waiting to fill our glass to overflowing!

Why do we so often, then, forget to be grateful? It is so easy to get caught up in our perceived "problems" and neglect all that is going right in our lives. We worry about the future and focus on the things we want to change. Yet, most of us can admit that we do have much to be thankful for. When we think more about what is going right in our lives, we allow more of that goodness to flow toward us. What we think about expands. What we focus on, we get more of. It's as if the Universe is a benevolent parent who wants to give Its children everything under the stars (and more). As a loving parent, the Universe also wants what is truly best for us. We must learn to appreciate what we have, or we will never be happy no matter what we are given. We must learn to be grateful, content, and conscious in order to fully receive. The Universe loves us unconditionally, and is waiting patiently for us to learn and grow. Being grateful makes this whole process so much easier, and so much more joyful as well.

One of the most beautiful changes we can make in our lives is to become "unconditionally grateful." This is something that may seem like a new concept, as many of us are used to only being grateful for pleasant experiences and material rewards. However, learning to say "thank you" when we are confronted with unpleasant situations is absolutely life transforming. If we are placed in a dark room and can say "thank you for the darkness," a light will appear. If we are faced with a loss and can be grateful for it, we will gain something beautiful and unexpected. Nothing is by accident, and the Universe is truly loving and kind. Negative experiences are given to us for a reason. If we can look at them as opportunities, everything will shift. Our consciousness will shift, and the situation will turn around. When we learn our lessons, we don't have to repeat them. Unconditional gratitude can be an incredibly powerful tool to use in your life. Even if it is challenging at first to say "thank you" when faced with an unpleasant experience, say it anyway. Even if you don't really mean it, you will get the ball rolling. Soon, you will understand why you are having the experiences you are having, no matter what they are. You will become totally aligned with joy, awareness, and *genuine* gratitude when you put this practice into your daily life!

Suggestion for practice: Each day, think of at least five things you are grateful for. Also, think of one thing that you are not comfortable with in your life—a "problem" that is vexing you. Say "thank you" for that problem. Think of at least one important thing that "problem" may be here to teach you. Think of at least one good thing that has happened because of that "problem." Be as open as you can to the reasons why you needed this experience. Also, be open to possible steps you can take to change the situation. The more you can incorporate this practice into your life, the more you will receive firsthand knowledge of the beauty of unconditional gratitude. Thank you God, thank you Universe, thank you Infinite Benevolence!

MEDITATION = VACATION

For many people these days, stress has become a way of life. It has become second nature to rush from one activity to the next without much of a break. Often, the only hope for relief in this kind of fast paced existence is the thought of a vacation. However, despite the release and enjoyment a vacation provides, it is still only a temporary solution. Once the party is over, we return to our regularly scheduled lives and continue our old habits. Now don't get me wrong—I have absolutely nothing against vacations and wouldn't mind taking one myself! However, I would rather be rejuvenated on a daily basis as well. And the easiest, most effective method of revitalization I have found is through meditation. Now, if this conjures up images in your mind of sitting on a hard floor, painfully stuck in a yoga pose, then you are in for a pleasant surprise. You can actually sit just as uncomfortably on a carpeted floor and get the same results! Just kidding. You don't have to be uncomfortable at all. In fact, if you feel relaxed and physically comfortable, you will be able to focus more easily and get the most out of your time.

So, if meditation is so rejuvenative and easy, why don't more people do it? Great question. Although meditation is considered a normal part of life in places like India and East Asia, it's still a fairly unusual concept in the western world. Unfortunately, we are taught here to depend upon external things to provide us with answers and fulfillment. It's a little harder for the western mind to believe that such a perfect solution to life's stress and trouble is sitting right within us. Yet, that's exactly where it is. Meditation is not only rejuvenative, it is also relaxing, uplifting, and powerfully healing. It creates deeply beautiful changes in our lives and brings us into harmony with our intuition and inner wisdom. Meditation makes us calm, focused, joyful, and clearheaded. As we meditate more and more, we transition into a state of total alignment with our highest self. Plus, we automatically share that inner wealth will all those around us without ever saying a word. Just by being in a higher state of consciousness, we create a beautiful ripple effect all around us. And the best thing is, it doesn't cost a dime! You can get everything you need from meditation just by sitting in the comfort of your own home and enjoying some high quality quiet time.

To begin any meditation practice, the first step is to find a place that is relaxing and free from distractions. You can start by finding a comfortable chair that is in a private (or at least quiet) location. Alternatively, you can meditate lying down if you feel confident that you will remain awake. The ideal position is one that encourages both comfort *and* alertness. Once you have found the right spot, you can then decide on a method of meditation. This is the fun part! Feel free to choose whichever of these methods you are the most drawn toward. As you continue your practice, you may wish to try several of these suggestions or even something different.

1. OBSERVATIONAL MEDITATION: This is similar to a practice that is referred to as transcendental meditation. Begin by allowing your body to relax. Next, imagine that you are sitting inside of your forehead, back toward the pineal gland. You are now an observer, viewing the activity of your mind. As if you were watching a movie, simply view your thoughts and mental images as if they were on a screen. Don't judge yourself or the images—just be *aware* of them. Get familiar with what is going on in your consciousness. Once you master this practice, it can be used at any time (and before longer meditations) to instantly produce clarity and understanding. Yes, it really is that magical!

2. RELAXATION STATION: This is a good type of meditation for relieving stress and also for healing yourself if you have any ailments. Begin by allowing all of your muscles to relax completely. Start with your toes and slowly work all the way up to the top of your head (crown), allowing all of the stress to melt away in each area as you go. Although many practitioners of meditation begin with the head and work their way down, I encourage you to try it this way as working your way *up* the body will help you maintain a higher state of consciousness. After you have relaxed all of your muscles, think of the most beautiful color of light you can imagine. See that beautiful light filling your toes and feet completely. Next, bring that beautiful, healing light slowly upward through every part of your body until you are totally saturated in that light from toe to head. Be as open as you can, and really *feel* the healing energies of that light in each part of your body. Send extra light and love to any part of your being that needs it and continue to be open to healing on all levels. Enjoy this state of peace and relaxation for as long as you like. Or longer.

3. MANTRA MEDITATION: This form of meditation is simply the repetition of your happy thoughts (a mantra or affirmation from the "Change your Mind, Change your Life" section on page 24). To do this, sit comfortably and mentally repeat your mantra over and over. If possible, focus your attention at the pineal gland, or at least in your forehead. If you can feel the beauty and truth of the words as you are repeating them, you will grow to enjoy this process more and more. *Honest.*

4. AFFIRMATIVE BREATH MEDITATION: This was a lifesaver for me during a really rough time in college. I had been suffering from intense anxiety attacks and was trying desperately to change my state of consciousness through meditation, affirmations, and visualization techniques. I still remember the elation I felt when I realized that this was actually working! One way to use this method is to create a phrase based on something negative that you want to let go of, along with something positive that will replace it. Then, coordinate that phrase with your breathing. For example, I used to say "I let all darkness go" as I exhaled and "I allow light and healing" as I inhaled. Alternatively, you can use this breathing affirmation in a solely "positive" way. For example, you could say "only love flows to me" as you inhale and "only love flows from me" as you exhale. Simply choose whatever works best for you right now. You can always change it at any point if you need to. Finally, it also helps to keep your palms in an upright position as you do this exercise as it will help you maintain an increasingly receptive state of mind.

Suggestion for practice: To begin with, choose your special spot: a place for you to meditate that is comfortable and quiet. Make it as conducive to concentration and relaxation as possible. If you like, you can place candles nearby (or anything else that helps set the mood). It should be an inviting space that feels good to you. Next, set aside a daily period of five minutes to devote to your practice. If it can be the same time each day (such as 7:00-7:05 a.m.), that is ideal because it will help you establish a habit. Although a longer amount of time would be even more beneficial, I find that people are more likely to stick with something if it is *totally* achievable. If you begin by establishing a daily five minute practice (preferably in the morning) for a period of three weeks, it will naturally become part of your routine. You can extend the practice whenever you like, but just make sure you stick with the minimum of five minutes. Five little minutes, five thousand big changes!

LOVE YOURSELF—YOU ARE BEAUTIFUL!

One of the most helpful and empowering things you can do only takes about ten seconds. If you can look at yourself in the mirror every day and feel a greater and greater love for yourself, you will soon become aware of how powerful this practice is. Self-love is a *natural* motivator since we automatically treat the ones we love with kindness, respect, and care. By choosing to love yourself unconditionally, you will begin to experience life with a newfound gentleness and deeply soothing peace. You will also become open to greater levels of joy and your life will automatically transform for the better.

However, if you initially find there is too much resistance in saying "I love myself," you may instead wish to begin by saying "I am *willing* to love myself." When we become willing and open, it automatically creates the space for greater love and empowerment.

Another way to get on the groovy love train is to simply be *aware* of what your internal dialogue is as you look in the mirror. Are you thinking that you need to change in some way before you can love yourself? Be aware of those thoughts and allow them to transform. Remember, just because you can become *more* beautiful does not mean that you aren't already beautiful right now! Try to see all of the things that make you beautiful in this moment. Can you see yourself in the way your creator (or higher self) does, with overflowing love, appreciation, compassion, and understanding? Resist the tendency to put yourself down in *any* way, as negative self-talk is never useful. Isn't it funny the things we say to ourselves, when we would never say those sorts of things to someone else we love? Give yourself the same respect you would a good friend, and learn to speak in kind and loving ways to yourself.

Another aspect of self-love is self-forgiveness. How many of us hold unspoken grudges against ourselves? We are taught guilt from a young age, unfortunately, by people who have a less than full understanding of how unconditionally loving and forgiving the Universe is. Yes, we have all made mistakes. But why hold onto them? We are in the process of being human, and until we become fully enlightened, we will continue to make mistakes. This is how we learn! No matter what we have done in the past, we can move forward with forgiveness and light. Holding onto negative feelings helps no one. If you truly feel bad for something, do what you can to make it right. Make it right and move on. You are still loved, you are still beautiful, and you are still learning.

Suggestion for practice: Every day, take a few moments to look in the mirror. Say "I love myself" as you look at that beautiful, Godly image staring back at you. Think of all of the reasons why you are, in fact, very lovable right now. Alternately, you can say "I am open to loving myself more" and/or "I forgive myself completely." Finally, be sure to focus *only* on the positives as you look into the mirror. You are no longer allowed to criticize your stomach, hair, eyebrows, or earlobes. During this time, see only the beautiful aspects of who you are. As always, what we focus on expands!

BALANCE CAN BE LIBERATING!

I read a fascinating article in Prevention Magazine a few years ago about the differences between how men and women lose weight. The article, called "Lose Weight Like a Guy," enumerated the ways in which men tend to do things right in this department. Now, I am a feminist by nature, but this really intrigued me as I am fully aware of how much my own perfectionism has created unnecessary stress in my life. One thing the article noted was that men don't usually ban their favorite foods. Instead, they "negotiate." They might eat less of a richer food, or make time for some extra exercise that day. Women tend to be more likely to think in an all-or-nothing type of way, which can often lead to overeating and other extremes. "Nothing can scuttle your good intentions like feeling deprived" states Denise Foley, the author.

Another difference she noted was that men often have less guilt about taking time for themselves. When they need to get away, they do it! Women often feel as though they need permission to pamper themselves. Many women think it's a luxury to make time for their own desires and needs, whereas men often consider it a basic right. Plus, if you are like most people, eating can become your only pleasure when you don't pamper yourself in healthy ways. Therefore, if you (no matter what your gender) could rearrange your life just a little, you could begin to make your own ultimate wellness your number one priority. This may sound selfish, but if you do this, you will actually, really, and truly find that you'll end up having infinitely more to give others.

Finally, men seem to have less of a tendency toward perfectionism. When women don't succeed one hundred percent, they often feel like failures. Pamela Peeke, author of *Body for Life for Women,* has a great suggestion. She says: "Hit your weight loss goals 80% every single day you can. One day, it'll be 120% because it happens to be a great day. Other days, you'll hit 50% or even 20%... Just make sure it averages out to 80%."

Whether you are male or female, balance is about avoiding extremes. It's about indulging in the foods you love—in moderation—from time to time *without guilt.* It's about taking care of your own needs first so that you will have more to give others. It's about pampering yourself in healthy ways so that you can be nourished on all levels. Give yourself some slack. See how much you are already doing right, and love yourself…just as you are.

Suggestion for practice: Write down at least five things that you're already doing right on a regular basis. Give yourself a pat on the back (if you can reach). Next, write down five things that you love to do. List some ways that you could start taking the time to do them. Finally, list five ways you could begin pampering yourself. Get out your schedule book and make it happen!

CHANGE YOUR MIND, CHANGE YOUR LIFE

Did you know that you are already doing something incredibly powerful in every moment? Although it may not be intentional or conscious, you are actually shaping your life with your thoughts all of the time. We become what we think about continually, and our lives are a direct reflection of the quality of our thoughts.

Have you ever taken a minute to observe the activity of your mind? It never stops. It's always busy thinking and repeating, thinking and repeating. It is the natural tendency of the mind to never shut up. However, we can use this to our advantage by replacing the unhelpful, negative chatter with helpful, positive chatter. This is what mantras and affirmations are all about. A positive thought, used over and over, can make an absolute world of difference in a person's life. Many years ago, I knew of a case where a very depressed, suicidal man used a positive mantra for several days. After that time, he not only wanted to live, he was transported to a state of absolute bliss! All he had done was to replace thoughts such as "there is nothing to live for" and "I hate myself" with thoughts like "there is beauty everywhere" and "I love myself and I forgive myself." He repeated those thoughts continually as if his life depended on them— because it did. He found out (as we all would) that, no matter how bad a situation seems or how hopeless we feel, things can turn around in the blink of an eye. *It is all about our consciousness.* We have it in our power to create the most beautiful, rewarding life imaginable for ourselves. All we have to do is put forth the effort to align our *thoughts* with what we truly want.

Suggestion for practice: Now, the fun starts! To begin, take a few moments to relax and become aware of the thoughts that are present in your mind. Pretend that you are an impartial observer viewing your thoughts as words or pictures on a screen. On a large sheet of paper, list the negative thoughts that you observed, leaving room underneath each one. Next, look at the first thought on your list. What is the subject matter of that thought? Once you have defined the subject matter, try to think of the highest, most positive thought possible on that subject. Write it down as a present moment *statement* below the negative thought. For example, let's pretend your first negative thought was "I never have enough money." What is the subject matter here? Money and fear. Therefore, your affirmation beneath it could be something like "I am always safe and I am always provided for. I am deeply grateful for the abundance in my life." After you have made your list, you can use it in several ways. Any time you are aware of an old, negative thought, you can replace it with the new, positive statement. You can make your affirmations the first thing you think each morning and the last thing you think each night. You can even repeat them aloud while looking at yourself in the mirror. Just remember that, as with any change, every little bit counts. Just keep putting forth the effort and you <u>will</u> be rewarded with renewed hope and joy.

Another powerful tool we can use to change our thought patterns is a mantra. Simply put, a mantra is a positive word or phrase that you mentally repeat over and over in order to change your state of consciousness. If you are especially fond of one of your positive affirmations (one of your present moment statements from the above exercise), you can choose that as your mantra. Alternatively, you can use a Sanskrit mantra such as *"om mani padme om"* (meaning "I am the jewel in the lotus") or *"om namah shivaya"* ("I bow to God within myself") if you prefer. Some other helpful mantras include *"only good can come to me, only good can come from me," "I live in gratitude and love,"* and *"every day in*

24

every way, I am getting better and better."

Once you have decided on a mantra, you can begin to use it to change your life. Every day, you are given a period of twenty-four hours. Some of that time your mind is in an unconscious state of sleep and some of that time your mind may be occupied with an engaging task. However, most people have more time each day than they realize to use their minds creatively. Whether standing in line at the grocery store, getting dressed, or taking a shower, our minds are often free and ready to be put to good use. The perfect time to do our mantra! It will not hinder our work or disrupt our lives in any way. In fact, the more we mentally repeat our mantra, the more effective, peaceful, productive, and joyful we become. And the more quickly and surely we become aligned with our highest self and most beautiful, ideal life.

BE KIND AND PLEASE REWIND

An *unexamined* life (and state of mind) is like a tape that is playing over and over. The tape continues to play the same thoughts, fears, tendencies, and habits each and every day. The tape *player* (the real self) listens and lives in accordance with its tape because that is its "program." Nothing much changes because the player of the tape is just sitting back, letting that same old tape play. Despite the defects in the tape, the player just lets it keep on going. It doesn't realize that it has the power to change its tape. It doesn't know that it is something much more powerful (and separate from) the tape. Yet, the player *does* control the tape. You (the real self) always have the ability to remove the defects from your tape so that it will run more smoothly. You can even choose to play an entirely different tape if you want to. It is your choice.

How do you change your tape? The easiest, most natural way to begin a cycle of positive change is with awareness. Observe your tape. Reflect on it. Rewind it and check it for defects. By doing so, you will soon become consciously in control of what you are creating and allowing to happen in your life.

Every evening, you can put this into practice by rewinding your day. Review what has gone on that day. Be aware of everything that you did right. Be grateful for all of the little things that went well. Next, reflect upon how you could have done things differently. Try to be thankful for the things that did *not* go well also, as they are opportunities for you to grow and become more free. See if you can change your consciousness about them. Visualize yourself acting or speaking in a way that would have felt better to you. Imagine yourself being faced with those same situations and handling them ideally. It is as if you are visualizing yourself going through the same day you just lived, but as a much more conscious, loving being.

Suggestion for practice: Before bedtime, set aside ten minutes to sit quietly and comfortably. Close your eyes and begin to "watch" your day, starting from the moment you woke up. Do your best to see it from a detached, observational standpoint without judging yourself or becoming emotionally attached to what you are watching. View yourself with compassion, love, and kindness. Next, visualize yourself being faced with those same situations, but instead see yourself acting, speaking, and thinking in higher ways. In a nutshell, you are visualizing yourself living the day you just went through, but as your highest self. If you can, do this practice every day for a month and journal your progress. I can tell you for a fact that if you take just ten minutes to do this every evening before bed, you will begin to align with your ideal self without even trying. It is that powerful! Be kind to yourself by rewinding your day, and that kindness will create a beautiful ripple effect that will spread out in circles all around you.

Chapter Three: The Two-Week Ultimate Radiant Health Plan!

Here is a very rejuvenative program that can be used anytime that you feel your body and mind need some fine tuning. It is a plan for people like me who want to do a "cleanse" while still maintaining normal daily activities. I have no interest in feeling weak, famished, or deprived. And if you don't either, I know this plan can assist you in achieving a higher level of radiant health and ultimate wellness.

What can you expect by following this plan for two weeks? First of all, it is a great way to begin making healthy habits a natural part of your daily life. Also, it will infuse you with a greater sense of well-being and joy as you remember to nurture and care for your holistic needs. Of course, if you want to lose weight or correct any existing health concerns, this plan is a fabulous jump-start! It will help you drop weight quickly *and* safely, lower your cholesterol, and begin to overcome a variety of other health issues. In a nutshell, you can expect to look and feel better than ever after only two weeks (heck, two days!) on this program.

And although this plan should be perfectly safe for any health condition, I recommend consulting a knowledgeable health-care practitioner before beginning if you have any health issues or concerns. Finally, I wish you inner and outer strength in this endeavor, as well as the knowing that a higher level of well-being *can* be yours...soon...and that it can be achieved with happiness, ease, and enjoyment!

> ## YOU DO NOT NEED TO BE HUNGRY ON THIS PROGRAM!

As always, *listening* to your body is so important. Each person who follows this plan will have his or her own unique metabolism, level of activity, and goals. This is why I've provided a basic structure, but with flexibility. For example, you can always add extra "green" recipes (please see pages 45 and 254) throughout the day if you're hungry. If you are still hungry (and especially if you're very physically active or not trying to lose weight), you may need to add in some extra "blue" recipes and higher-fat plant foods (such as nuts and avocados) as well. As long as you are stopping at level three (see the hunger and fullness gauge below) and following the plan otherwise, you are still "on the wagon!"

Of course, drinking enough water goes a long way too. It is very easy to confuse the body's signs for thirst with those for hunger. It never hurts to drink a little water before you eat to make sure your thirst requirements are satisfied. As always, try to tune into the signals your body gives you.

AS A REMINDER, HERE AGAIN IS THE HUNGER AND FULLNESS GAUGE FROM CHAPTER THREE:

1. You are so hungry that you feel ravenous! You might have trouble concentrating and you may even feel weak. Headaches, stomach pains, crankiness, and dizziness are also possible at this level because of excessive hunger. If you allow yourself to get to this point, you will be much more likely to make unconscious choices about *what* you eat, as well as *how much* to eat. You are just too darn hungry to think straight!

2. You are hungry, but are not experiencing the negative side effects of the first level.

3. You have eaten *just* enough to satisfy your hunger. Your taste buds and learned instincts may entice you to eat more, but your body would feel fine without more food. You feel light, nourished, and physically satisfied. Try to gravitate toward this ideal level as much as you possibly can.

4. You have eaten past the point of simply satisfying your physical hunger. You still feel fine for the most part, but a little full. You didn't need to eat quite as much as you did.

5. You have eaten so much that you feel very unpleasantly full. You may have binged, or you may have even started eating when you weren't hungry. Any eating at this stage is a form of self-sabotage and abuse. However, you **can** heal this habit, no matter how long you have been in this cycle!

WHAT TO EAT ON THE TWO-WEEK RADIANT HEALTH PLAN

The following foods are to be emphasized during this time: vegetables, beans, whole grains, fruits, organic foods, and sprouted foods. In the bread department, sprouted grain breads and tortillas are the ideal choice, as they are high in fiber and provide maximum nourishment. Some examples are the *Food For Life* (Ezekiel 4:9) sprouted grain breads and sprouted grain tortillas. Tofu and seitan are allowed in moderation during this plan, although tempeh is preferable.

For the optional breakfast cereal, you may either eat oatmeal (or other *whole* grains), the "Indian Spiced Supergrain Cereal" (page 52), or a packaged high fiber breakfast cereal (choose a vegan, 100 percent whole grain cereal with at least six grams of fiber per serving such as *Barbara's* GrainShop).

The following vegetable oils are allowed in moderation during the two weeks: olive, coconut, flax, sesame (or toasted sesame), hemp, or sunflower. If you are hungry or in need of more calories, you may also eat some higher-fat plant foods during this time. These include nuts (especially almonds and walnuts), seeds, tahini, nut butters (especially almond butter), and avocado.

The following sweeteners are allowed in moderation during the program: pure maple syrup, agave nectar, organic sugar (or organic sucanat), and brown rice syrup. If you have a hankering for something sweet during this time, you may choose one of the "green" or "blue" dessert recipes from this cookbook, but they should be limited to a *maximum* of one small serving per day, sugar baby.

FOODS NOT ALLOWED ON THE TWO-WEEK RADIANT HEALTH PLAN

These "foods" are off limits during the two-week program: meat, poultry, fish, eggs, dairy products, and any foods that contain animal products (including gelatin, whey, fish oils, chicken broth, egg whites, etc.).

Also off limits are hydrogenated oils, alcoholic beverages, soft drinks, caffeine/coffee (see the final notes below if this one is difficult for you), aspartame (or other artificial sweeteners), high fructose corn syrup, corn starch (use arrowroot instead), artificial colors or flavors, preservatives, MSG, refined white sugar, and deep-fried foods. *Whole* foods (brown rice vs. white rice, for example) should be emphasized over refined foods as well.

FINAL NOTES BEFORE YOU BEGIN:

♥I would suggest taking a few moments to reflect before you begin. Write down a list of reasons why you are choosing to follow this program and what your goals are, *exactly*. It's also helpful to take stock of your current health before beginning. Make a note of what you weigh, how you feel, and any other health or wellness concerns you currently have. Finally, take a little time to decide what you will be eating over the next two weeks and shop accordingly. The journal and planner (pages 258 and 259) are also great tools to help you get organized and stay focused.

♥If possible, try to stop eating earlier in the evenings (and choose your larger meal for lunch vs. dinner), as our bodies don't burn carbohydrates and calories as effectively while sleeping.

♥If you are having difficulty eliminating caffeine completely, you may try drinking a moderate amount of yerba mate or green tea each day. Although they still contain some caffeine, these herbal drinks at least contain high levels of nutrients and antioxidants.

♥As with any cleansing program, it is possible that you will experience symptoms of hunger and detoxification *for the first few days*. However, this is simply part of the body's natural response to letting go of toxins. The amount of symptoms you experience will depend on your level of health and what your habits were prior to beginning this cleanse. Although many people don't experience any side effects, most of the people who do usually find that their symptoms subside within a few days. They also report feeling better than ever after the initial detoxification period as well, so don't give up!

♥Because of the abundance of fiber-rich foods, it is <u>very</u> important to drink lots of water during this time. This plan is meant to *clean you out*! Needless to say, you can wave goodbye to any constipation issues. But don't worry—you can still send them a postcard.

♥If at any time you are hungry on the program, begin by drinking water and eating vegetables. Next, add in "green" items. If you are still hungry, you may eat any of the following: nuts (especially walnuts and almonds), avocado, sprouted grain bread with almond butter, or other "blue" foods.

♥If you are trying to lose weight, you will probably do so most quickly if you stick to the plan and emphasize vegetables and "green" foods. Also, if you opt for *whole* fruit in the morning (instead of the smoothie) it will speed up your weight loss. However, you can still lose weight eating "blue" foods, so don't be afraid of them! Especially if you are physically active, you will want to eat enough calories in order to feel strong and stay in balance. Whatever works, baby!

♥Remember to refer to the "green" and "blue" foods listing (starting on p. 254) for recipe ideas.

♥During these two weeks, make sure to eat (at least) the recommended amount of fruits and vegetables. This means two cups of fruit and six cups of vegetables each day. Remember, you are an absolute veggie monster on this plan! You simply cannot eat too many fresh, organic vegetables. They will assist you greatly in your quest for wellness, weight loss, and overall health.

♥If, after your two weeks are up, you wish to continue for longer on this program, there is no reason not to. *Go for it*! As long as you are eating enough and feel satisfied, it is perfectly safe.

THE TWO-WEEK ULTIMATE RADIANT HEALTH PLAN!

DAILY ACTIVITY COMMITMENT:

•At least ten minutes of being outside in the fresh air
•At least twenty minutes of exercise

DAILY EATING COMMITMENT:

Throughout the day:

•3-4 quarts of fresh, filtered (or spring) water (you may add fresh lemon juice to the water if you like) or "Liquid Radiance Tea" (page 197)

Breakfast:

•*First thing:* lemon water (the juice of ½ fresh lemon squeezed into a glass of water)
•*Second thing:* two cups of fruit (either two servings whole fruit or a 16 oz. fresh fruit smoothie (use only pure fruit and juice)
•*Optional thing (to be taken at least thirty minutes after the lemon water and fruit to allow for optimum digestion)*: high fiber cereal (or oatmeal, cooked whole grains, or "Indian Spiced Supergrain Cereal") with nondairy milk

Mid-morning snack:

•Two servings of fresh raw vegetables

Lunch:

•1 cup of fresh vegetables (raw or lightly cooked)
•*Meal of your choice!* (choose from "green" or "blue" recipes and eat only until level 3 of the hunger and fullness gauge)

Afternoon snack:

•1 serving of fresh vegetables (or two fresh spring rolls from the "starters" chapter)

Dinner (*do not eat past 7 p.m.*):

- *Eat first*: large green salad (with a "green" dressing, vinegar, or other lowfat natural dressing)
- *Main dish*: choose from "green" recipes and be sure to include a serving of beans (legumes)

DAILY TEN-MINUTE INNER WEALTH COMMITMENT:

Once each day:

- Look in the mirror and say "*I love myself*" (and/or "*I am open to loving myself more*")
- Think of at least five things you are grateful for
- Visualize being the ideal version of yourself
- Meditate for at least five minutes (or just sit quietly and observe your thoughts)

AN OPTION FOR THOSE WHO WANT EVEN QUICKER RESULTS: THE TWO-WEEK ULTIMATE, ULTIMATE RADIANT HEALTH PLAN!

O.K., I'll admit it—this is my favorite way to lose a few pounds in record time! This plan is a new twist on an old fitness trainer trick that *really* works to quickly and safely melt the fat off of your body. However, if needed, you may adjust the 3 p.m. "cutoff" time (preferably to no later than 5 p.m.).

Overall requirements to be filled throughout the day:

- 3-4 quarts of fresh, filtered (or spring) water or "Liquid Radiance Tea" (page 197)
- 4 cups organic, *raw* vegetables plus an additional 2 cups of organic vegetables (raw or lightly cooked) for a total of 6 cups of vegetables per day

Breakfast:

- *First thing:* lemon water (the juice of ½-1 fresh lemon squeezed into a glass of water)
- *Second thing:* 1-2 cups of whole, fresh fruit

Foods to munch and crunch upon until 3 p.m:

- "Green" recipes will comprise the majority of your daily food intake. Take care to eat enough so that you aren't overly hungry, but do remember to keep up with your water and vegetable requirements as you go. Also be sure not to exceed the feeling of being *just* satisfied as you eat. In other words, never go above level 3 on the hunger and fullness gauge. Note: On this plan, you may consume up to one serving of any "blue" recipe each day.

Foods to consume after 3 p.m. (or up to 5 p.m. if needed):

- Fat-free or low fat bean dishes (a maximum of 1 teaspoon of oil is allowed after this cutoff time)
- Unlimited raw or steamed vegetables (no avocados or olives though—they're fruits, anyway!)
- That's it!

Daily physical activity:

- At least ten minutes of being outside in the fresh air
- At least 30 minutes of exercise

Once each day:

- Look in the mirror and say "*I love myself*" (and/or "*I am open to loving myself more*").
- Think of at least ten things you are grateful for.
- Visualize being the ideal version of yourself.
- Meditate for *at least* ten minutes (or just sit quietly and observe your thoughts).

Good luck...I know you can do it!!!

Chapter Four: In The Kitchen

PART ONE: A HEALTHY KITCHEN SET-UP

Wouldn't it feel refreshing to have a healthy, happy, organized kitchen that you could *easily* create nourishing, delicious meals in every day? Well, dream no more, because here's the skinny to make it happen! If you stock your kitchen according to these guidelines, you'll be able to create any of the recipes in this book with ease because you'll have all of the basics on hand. Incidentally, if you are unfamiliar with any of these ingredients, many of them are listed in the glossary (page 251).

DRY FLOURS:

These can usually be bought in bulk at your local health food store. If you live in an arid climate, these should store indefinitely in airtight (preferably glass) containers at room temperature. If you live in a more humid area, you can freeze (or refrigerate) what you won't be able to use up within a month or two.

•Whole wheat pastry flour—this is a wonderful way to eat a whole grain flour while retaining the lightness of white flour (You may substitute a gluten-free all-purpose flour if you're gluten intolerant.)
•Whole wheat flour
•Cornmeal
•Rice flour (white or brown rice flour)

DRY WHOLE GRAINS:

These can usually be bought in bulk at your local health food store. Most will store for several months in airtight (preferably glass) containers at room temperature.

•Quinoa (pronounced keen-wah)
•Millet
•Amaranth (tiny pearls of fabulousness)
•Rolled oats (*not* quick oats or instant)
•Dry polenta (Once you see how inexpensive and easy it is to make creamy polenta, you may never spend the money on precooked polenta again!)
•Rice: brown basmati, short grain brown rice, long grain brown rice, Jasmine, and sushi rice
•Popcorn
•Sprouting goodies (alfalfa seeds, dry garbanzo beans, and dry whole barley)

SWEETENERS:

These can usually be bought in bulk at your local health food store. Aside from the maple syrup, most will store for several months in airtight (preferably glass) containers at room temperature.

•Organic "white" sugar (This all-purpose sweetener is simply a fine-grain sugar that has not been bleached or processed with chemicals or bone char.)
•Brown rice syrup (So good, you may want to eat this natural sweetener with a ladle!)

•Sucanat and organic brown sugar
•Organic powdered (confectioner's) sugar
•Molasses (not blackstrap)
•Pure maple syrup (this should be refrigerated unless you live in a very arid climate)

Dry Legumes:

These can usually be bought in bulk at your local health food store. They will store for several months or more in airtight (preferably glass) containers at room temperature.

•Black beans
•Pinto beans
•White beans (navy, cannelini, or great white northern)
•French lentils (Le Puy)
•Red lentils
•Garbanzo beans (chickpeas)
•Yellow mung (moong) beans or yellow split peas
•Adzuki beans (red, small, and fabulous!)
•Black-eyed peas

Baking Items:

These will all store at room temperature in their original containers for several months.

•Aluminum-free baking powder
•Baking soda
•Arrowroot (a healthy cornstarch substitute)
•Ener-G egg replacer (This will last for years in your pantry—or at least in *my* pantry.)
•Carob powder (incredibly nourishing—I prefer the roasted variety)
•Cocoa powder (don't use Dutch alkali-processed cocoa powder for baking—also labeled as European)
•Sea salt
•Yeast (not nutritional yeast; standard baking yeast)
•Dry, ground gluten (helps to lighten whole wheat flour when used in breads)
•Pure vanilla extract and mint extract

Liquid Seasoning Staples:

These items are always in a cabinet near my stove for easy (lazy!) access.
They will all store at room temperature in their original containers for several months.

•Organic soy sauce, shoyu, or tamari (If you are gluten-free, make sure your tamari is too—some brands contain wheat.)
•All-purpose oil (I use coconut or non-virgin olive oil for this although sunflower and safflower are fine.)
•Extra-virgin olive oil
•Coconut oil
•Toasted (dark) sesame oil
•Vinegars: apple cider vinegar, red wine vinegar, brown rice vinegar, and balsamic vinegar
•Sriracha Thai chili sauce (This is often referred to as "rooster" sauce, although no actual roosters were harmed to make it! It's available in supermarkets, Asian groceries, and some health food stores)
•Cooking wine or sherry

Always on my Counter:

If these items *aren't* on my counter, it means I need to go to the store!

•Fresh limes and lemons
•Fresh garlic
•Ripening bananas (I'm constantly ripening bananas so that I can freeze them for smoothies and shakes.)
•Fresh fruit (a great way to start the day!)

In the Freezer:

•Frozen broccoli, peas, and corn (These make it so easy to add veggies to any dish in a pinch!)
•Frozen bananas and berries (for smoothies and shakes)
•Extra spices and flours (if I know it will be a while before they are used up)
•Organic phyllo dough
•Puff pastry dough
•Woodstock Farms sliced, frozen shiitake mushrooms (I drive an hour to get these because I love them so much!)
•Finely shredded coconut (This can also be stored in the fridge, but if you use it as infrequently as I do, it will store better in the freezer.)

In the Fridge:

•Organic produce is the rock star of my fridge. I keep it in a highly visible, accessible spot (rather than worrying about where I "should" put it). For me, this means the entire top shelf of the fridge. Doing this makes it easy to stay focused on emphasizing the most health-supporting food of all—vegetables. No more tossing them into the vegetable crisper where they are out of sight and out of mind!
•However, in the vegetable crisper, I do keep *staple* veggies such as onions, carrots, and potatoes, as they take up too much room on the top shelf. Also found here are "fragile" veggies (fresh herbs, lettuce, cilantro, etc.) that can freeze in certain refrigerators (mine).
•Seeds: sesame, sunflower, poppy, and golden flaxseeds
•Nuts: pine nuts, whole almonds, sliced or slivered almonds, walnuts, dry-roasted peanuts, and pecans
•Ground flax meal (a healthy, inexpensive egg replacer for baking when combined with boiling water)
•Nutritional yeast (I use Red Star vegetarian support formula as it is vegan and very high in B-vitamins, including B-12)
•Dark miso and mellow white miso
•Organic ketchup
•Mustards: dijon and yellow
•Good quality barbecue sauce (such as Annie's)
•Green and red curry pastes (Thai Kitchen makes delicious, vegan versions of both)
•Vegenaise brand vegan mayonnaise (found in health food stores)
•Nut butters (natural, organic peanut butter and raw almond butter)
•Raw tahini (sesame seed butter)
•Fruit spreads (think jam without massive amounts of sugar)
•Pure maple syrup (ah, sweet elixir of tree)
•Orange juice (the "not from concentrate" kind, as it's the closest thing to fresh squeezed)
•Earth Balance margarine (I use the sticks or otherwise non-whipped kind for cooking/baking and the whipped kind for toast)
•Firm, water-packed tofu
•Five-grain tempeh (which also freezes well and will not change in consistency when frozen and thawed)

•Organic corn tortillas (choose *sprouted* corn tortillas for extra super-powers)
•Aseptic pack (liquid) vegetable broth; great for lowfat sautéing
•Whole grain (or sprouted) tortillas and whole grain (or sprouted) bread

Staples to Keep on Hand in the Cupboard:

•Organic canned beans (pinto, garbanzo, kidney, and black beans)
•Canned, diced organic tomatoes
•Pasta: penne, linguine, and buckwheat soba noodles
•Bean thread noodles (found in Asian markets and many grocery stores), see page 251 for riveting details
•Organic, high fiber breakfast cereal
•Spring roll skins (sounds creepy, but it's just rice paper)
•Dry wasabi powder
•Raisins, dried dates, and dried cranberries
•Silken tofu (aseptic pack); firm or extra-firm, see page 42 for more information
•Canned coconut milk (I use the full-fat variety because when I want coconut, I want coconut!)
•For snacking (totally optional): fun dried fruits such as mango, strawberries, and apples
•Nondairy, high quality semi-sweet chocolate chips
•Sun-dried tomatoes and kalamata olives (once opened, they go in the fridge)

Sea Vegetables:

I actually have a "sea veggie section" in one of my cupboards. Disturbing or inspired? You make the call.
These all store for several months at room temperature if kept in a dry, airtight package.

•Nori (packaged in large square sheets and available toasted or untoasted—either version is fine)
•Dulse flakes
•Ground kelp powder
•Kombu strips (I religiously add these to every pot of beans I cook)
•Agar-agar (also called agar); very nutritious and tasteless (in a good way), this is used as a thickener

Herbs and Spices:

I store these in glass jars (at room temperature) and refill them using bulk herbs and spices from
the health food store. This is the cheapest, freshest, and least wasteful way to go!
I always keep the following on my spice rack:

Amchur, asafetida, basil, oregano, thyme, rosemary leaf, salt-free lemon-pepper, seasoned salt, Mexican oregano, sage leaf, dried (ground) turmeric, cayenne powder, chili flakes, chili powder (the seasoning mix, not straight ground chilies), cumin powder, cumin seeds, ground coriander, black pepper, white pepper, fenugreek seeds, black mustard seeds, onion and garlic granules,* dill weed, bay leaves, celery seed, green cardamom pods, ground cinnamon, cinnamon sticks, ground ginger, ground mustard, minced onion, paprika, parsley, ground nutmeg, and whole cloves.

*Granulated onion and garlic (also called onion and garlic granules) taste much better than the powdered variety. However, they are often still labeled as "powdered" onion or garlic. What you are looking for is a product that has the consistency of tiny granules rather than powder. Think "tiny edible sand particles."

SEASONING BLENDS:

Most of these will keep for several months stored at room temperature.

•"Chicky Baby Seasoning" (page 194)
•"Indian Seeds and Spice Blend" (page 195); If you adore Indian food, you really should consider keeping these mixes on hand.
•"Seaweed Gomasio" (page 194); This may need refrigeration if you live in a humid climate.
•Seasoned salt (make sure it does not contain MSG)
•Zatar (a premixed Mid-Eastern seasoning blend…*so good*! See page 253 for the intimate details)

PART TWO: TOOLS FOR A THRIVING KITCHEN

Here are the items that you will want to stock your kitchen with in order to unleash your inner chef. For once, buying more stuff will actually *uncomplicate* your life.

GENERAL COOKWARE:

These are the most commonly used items of cookware in my kitchen.

•Cast iron skillets
•Stainless steel pots (small, medium, and large) with tight fitting lids
•Wok or very large skillet
•Pressure Cooker (Don't be scared—once you learn how easy and convenient this is to use, you won't know how you survived without it!)
•Strainer (one medium-large strainer for pasta, quinoa, fool's gold, etc.)
•Good knives (quality is more important than quantity here)
•Cutting boards (I prefer wood to plastic)
•Assorted size metal bowls (small, medium, large, and huge)

BAKING COOKWARE:

•Large lasagna size pan (preferably glass)
•Muffin tins
•Round glass pie pan
•Nonstick cookie sheets (place a silicone baking insert on your cookie sheet for great nonstick baking)
•9 x 9-inch square baking pan

SMALL TOOLS:

•Wire whisks, cooking spatulas (heat proof), wooden spoon(s), vegetable peeler, kitchen scissors, can opener, soup ladle, metal slotted spoon
•Pastry brush (preferably silicone, as this kind will not leave annoying "hairs" behind)
•Measuring cups and spoons (keep a few sets on hand, they aren't expensive!)
•Garlic press (A good garlic press is indispensable—use a high quality one such as Pampered Chef that doesn't require the cloves to be peeled before pressing.)

•Fine grater (for ginger, grated zest, etc.) and a regular grater (for carrots, nondairy cheese, etc.)
•Small, handheld fine mesh strainer
•Cookie cutters
•Reusable storage containers with lids
•Rubber spatulas (I have several of these. They are one of the most commonly used items in my kitchen, perfect for making sure you get every last drop out of what you are cooking up!)

Optional, but Very Useful Small Tools:

Although these are categorized as optional, I would hate to be without them! I highly recommend that you stock your kitchen with these handy tools as they will make your life much easier. Especially useful are the handheld citrus juicer, citrus zester, and oil sprayer.

•Handheld lemon/citrus juicer: These are made of metal and cost around $10. They make quick work of fresh lemon and lime juices (they're a little small for oranges). For oranges, I recommend a standard non-electric juice extractor (plastic, glass, or metal).
•Citrus zester: I thought of zesting as a chore before I bought one of these! Probably about the best $10 I ever spent. When a recipe calls for minced (or chopped) zest, having this will make your life far easier.
•Oil sprayer (such as Misto): This wonderful invention makes lowfat cooking much easier and eliminates the need for wasteful, expensive non-stick sprays
•Mandolin: Decent mandolins usually start at around $50 and are ideal for making julienne cuts and thin, uniform slices of vegetables or fruits.
•Vegetable steamer insert (metal)
•Cookie scoop (a small handheld number that makes scooping cookie dough a breeze)
•Bamboo sushi mat
•Mortar and pestle (This is great for crushing spices, peanuts, etc. Plus it looks cool on your counter.)
•Pastry tool (for frosting): If you don't have one of these, you can cheat and use a small plastic bag with a hole cut out of a corner.
•Sprouting lids: These make sprouting clean and easy, especially compared to cheesecloth!

Small Appliances:

•Toaster oven
•Good quality blender (Cuisinart is a good brand)
•High quality food processor (Cuisinart again, and no, I don't see a dime)
•Juice machine (if you are a juicing novice, usually a fairly inexpensive one will suffice)
•Hand held electric beater: These are indispensable for making fluffy frostings and mashed potatoes; they are usually available for under $20

Optional but Fabulous Small Appliances:

•Soymilk/nondairy milk machine: This will pay for itself in no time and ensures that you are drinking the freshest and least processed milk possible—I recommend the SoyaPower brand (see page 260 for details).
•Rice cooker (These are inexpensive and cook rice perfectly every time—plus they're crazy easy to use.)
•Reverse osmosis water purifier: Although not really an appliance, these systems can be rented or purchased for your kitchen sink. They're also an easy way to use purified water in all of your cooking.
•Yogurt maker: Especially if you have a soymilk machine, this is an easy, affordable way to make and consume fresh, unprocessed nondairy yogurt.
•Excalibur food dehydrator: This makes for awesome dried fruits, veggies, roll-ups, tofu jerky, and more.
•Waffle maker (What's better than homemade waffles on a Sunday morning? Don't answer that.)

PART THREE: MENU PLANNING FOR SUCCESS

Menu planning is an invaluable tool to consider when upgrading your life. By taking a little time to plan in advance, you're creating the outline for an easier, healthier lifestyle. For a photocopiable (is that a word?) worksheet that you can use for menu and shopping planning, please see page 259.

WHY SHOULD YOU PLAN YOUR MEALS IN ADVANCE?

☺ Your wallet will thank you. You will be able to stick to a budget much more easily when shopping with a list, rather than roaming around aimlessly in the frozen foods section. Plus, when you know you can make a delish dish at home, you'll be *way* less tempted to eat out!

☺ Greater health! You will be much more likely to eat healthy, fresh foods at home if you have a plan. Tired and hungry? Instead of reaching for a processed meal, you can look at your menu list (conveniently posted on the fridge) and see some of the dishes you can prepare in no time. And, you will have all of the necessary ingredients on hand to do so!

☺ Children love being part of activities in the kitchen. Get them involved in planning meals, shopping, and preparing foods. It's a great way to increase family harmony and make an adult "chore" into something fun!

SOUND GOOD SO FAR? WANT TO KNOW WHAT TO DO NEXT?

•First, decide what meals and foods you would like to eat in the upcoming week. When deciding what you are going to be eating, keep *balance* in mind as well as the tips listed below. For example, you can choose a foundation of healthy, light dishes (such as "green" recipes) and include lots of fruits and veggies. Then, if you like, you can throw in a few treats as well, such as an "extravagant entrée" (pages 157-179) and a dessert from this book.

•A great tool to help bring balance into your daily eating habits is to use the color coding system outlined on page 45. For example, I mainly make "green" and "blue" recipes, with a few "purple" ones thrown in on occasion. There is, however, no exact science here to dictate which colors to use when. It depends on your current health goals, your metabolism, and your level of activity. For more information on the subject, please see page 45.

•Try to make your best guess as to how much your family will eat in the coming week and plan accordingly. Make sure you take the time to read through the recipes you will be making and write down every single thing you will need onto your shopping list.

•Go grocery shopping with your list and stick to it. If you forget your list, go back home and get it. *It's that important!*

•If it helps, you may want to set aside a day of the week to make some of the foods on your list. For example, can you make a casserole on Saturday and have it for lunch the rest of the week? Can you make some of the more time consuming elements of your meals (sauces, etc.) in advance when you aren't as busy, so that meals during the weekdays can be quick and easy?

TIPS TO MAKE MEAL PLANNING *REALLY* WORK FOR YOU

•Be sure to take stock of what you have on hand. Do you have some produce (or other) items that need to be used up very soon? Incorporate them into that weeks meals as soon as possible. Setting aside a special spot in your fridge for just such "emergency" items can also help you reduce waste.

•Using more in-season items not only makes for greater health, it is also better for your budget and the environment. Besides, fresh, in-season produce makes cooking a joy! What is more delicious than asparagus or strawberries eaten fresh and at the peak of their ripeness?

•Are there items that can be consolidated? This applies to both shopping and cooking. It will save you both time in the kitchen and money at the grocery store. For example, fresh mint can be purchased for both spring rolls and Fatoush salad. A larger batch of rice can be cooked and paired with a stir-fry or curry and then be used as a base for veggie fried rice the next day. Polenta makes a great side dish for dinner and can be used the next day for Mexican polenta pie.

•Be realistic. If you have goals, great! Be sure to work toward them in a way that is encouraging to you and reasonable to achieve.

•If you know there will be busier times (such as after a long day at work), try to plan some very easy, quick meals. You don't want to discourage yourself from eating well because you are too tired! Be sure to incorporate the necessary amount of "30 minutes or under" meals into your week so that you can *realistically* follow your menu plan.

•Combine new things you wish to try with old favorites. If you try too many new things at once, you may feel overwhelmed and be less likely to stick with your positive changes. *Slow and steady wins the race, bunnyheart*!

•If you want to make a time-consuming dish, you may wish to pair it with something simple or familiar.

•For menu ideas, check out the Menu Suggestions Chapter (pages 245-250). There are ideas there for just about any type of meal you would want to create.

•Set specific days for meal planning, grocery shopping, and cooking. For example, you may wish to make your plan on Wednesday, shop on Thursday, and do some of the cooking preparations on Sunday.

•Make a guideline for the upcoming week (or photocopy the one on page 259) to post on your fridge. The recipes you incorporate into it can all be made at a moment's notice because you will have done your shopping based on your plan. The following is an example of what a weekly guideline looks like (notice the emphasis on fruits, veggies, "green" and "blue" recipes, and the consolidation of items).

EXAMPLE:

RADIANTLY FABULOUS HEALTH FOR THE WEEK OF MAY 3-MAY 9!

MEAL PLANNING DAY: Thursday

SHOPPING DAY: Friday

COOKING DAY: Saturday (It will take under an hour and a half to prepare the veggies for the spring rolls and make the Creamy Hummus, The Peanut Sauce, the Classic Vinaigrette, and the chili-roasted almonds.)

BREAKFASTS:
•Whole fruits: grapefruit, mangoes, raspberries, and apples
•Tropical Smoothie
•High fiber cereal
•Sunday breakfast: Raspberry Lemon Zest Pancakes and Lemon-Rosemary Home Fries

LUNCHES:
•Fresh Greek Delight (using pre-made hummus)
•Dolmadas and a Greek Salad (with pre-made Classic Vinaigrette)
•Tasty Lowfat Tostadas (made using leftover Perfect Pinto Beans)
•Fresh Thai Spring Rolls (with pre-made peanut sauce) and Kid's Favorite Veggie Fried Rice (using leftover rice from the Skinny Dinny meal)
•Leftovers (Lemon Asparagus Linguine, Mexican Fiesta Rice, Mexican Polenta Bake, and Black-eyed Peas with Kale)

QUICK DINNERS OR MINI-MEALS THAT CAN BE MADE IN A HURRY:
•Fresh Greek Delight (using the leftover hummus)
•Light Night Asparagus-Bean Curry
•Creamy Polenta
•Greek Salad (with pre-made Classic Vinaigrette)
•Kid's Favorite Veggie Fried Rice (using the leftover rice)
•Fresh Thai Spring Rolls (since the veggies are prepped in the fridge and the sauce is on hand)

COMPLETE DINNERS:
1. Light Night Asparagus-Bean Curry, served with baked potatoes (bake a few extra for Sunday morning's home fries) and Kid's Kale
2. Black-eyed Peas with Kale, served with Creamy Polenta (make this version of polenta a day or two before you prepare the Mexican Polenta Bake) and a green salad with Classic Vinaigrette
3. Mexican Polenta Bake, served with the Avocado and Grapefruit Salad with Chili-Roasted Almonds
4. Dolmadas, Hummus, and Zatar Wedges, served with a Greek Salad
5. Perfect Pinto Beans, Mexican Fiesta Rice, and Avocado and Grapefruit Salad with Chili-Roasted Almonds
6. Skinny Dinny with a Fresh Thai Spring Roll and Asian Asparagus Wraps
7. Lemon Asparagus Linguine with Sourdough Bruschetta and a salad (Baby Greens with Arugula, Apples, and Caramelized Pecans)

DESSERT OF THE WEEK:
Quick, Light, and Outta Sight Turnovers (made using the thawed phyllo from the Asian Asparagus Wraps)

PART FOUR: SUPER HANDY KITCHEN TIPS!

This is the part where I pass on random (yet meaningful) advice that will hopefully save you time and stress in the kitchen. It is in handy dandy alphabetical format for your viewing pleasure.

◆ALMONDS: I always keep toasted, sliced (or slivered) almonds on hand. To toast raw sliced (or slivered) almonds, simply place them in a dry pan over medium-low heat for about 3-5 minutes. Stir or shake them often while they are cooking to ensure even browning. Be sure to watch them closely—they can burn quickly! When they are aromatic and golden brown, remove them from the pan immediately. Once cooled, store them in an airtight glass jar, either in the fridge or at room temperature.

◆**ALUMINUM FOIL**: Please do not use aluminum foil to cover anything that has tomatoes or fresh lemon juice in it, as those types of citric acids can leach aluminum out of the foil and into the food. I learned this one the hard way many years ago, after I found bits of silver in my food!

◆**ARROWROOT**: Working with arrowroot is fabulous as long as you understand that there is a fine line between perfectly thick and overly thick. If it is allowed to overcook (or if too much is added), arrowroot can become gummy. It is an effective, nutritious way to thicken just about anything in a pinch—it simply needs to be heated to work its magic. Please see the glossary on page 251 for the definition.

◆**ASPARAGUS**: To trim asparagus: Hold the bottom of one spear with your hand. Bend the top over with your other hand. The asparagus spear will snap and break in the exact position that will separate the tender portion from the tough base.

◆**BALANCE**: A key element to making a dish taste *just right* is balance. Being aware of the different types of flavors (sweet, salty, sour, pungent, rich, and bitter) will give you the ability to "round out" your dishes with proper balance. For example, a little sweetness can help mellow a savory dish, or a little lemon can bring balance to a sweet dish. Of course, not all flavors need be present in every dish—they are just something to be aware of as you experiment in the kitchen.

◆**BEANS (DRY)**: These little gems become much more digestible when soaked before cooking. Simply place them in plenty of water to cover and soak them overnight (or for 8-12 hours). My favorite time to start soaking them is first thing in the morning. That way, they are ready for dinner that evening. Simply drain and rinse them and they are ready to go. I have found that I need to reduce the water content a bit when using soaked beans (for example, from 3 cups of water down to 2½ cups of water). You may need to experiment just a bit, as everyone's cookware, stove, and method of cooking will create slight variations. Finally, I always recommend adding kombu to every pot of beans. Kombu will aid digestibility and help enhance the natural flavor of the beans (without adding unwanted flavors). Soaking the beans and adding kombu to them should keep people from singing the musical fruit song to you too often.

◆**BREADCRUMBS**: To make healthy breadcrumbs, take whole grain (or sprouted) bread and break it into pieces. Next, whirl it in a food processor until it turns into fine crumbs. It will then store in the freezer (in an airtight bag or container) for a month or more.

◆**BRIGHT BLUE**: This is the color you can magically get if you put fresh garlic *and* fresh lemon in a dish. I noted this here to prevent you from unnecessarily thinking your food is moldy!

◆**BROCCOLI**: The stems of broccoli are just as edible as the florets. Simply remove the stem's tough outer layer with a vegetable peeler and chop the inner stalk. Since the stem takes longer to cook than the florets, make sure you cut the inner stalk into very small pieces. That way, the cooking time will even out when cooking the florets and stem pieces together.

◆**CHILI/HOT PEPPERS**: To prepare a whole hot pepper, you may wish to begin by putting on some rubber gloves, as the hot oils can linger on your fingers for quite some time. Next, remove the stem portion. Cut the chili open lengthwise and remove the seeds (unless you want to triple the heat!). You will also want to remove the "membranes" (the white portions inside the pepper). Finally, chop or dice the pepper on a designated surface (please see the cutting board tip on page 40).

◆**CLEAN-UP**: When I'm in the kitchen, I always end up ahead when I clean as I go. For example, I'll rinse things (such as a cup that had almonds in it) immediately and put them in the drying rack. Conveniently, cookware that has had oil-free vegan food on it does not need to be washed with soap to become clean. Of course, anything with oil on it does require a more hot and soapy application. One item that I especially make sure to clean immediately after I use it is a strainer. It is far easier to rinse it out right after draining some pasta than it is to pick dried bits of noodles out of the holes an hour later!

◆COCOA: In my recipes, I use organic, non-alkali-processed cocoa powder, which can be purchased from health food stores and most supermarkets. If you use the Dutch process (European) cocoa for baking, it may prevent your dish from rising properly, as this type of cocoa is treated with alkali (which reacts differently to certain ingredients).

◆COOKING TIMES: As there are so many potential variations in ovens, altitude, and cookware, you may need to adjust the suggested cooking times. For example, if your oven is fairly old, things may take longer. If you are at sea level with a crankin' new stove, things may cook more quickly.

◆CUTTING BOARDS: I like to keep separate cutting boards for different uses. For example, I use the top side of my main cutting board for just about everything savory, including onions and garlic. However, if I want to chop up some apples for a pie, I do not want them to pick up those flavors! So, I keep a "neutral" cutting board for things like fruit. Lastly, I keep a separate spot (the *back* of one of my cutting boards) for chopping chili peppers, as their heat will linger on the board and will flavor anything else put in the same spot.

◆DIRT: You may need to wash certain foods more thoroughly, as they can occasionally be very dirt laden. This seems to happen randomly for some reason, so it is always a good idea to check your vegetables well, even if you are used to them being dirt-free. Some vegetables like leeks and green onions often hide dirt under their layers. Others such as cilantro and spinach can require several rinses when their leaves are exceptionally dirty.

◆FLOUR: You may notice that I use whole wheat pastry flour for just about everything. That's because this variety of flour retains the nutritional benefits of being made from only *whole* wheat, yet produces much lighter results than regular whole wheat flour does. Almost any time a recipe calls for white (all-purpose) flour, whole wheat pastry flour can be substituted. However, since it is low in gluten, I do not recommend using it in yeasted breads. Whole wheat pastry flour can be found in any health food store, and in many supermarkets as well. On a final note, there are some people who feel that even whole wheat pastry flour is "heavy," as they are used to consuming only refined flours. For these people, I have found that using half whole wheat pastry flour and half unbleached white flour is a great "transition trick." Of course, if you are gluten intolerant, you will use a gluten-free all-purpose flour (see the gluten tip below).

◆FRESHNESS: You may notice that I often minimize the cooking of many ingredients. This is because, although I am not a pure raw foodist, I do believe that foods should be eaten in their freshest state. I try to use heat minimally in order to preserve as many nutrients as possible. Many of the superfoods (such as garlic, lemon juice, ginger, and fresh herbs) can be added to a dish *after* it is already cooked. This helps to retain their nutrients as well as their bright flavors.

◆GARLIC: If you have a proper garlic press, you will hardly ever need to remove the paper-like skins. However, here is a little trick that makes life easier when (and if) you do need peeled garlic cloves. First, cut off the very end of the garlic. Using a chef's knife, press the flat side of the blade onto the clove of garlic (using your hand for pressure). This will lightly crush the garlic and loosen its skin, making it very easy to remove. For a recommendation on what kind of garlic press to use, please see page 34.

◆GINGER: Contrary to popular theory, it is not necessary to peel ginger. Since many of the nutrients are located very close to the skin, peeling ginger reduces its nutritional content. Of course, if you dislike the idea of tiny bits of ginger skin in your dish, you can peel it. Additionally, people are often surprised when I show them how much juice can be squeezed out of the ginger pulp. When you grate ginger, make sure to squeeze the juice from the stringy pulp. This can be accomplished just by using your fingers. Flavorful ginger juice—too good to waste!

◆GLUTEN: For those avoiding gluten, I have tried my best to include substitutions whenever possible. In my recipes, I have considered oats to be a gluten-free item. However, if you cannot eat oats, you may wish to try quinoa flakes. Please see page 44 for more details. Finding acceptable gluten-free products can be challenging, as they really vary in quality. I have found the "Tinkyada" brand of *brown* rice pasta to be less mushy than other gluten-free pastas. Also, "Bob's Red Mill" makes an affordable all-purpose gluten-free flour that works quite well in most recipes.

♦**JULIENNE CUTS**: The easiest way to make julienne cuts is to buy a good quality mandolin. However, making julienne cuts "from scratch" is not as hard as you may think. For example, to julienne a carrot, begin by peeling it and trimming the ends. Next, cut it into 3-inch segments. With a good chef's knife, cut each segment vertically to create several pieces that are about ¼-inch thick by 3-inches long. Finally, cut each piece lengthwise to create "matchsticks."

♦**LEMON/LIME JUICE**: You may have noticed that I call for a *lot* of fresh citrus juice in my recipes! To make life easier, I recommend purchasing a handheld citrus squeezer (please see page 35 for more details) or a simple citrus juicing insert (to be placed over a cup). There is also a little trick you can use that will help you extract the maximum amount of juice. Before you slice your fruit in half, roll it on the counter, pressing it firmly with your hand. This will help release the juices from the skin. Finally, I strongly suggest using freshly squeezed juice whenever it is called for in these recipes, as it makes a huge difference in the flavor and quality of the finished product.

♦**LOWER CALORIE SHAKES AND SMOOTHIES**: If you don't mind taking a wee little bit of flavor away from the shakes and smoothies in the breakfast section, you can easily substitute a small amount water for some of the nondairy milk or juice. Of course, they are not *quite* as tasty this way, but they are lower in calories and less expensive.

♦**MARGARINE**: The recipes in this book will work best with a *regular* non-hydrogenated margarine (not whipped or reduced fat). "Earth Balance" is a good brand, and they even carry sticks (which work well as they are so easy to measure). In our household, we do keep a lighter, whipped margarine on hand as well, but we use it mainly for spreading on toast.

♦**MEASURING CUPS**: When measuring something sticky (such as molasses or brown rice syrup), it helps tremendously to spray (or lightly coat) the inside of the measuring cup with oil. That way, what you are measuring will pour right out without sticking to the cup.

♦**MEYER LEMONS**: These are a delicious and unusual variety of lemons that are much sweeter than regular lemons. However, since the recipes in this book call for regular lemons, I do not recommend substituting Meyer lemon juice or zest.

♦**OIL USAGE**: Here is a trick to minimize oil usage when pan-frying foods: You can keep a one teaspoon measuring device next to the oil in your cupboard. That way, you can start with just a little oil (which is often enough) and only add more if needed.

♦**OLIVES**: I tend to buy pitted olives as they are much less time consuming to prepare. However, if you do need to pit some olives, here is a trick: Using a chef's knife, press the flat side of the blade onto the olive (using your hand to create pressure). This will loosen the pit from the flesh of the olive so that you can remove it with ease. One final note: There is a reason why I always call for high quality olives such as kalamatas. Canned black olives have very little flavor, and often retain a "tinny" taste.

♦**ORANGE JUICE**: As you may notice, I use a lot of orange juice in my recipes, and I often say "the fresher the better." For this purpose, "fresh squeezed" refrigerated orange juice works quite well. Just make sure it says "not from concentrate" on the label. It is almost as good as squeezing it yourself, but much less work.

♦**PEANUTS**: Generally, I call for *crushed* peanuts in my recipes, as their flavor is much more pronounced this way. Crushing them is quick and easy. Simply place dry-roasted peanuts in a plastic bag. Press most of the air out of the bag, then seal it. From there, you can go over the bag with a rolling pin until the peanuts are crumbly. If you don't have a rolling pin, you can use any heavy object to lightly pound on the bag. Another way to go (that has nothing to do with a plastic bag) is to place your peanuts in a mortar and pestle and crush them that way.

◆PHYLLO: For some reason, working with phyllo (also called *filo*) can be very intimidating (or downright scary!) for people who are unfamiliar with it. However, it really is very easy to use and works fabulously for making quick, impressive dishes. *Here are a few tips for working with phyllo*:

•Phyllo does not like fresh air. If it is allowed to sit uncovered for very long (or is not securely wrapped when stored), it will dry out. Dry phyllo=sad phyllo.

•When making a dish that calls for phyllo, you may find it helpful to cover most of the phyllo dough with a slightly damp towel so that it doesn't dry out.

•I have found that patience makes a big difference when working with phyllo. Take your time unfolding the phyllo and separating its layers. Do not allow the fear of it drying out make you work too quickly! Of course, this does not mean that you should have detailed phone conversations while making baklava. It is still important to expedite any phyllo making process, as the dough will be easier to work with that way. The reason I mention this is because when I was a phyllo novice, the common advice to "work quickly" always made me feel stressed, and I worked a little *too* quickly! A happy medium of an efficient, yet *relaxed* process when using phyllo is the ideal.

•Always plan ahead when making a dish that calls for phyllo. If your phyllo is frozen, you have two options. If you have enough time, you can put it in the refrigerator for 24 hours before you begin. If you are short on time, the phyllo can sit (securely packaged) at room temperature for a few hours.

•Have all of the necessary filling (and other) ingredients ready to go before you unwrap your phyllo. It is also a good idea to have your work area clean and organized before you begin.

•If your phyllo has been in the fridge, you may find it helpful to let it sit at room temperature (securely packaged) for up to an hour before using it.

•Any unused phyllo dough can be rewrapped securely in plastic (make sure not to leave any air gaps). Wrap it in a second plastic bag (airtight again), and store it in the refrigerator for up to a month.

◆SESAME SEEDS: Toasting sesame seeds brings out their fullest flavor. To toast raw sesame seeds, place them in a dry skillet over low (or medium-low) heat. Shake the pan often to evenly brown the seeds. Toast them for several minutes, or until they are lightly browned and aromatic. Remove the seeds from the pan immediately, since they can over-brown quickly if left in contact with a hot pan.

◆SCALLIONS (GREEN ONIONS): To trim scallions, simply cut off the rootlets at the base, as well as the very top of the green portion. Although some cookbooks tell you to toss out the green parts of the scallion, I always use them. Whenever scallions are called for in my recipes, you can use the entire portion of the trimmed scallion (both white and green parts).

◆SUGAR: The most commonly used sugar in my recipes is usually referred to as "organic white sugar." This refers to an unrefined, light colored, granular sugar. The other types of dry sugars used in this book include brown sugar (available organically grown), sucanat (a coarser type of brown sugar), and powdered sugar (less sweet and more fluffy; perfect for pie fillings and frostings). If I do not specify the type and simply call for "organic sugar," you may use organic white sugar, brown sugar, or sucanat.

◆THE THRILLS OF TOFU: "What type of tofu should I use?" is something I hear very often. I like to keep things simple in life, so there are only two types I *ever* use. Here's my version of Tofu 101:

•The first kind of tofu I use is silken tofu. This is usually not refrigerated when you buy it (unless the store manager needs a tofu clue), and is found in aseptic packaging. I mainly use this kind for desserts. As far as firmness goes, I buy either firm or extra-firm silken tofu. When one of my recipes uses silken tofu, it will call for 12.3 ounce package(s) of tofu, and the word "silken" will be used.

•The second type of tofu I use is fresh, water-packed tofu. This type is *always* kept refrigerated.

For this type of tofu, I only use the extra-firm variety (or firm, if extra-firm is unavailable). This kind of tofu is perfect for stir-fries and savory entrées. If a recipe just calls for tofu (and does not say *silken*), this is the kind you will need to use.

•To store tofu once it has been opened, place it in a container that has a tight fitting lid. Pour enough water over the tofu to cover it. Place the lid on the container and store it in the refrigerator. Every other day, replace the old water with fresh water. The tofu will store for up to a week this way.

•Freezing your tofu will give it a "fishy" (or meaty) type of texture. To freeze tofu, simply pop the whole container into the freezer and let it sit overnight (or up to several months). The next morning, set it out to thaw. Once it has thawed, there will be lots of water to squeeze out. Once you have gently squeezed the excess water out with your hands, the tofu will be ready to use. Incidentally, you can use either type of tofu for this purpose as they will both go along willingly on this one.

•Pressing tofu takes only minutes, but really makes a difference. Pressed tofu browns more easily, is firmer, and also soaks up marinades more thoroughly. To press a pound of tofu, cut it into eight slabs. Place the slabs in a single layer over paper towels (or lint-free cloth towels). Cover the tofu with more paper towels, then place a cutting board or cookie sheet over the top. Next, place "weights" on top of the board or sheet to help compress the tofu. Examples of weights you can use for this purpose include canned beans, a gallon of water, a sleeping cat, or a calm child. Allow the tofu to rest in this position for as long as you can. Even ten minutes will improve the texture of your tofu!

•Another way to maximize the texture of tofu when using it in a savory dish is to brown it first (usually in oil, garlic, and tamari) and then remove it to a plate. After the rest of the dish has cooked, the tofu gets added back in as a final step. This way, the tofu retains a nicely browned, crisp appearance and texture, rather than becoming soft and mushy.

◆**VEGETABLE OIL (SOYBEAN OIL)**: This oil may be marketed as "healthy," but is actually a highly refined by-product of the soy industry. In traditional Chinese medicine, it is considered toxic. Better choices for an all-purpose oil would include coconut, sunflower, or non-virgin olive oil.

◆**WATER**: I recommend using purified water to cook with whenever possible. Not only is it healthier, it makes everything taste better.

◆**ZEST**: I call for a fair bit of citrus zest in my recipes. Surprisingly, this is not meant to annoy you. There is just nothing like it to uniquely flavor a dish and add a touch of elegance. Plus, citrus zest is the bomb, nutritionally speaking! However, I always recommend using *organic* citrus fruits for zesting because citrus peels aren't considered a food by the USDA. Therefore, non-organic citrus peels are subject to excessive amounts of chemicals and dyes. To zest a citrus fruit, I recommend a handheld citrus zester. They are available from around $10 and make zesting fun and easy! For real. Another way to zest is to use a very fine, sharp grater. Either way, be careful not to use the white portion underneath the colored exterior, as it is very bitter. Kind of like you might have been before you realized there was a legitimate reason for all the zesting.

Chapter Five: A Guideline for Using the Recipes

After over a year spent writing this book (and fifteen years of preparing for it in other ways), it is *finally* in your hands, my friend! I do hope you love it. Dozens of recipe testers have helped me make extra sure that things will work as smoothly as possible. In this process, I found it enlightening to observe how varied their palates were. For example, one person would say a recipe was too salty, while the next one would increase the salt! Therefore, I ask that you use these recipes as a guideline. However, as I have personally made these recipes many times for family, friends, and clients, I have found them to be best received *exactly* as they are written. In fact, this was a major goal I had when writing this cookbook. I wanted to make everything as specific as possible so that the reader could replicate my results when following these recipes just as they are written. However, if you do find that you need to increase or decrease a particular ingredient in several recipes, this will give you an indication that you can alter the rest of the recipes in a similar way.

The testers also helped ensure that the recipes would work at low altitude. In my kitchen, everything was as it should be, but I was at an altitude of 7,500 feet! I was slightly panicked. How would I make sure that these recipes would also work at sea level? Well, thanks to my lovely low altitude recipe testers, I have made adjustments to ensure that they should work very well at sea level. However, if you do live at high altitude, you can slightly *decrease* leavening amounts (baking soda and baking powder) and slightly *increase* liquids. Recipes may also take a little longer to cook at higher altitudes. All in all, I have tried my best to make these recipes work for a standard, sea level kitchen. Although I have not found this to be an exact science, I hope this helps if you do end up having to "tweak" any of the recipes because of our variations in altitude.

You may also find it very helpful to check out the section on "Super Handy Kitchen Tips" (pages 38-43) before you begin. Additionally, if you aren't sure what an ingredient is all about, please refer to the glossary (pages 251-253).

Finally, it is always a good idea to read through the recipe that you are about to make beforehand. That way, you will become familiar with all of the steps involved and know in advance what you will need to have on hand.

WHAT ARE THE SECRET CODES AT THE BOTTOM OF EACH RECIPE ALL ABOUT?

GF = GLUTEN-FREE GF means that the recipe is either already gluten-free, or that it can be made gluten-free with the suggested substitution(s). For those truly dedicated to eating a gluten-free diet, oats are often a point of contention. Some people believe that oats may be contaminated with gluten. Others believe that although oats are technically gluten-free, they can *feel* like gluten in their systems. For these people, I would suggest that quinoa flakes (not to be confused with whole quinoa) offer the best replacement (nutritionally and functionally) that I know of. Quinoa flakes can be purchased in most health food stores. In certain areas, you may also be able to locate a relatively new product, gluten-free rolled oats. Additionally, recipes that call for tamari have been labeled as gluten-free, since you can use wheat-free tamari (available in health food stores and many supermarkets).

SF = SOY-FREE For those who do not wish to consume soy products in any form, I have labeled the soy-free recipes as SF. When a recipe calls for margarine, I do not label it as soy-free because the non-hydrogenated margarine I am familiar with contains some soy. Additionally, many recipes are not labeled as soy-free because they contain tamari. I do know of several people who avoid soy, yet do not have a problem with a little tamari in their food. If this exception applies to you as well, many more recipes will become available.

30 MINUTES OR UNDER! This applies to recipes that can be made in, yes, thirty minutes or less, start to finish. However, many other recipes without this tag are just as *easy* to make. They may simply require soaking, marinating, or sprouting. It is always best to read through a recipe before you begin, as this will give you a good idea of the exciting journey that lies ahead.

COLOR CODES ("GREEN," "BLUE," OR "PURPLE") This system was devised as a quick reference as to which recipes are best eaten in moderation and which should be emphasized. Keep in mind, however, that each color category also contains variations. Not all purple foods are considered equal, and so on. Additionally, if you would like a list of all of the "green" and "blue" recipes from this book (as well as other "green" food ideas), please see the reference guide on pages 254-257.

• **GREEN:** Green means go! These recipes are low in fat and calories, and high in fiber. They are the ideal foods to emphasize in our daily diets for optimum health.

• **BLUE:** These recipes are still suitable for everyday eating, but are a little richer than the green category. However, most people can still thrive while eating many "blue" foods.

• **PURPLE:** These are the richest recipes in this book as they contain higher amounts of fats and sugars than the others (and the occasional refined ingredient). Even so, keep in mind that even the "purple" foods from this book are a relatively healthy choice when compared with what is typically eaten in the standard American diet.

Given all of this, please remember that no dietary system is an exact science. Every person is different. Everyone has individual health goals, metabolism, levels of activity, and current states of health. Do you need to lose weight? Eating all "green" foods will probably get you there the fastest. You can certainly still lose weight eating "blue" and "purple" foods, but it might take longer. Of course, exercise also plays a role, and if you are very active, your body may *need* more "blue" foods to sustain itself. Which color codes you should frequent also depends on how much you eat. If you eat smaller amounts of food in general, you can allow more "blue" and even "purple" foods since you will not be eating as *much*. Of course, anyone wanting to opt for the ultimate vitalizing diet cannot go wrong eating lots of fruits and veggies, and emphasizing mainly "green" recipes, as they are light and nourishing.

Am I confusing you? I certainly hope not. The point of all of this is: Please use this information as a helpful tool to determine what *your* body needs. Only **you** know what your level of commitment is and what will work for you in this moment. Rely on your inner wisdom and common sense, factoring in how much you exercise, how *much* you eat, and what your goals are. This is just another tool you can use for your benefit to help you achieve the radiant health you truly deserve!

Chapter Six: A Beautiful Start to Your Day!

Whether you want a large brunch to impress guests with or a light and healthy breakfast just for yourself, you're in the right section! Of course, some of the best things to eat for breakfast aren't even listed here. Fresh fruit, high fiber (whole grain) cereals, green drinks (such as wheatgrass), and cooked or sprouted grains are all great choices as well. One of my favorite ways to greet the morning is to squeeze a fresh lemon and drink it mixed with water. It is a cleansing, alkalinizing, and zippy way to start the day off right!

Frozen Bananas

This is more of a technique than a recipe, but I've heard too many disturbing stories about poor banana freezing methods to leave it out! I like to use *very* ripe bananas for this purpose. I find that I can always omit added sweeteners from my smoothies and shakes because a really ripe banana lends the perfect amount of sweetness.

INGREDIENT: BANANAS (RIPE OR VERY RIPE)

1. Peel the bananas and discard the peels (not onto the floor).
2. Break into 1 or 2-inch pieces and place in a plastic bag. Leave enough room (don't overpack the bag) so that the chunks can freeze individually. Seal the bag so that it is airtight.
3. Place in the freezer, laying the bag flat, so that the pieces can spread out and won't freeze together too much. After they have been frozen for 8-10 hours, they will be ready to use. They will keep for several weeks or longer in the freezer. If, at some point they do freeze together, simply thump the bag on the counter with feigned rage. They will separate out of fear.

SERVES: THE PURPOSE; 30 MINUTES OR UNDER! GF/SF/Green

Mango Ginger-Mint Power Smoothie

This smoothie is very unusual and chock full of some of my favorite superfoods. Mint and ginger are cleansing, energizing foods, and also aid in circulation and digestion. Flax is cleansing as well and is a great source of fiber and essential Omega-3 fatty acids. Incidentally, it doesn't really matter which of these fruits are fresh or frozen. What matters is to make sure at least two are frozen to maintain a proper level of thickness. All in all, this is a zippy, zesty, nourishing way to kick start the morning!

1 TABLESPOON GOLDEN FLAXSEEDS (OR GROUND FLAX MEAL)

1 CUP FROZEN PINEAPPLE CHUNKS

1 LARGE, FRESH MANGO (1½ CUPS PEELED AND CHOPPED MANGO)

1 FROZEN BANANA (SEE ABOVE RECIPE)

1 TABLESPOON (PACKED) FRESH MINT

1-2 TEASPOONS GRATED FRESH GINGER*

1¼ CUPS ORANGE JUICE (OR MANGO JUICE), THE FRESHER THE BETTER

1. If you are using whole flaxseeds, place them in the blender first along with a little of the juice. Blend until the flaxseeds are as emulsified as possible.
2. Next, place the fruits, mint, and ginger in a blender and pour just enough of the juice in to blend. Once all the chunks, bits, pieces, and parts are emulsified, add the rest of the juice and blend thoroughly. If needed, you may add a little more orange juice until smooth. Drink it. Feel gooooood.

SERVES 2-3; 30 MINUTES OR UNDER! GF/SF/Green

*1 teaspoon of grated ginger will yield a subtle ginger taste, whereas the full amount makes a bold ginger statement. Many people find that 1½ teaspoons is the perfect amount.

Virtuous Vanilla Shake

This shake is probably #1 on my list, as well as my daughter's! It tastes delicious and we always have the ingredients on hand. I absolutely adore the simplicity of this shake. Who would guess that only three ingredients would come together for such a sweet and satisfying meal in a glass? Be sure the bananas you are using are ripe enough, however, or your shake won't be sweet enough.

2 FROZEN BANANAS (SEE PAGE 47)

1-2 CUP(S) NONDAIRY MILK (*SEE NOTE AT THE BOTTOM OF THIS PAGE)

1 TEASPOON VANILLA EXTRACT

Place the frozen bananas, 1 cup of the milk, and the vanilla in a blender. Blend on low, and then turn to high for several seconds to fully emulsify. Add more milk *only* as needed. Serve immediately.

SERVES 1-2; 30 MINUTES OR UNDER! GF/SF/GREEN

Four Goodness Shake

This incredibly simple shake is a meal in a glass and sooo nourishing. Carob is very alkalinizing and is also high in calcium, potassium, fiber, and top notch good vibes.

2 FROZEN BANANAS (SEE PAGE 47)

1-2 CUP(S) NONDAIRY MILK*

2 TABLESPOONS CAROB POWDER

OPTIONAL: 1 TABLESPOON PURE HEMP PROTEIN POWDER (SUCH AS NUTIVA BRAND)

Place the frozen bananas, 1 cup of the milk, and the carob in a blender. Blend on low, and then turn to high for several seconds to fully emulsify. Add more milk *only* as needed. Serve at once.

SERVES 1-2; 30 MINUTES OR UNDER! GF/SF/GREEN

*The less liquid you add to a shake, the richer and thicker it will be. I give an estimated amount here, as it will depend on your blender and the size of the bananas as to how much milk you will have to add. Simply start with the lesser amount given, and add a little more at a time until you have *just* enough liquid to blend with.

Peanut Butter Cup Shake

As you may have guessed, this is slightly more decadent than the other breakfast drinks. However, it still contains loads of nutrients and is very filling. This also works well as a meal in itself anytime you are hungry and want something quick and satisfying. And *gooooood.*

2 FROZEN BANANAS (SEE PAGE 47)

2 TABLESPOONS NATURAL, CREAMY PEANUT BUTTER

1-2 CUP(S) NONDAIRY MILK* (SEE NOTE AT THE BOTTOM OF THIS PAGE)

1 CUP NONDAIRY ICE CREAM (VANILLA)

3 TABLESPOONS COCOA POWDER

2 TABLESPOONS PURE MAPLE SYRUP (YOU MAY OMIT IF USING SWEETENED MILK)

2 TEASPOONS VANILLA EXTRACT (NOT ARTIFICIAL VANILLA)

Place the bananas, peanut butter, and a little of the milk in your blender. Blend until the bananas are smooth. Add all of the other items and *just* enough of the milk to blend. Serve immediately.

SERVES 2; 30 MINUTES OR UNDER! GF/SF/Blue

Dark Chocolate Shake

Are you craving the taste of pure chocolate goodness? Want to feel relatively good about indulging in said goodness? Look no further. This shake is delicious, rich, satisfying, and still manages to be good for you.

2 FROZEN BANANAS (SEE PAGE 47)

1-2 CUP(S) NONDAIRY MILK (UNSWEETENED OR REGULAR)*

1 CUP NONDAIRY ICE CREAM (VANILLA)

3 TABLESPOONS COCOA POWDER

2 TABLESPOONS MAPLE SYRUP (YOU MAY OMIT IF USING SWEETENED MILK)

2 TEASPOONS VANILLA EXTRACT (DON'T USE ARTIFICIAL VANILLA)

Place the bananas and a little of the milk in your blender. Blend until the bananas are smooth. Add all of the other items and *just* enough of the milk to blend. Serve immediately. This is a chocolate emergency.

SERVES 2; 30 MINUTES OR UNDER! GF/SF/Blue

*The less liquid you add, the richer and thicker it will be. I give an estimated amount here, as it will depend on your blender and size of the bananas as to how much milk you'll have to add. Simply start with the lesser amount given, and add a little more at a time until you have *just* enough liquid to blend with.

Triple Green Purple Power Shake

Want to start your day like a triathlete winner—without those annoying training procedures? This powerhouse will win you a virtual gold metal in no time. Hemp is a wonderful source of chlorophyll and fiber, as well as essential Omega-3 fatty acids. Parsley is purifying, high in vitamins, and even anti-carcinogenic. "Green powder"* contains a vast array of powerfully strengthening and cleansing ingredients such as wheatgrass and spirulena. Blueberries are not only in the game to neutralize the flavor, they are also known for being extremely high in bioflavonoids and vitamins. By using the almond milk, you also benefit from the vast nutrients and alkalinizing power of almonds. You go, champion!

2 FROZEN BANANAS (PLEASE SEE PAGE 47)

¼ CUP (LIGHTLY PACKED) FRESH CURLY PARSLEY

2 TABLESPOONS PURE HEMP PROTEIN POWDER (NUTIVA IS A GOOD BRAND)

1-3 TEASPOON(S)** "GREEN POWDER"* OR SPIRULENA

1 CUP BLUEBERRIES, FRESH OR FROZEN

2 CUPS NONDAIRY MILK, PREFERABLY ALMOND MILK (RECIPE ON PAGE 187)

Place all of the ingredients in a blender. Blend on low for a bit, and then on high for several seconds to fully emulsify. Serve immediately and feel the magic.

SERVES 2-3; 30 MINUTES OR UNDER! GF/SF/GREEN (TRIPLE GREEN, THAT IS!)

*"Green powder" is a mixture of green superfoods, which is usually added to water or other beverages. It is important to choose a brand that is organic, minimally processed, and without unnecessary additives.

**I have given a range of one to three teaspoons because it can greatly alter the flavor of the shake. With only one teaspoon of green powder, the shake will still taste quite neutral and retain a berry flavor. If you add three teaspoons, the nutrients will be much higher, yet the taste will be much more "green." I encourage you to experiment with the combination that works best for you.

Super Antioxidant Smoothie

This morning drink could not be simpler, and it is absolutely *delicious*! It also happens to be overflowing with some of the best superfoods currently available to the human race: blueberries, pomegranate, and acai. Blueberries have been receiving lots of press in the last few years due to their rich levels of antioxidants and impeccable nutritional profile. Pomegranate and acai (pronounced ah-sigh-EE) are newer finds to the western market, but are also extremely high in antioxidants and vitamins. You can feel great about enjoying this yummy super-drink!

1 FROZEN BANANA (SEE PAGE 47)

1 CUP FRESH OR FROZEN BLUEBERRIES

1 CUP POMEGRANATE-ACAI JUICE (OR OTHER PURE FRUIT POMEGRANATE JUICE)

Place the frozen banana, berries, and juice in a blender. Blend on low, and then turn to high for several seconds to fully emulsify. Add more juice only if needed.

SERVES 1; 30 MINUTES OR UNDER! GF/SF/GREEN

Berry Good Morning Shake

This shake is so rich and delicious that it's hard to believe it's so healthy and simple. Since berries are one of nature's best sources of antioxidants, vitamins, and fiber, you can drink up and feel fabulous!

2 FROZEN BANANAS (PLEASE SEE PAGE 47)
1 ½ CUPS BERRIES OF CHOICE*
1 ½ -2 ½ CUPS NONDAIRY MILK**
1 TEASPOON VANILLA EXTRACT

Place the frozen bananas, berries, 1½ cups of the milk, and the vanilla in a blender. Blend on low and then turn to high for several seconds to fully emulsify. Add more milk *only* if berry necessary.
SERVES 2-3; 30 MINUTES OR UNDER! GF/SF/GREEN

*If you are using a fairly sweet berry such as strawberries or blueberries, it should yield a sufficiently sweet shake without the need for added sweeteners. However, if you are using a more tart berry (such as raspberries), you may wish to add a bit of pure maple syrup. Incidentally, if you are using blueberries, be sure to check your teeth when you are finished! Social suicide averted yet again.

**The less liquid you add to a shake, the richer and thicker it will be. I give an estimated amount here, as it will depend on your blender and the size of the bananas as to how much milk you will have to add. Simply start with the lesser amount given, and add a little more at a time until you have *just* enough liquid to blend with.

Tropical Smoothie

Drinking this concoction of sweet, tropical fruits will make you feel like you woke up on the beach!
Perfect for breaking the overnight fast, this drink is filling, chock full of vitamins and fiber,
and will get your digestive enzymes pumping!

1 CUP FROZEN STRAWBERRIES
1 CUP FRESH OR FROZEN PINEAPPLE CHUNKS
2 FROZEN BANANAS (PLEASE SEE PAGE 47)
2 CUPS ORANGE JUICE (THE FRESHER THE BETTER)

Combine well in a blender. I usually start the blender on low, and then turn it up to high to make sure everything is mixed well. Enjoy your imaginary tropical getaway!
SERVES 2-3; 30 MINUTES OR UNDER! GF/SF/GREEN

LIL' TIP: IT DOESN'T REALLY MATTER WHICH OF THESE FRUITS ARE FRESH OR FROZEN.
WHAT IS MOST IMPORTANT IS TO MAKE SURE AT LEAST ONE OR TWO OF THE FRUITS
ARE FROZEN IN ORDER TO MAINTAIN THE FROSTY, THICK CONSISTENCY.

Indian Spiced Supergrain Cereal

Here is a fabulously healthy way to start the day when you *really* need some nourishment!

¼ CUP <u>EACH</u>: DRY AMARANTH *AND* DRY QUINOA, WASHED WELL AND DRAINED

1 CUP WATER

5 WHOLE CARDAMOM PODS (PREFERABLY GREEN)

⅛ TEASPOON GROUND GINGER

½ TEASPOON GROUND CINNAMON

¼ TEASPOON VANILLA EXTRACT

¼ CUP NONDAIRY MILK

1 TABLESPOON PURE MAPLE SYRUP

<u>OPTIONAL</u>: 2 TABLESPOONS RAISINS (OR PITTED, CHOPPED DRIED DATES)

1. In a small pan, bring the amaranth, quinoa, water, cardamom, ginger, cinnamon, and vanilla to a boil over high heat, stirring well.

2. Reduce heat to low and simmer for about 10 minutes, or until the grains are tender and the liquid is absorbed.

3. Remove the cardamom pods and add the remaining ingredients. Stir well and serve. Feel the power. Be it. Love it.

SERVES 1-2; 30 MINUTES OR UNDER! GF/SF/GREEN

IF YOU DON'T CARE FOR INDIAN SPICES, YOU CAN MAKE THIS WITHOUT THE CARDAMOM PODS. YOU CAN ALSO ALTER THE SPICE COMBINATION IN ANY WAY THAT FLOATS YOUR BOAT. WHAT MAKES THIS CEREAL SPECIAL IS THE COMBINATION OF THE TWO SUPERFOODS, AMARANTH AND QUINOA. THESE AMAZING GRAINS WILL FUEL YOU UP LIKE NOTHING ELSE!

Love Bug Parfaits

When my daughter first tried this, she took one bite and said: "Can you make this again for me…very, very soon?" She then began to sing about how someone loved her so much that they fed her parfaits for breakfast. Thus, the title of this dish was born! I have also served this to many adults, all of whom were (almost) equally impressed with its delicious, fresh taste and satisfying feel. If you are short on time, you can substitute a nondairy yogurt for the strawberry cream. However, I do urge you to try the cream, as it is very easy to whip together and incredibly tasty!

GOOGY GRANOLA:

1 CUP ROLLED OATS

¼ TEASPOON PLUS ⅛ TEASPOON EACH: SEA SALT AND GROUND CINNAMON

1 TEASPOON FLAXSEEDS (WHOLE)

2 TEASPOONS GROUND FLAXSEED (FLAX MEAL)

1 TABLESPOON EACH: RAW SUNFLOWER SEEDS, SHREDDED COCONUT, AND ORGANIC SUGAR

1 TABLESPOON OIL (COCONUT, SAFFLOWER, NON-VIRGIN OLIVE, OR SUNFLOWER)

¼ TEASPOON VANILLA EXTRACT

3 TABLESPOONS PURE MAPLE SYRUP

3 TABLESPOONS RAISINS

STRAWBERRY CREAM:

1 2.3 OZ. SILKEN TOFU, FIRM OR EXTRA-FIRM (ASEPTIC PACKED)

4 TABLESPOONS PURE MAPLE SYRUP

⅛ TEASPOON SEA SALT

2 TEASPOONS VANILLA EXTRACT

4 LARGE STRAWBERRIES (FRESH OR FROZEN)

2 TABLESPOONS OIL (SUNFLOWER, SAFFLOWER, NON-VIRGIN OLIVE, OR COCONUT)

BERRY IMPORTANT:

1 CUP BERRIES, FROZEN OR FRESH (SLICED STRAWBERRIES OR BLUEBERRIES ARE IDEAL)

1. Preheat your oven to 325° F. Combine the first eight (dry) ingredients for the granola in a medium bowl. Stir in the oil, vanilla, and maple syrup. Combine very well.

2. Spread evenly on a cookie sheet and bake for about 25-35 minutes, stirring every 10 minutes or so, until fragrant and lightly browned (be careful not to overcook). Remove from the oven and allow to cool. Mix in the raisins and set aside.

3. In a food processor, blend all of the ingredients for the strawberry cream. You may need to use a rubber spatula to scrape down the sides in order to make sure that there are no chunks of tofu or strawberries remaining. Process until velvety-smooth.

4. *To create parfection*: In a pretty glass or parfait cup, layer the cream with the granola and berries. Top with a few additional berries and serve immediately. *Ahhhhhh…*

MAKES ABOUT 4 SERVINGS; GF (CONTAINS OATS)/BLUE

Juice of Empowerment

The lemon is the secret. This drink would be far less palatable without its uplifting tang! However, if you don't like quite so much tartness, you can try using half of the recommended amount. This drink is just the thing for when you want to rev up your immune system.

2 CARROTS, WASHED

2 LARGE STALKS CELERY, WASHED

LARGE HANDFUL OF FRESH PARSLEY, WASHED

½ ORGANIC LEMON (DO NOT PEEL), WASHED AND CUT INTO WEDGES

OPTIONAL ADDITIONS:

½ BEET, WASHED AND UNPEELED

½ TO 1-INCH CHUNK OF FRESH GINGER, WASHED AND UNPEELED

Juice according to the manufacturer's guidelines for your juicer—unless you're a rebel. Stir to mix. Freshly made juices such as this are best served *right away*, as they begin to lose their vitamins quickly upon juicing.

SERVES 1; 30 MINUTES OR UNDER! GF/SF/GREEN

Kiddie Power Drink

This juice is the perfect way to get an entire day's worth of fruits and veggies into a child who otherwise might not eat them. My six-year-old daughter intuitively requests this juice when all of the kids at school are "coming down with something."

1 APPLE, CORED (EVERYTHING BUT THE SEEDS) AND WASHED

1 STALK CELERY, WASHED

1 LARGE CARROT (OR 2 SMALL CARROTS), WASHED

SMALL HANDFUL FRESH CURLY PARSLEY (OR OTHER DARK LEAFY GREENS), WASHED

¼ ORGANIC LEMON, UNPEELED AND WASHED (CUT INTO WEDGES)

Juice according to the manufacturer's guidelines for your juicer. Stir to mix. Freshly made juices such as this are best served *right away*, as they begin to lose their vitamins quickly upon juicing. Savor the abiding peace and giddiness that comes with seeing your child drink this.

SERVES 1; 30 MINUTES OR UNDER! GF/SF/GREEN

Carrot-Orange Juice

Do you have anyone in your life that you feel should be ingesting more carrots? This drink will put an end to any and all struggles in that department! I have given this to small children, notoriously the pickiest of all eaters, and they've all invariably drank it down gleefully. It tastes like fresh oranges with an almost imperceptible undertone of carrots. *Delicious*!

2 LARGE ORANGES, PEELED
2 SMALL CARROTS, WASHED

Juice according to the manufacturer's guidelines for your juicer. Stir to mix. Freshly made juices such as this are best served *right away*, as they begin to lose their vitamins quickly upon juicing. *Please note*: an immediate desire for more of this juice is a perfectly normal side effect and generally subsides after about an hour. Or not.

SERVES 1; 30 MINUTES OR UNDER! GF/SF/GREEN

Carrot-Apple-Ginger Juice

You may have already heard of this classic juice, but I include it here because it is another easy way to get people to eat carrots! It's also a great way to take advantage of the magic of ginger. Fresh ginger boosts circulation and the immune system, and is cleansing and medicinal in a myriad of ways. I won't get into all of them right now. Just enjoy your juice.

1 LARGE APPLE, CORED (EVERYTHING BUT THE SEEDS) AND WASHED
2 MEDIUM SIZED CARROTS, WASHED
1/2 TO 1-INCH CHUNK OF FRESH GINGER, UNPEELED AND WASHED

Juice according to the manufacturer's guidelines for your juicer. Stir to mix. Freshly made juices such as this are best served *right away*, as they begin to lose their vitamins quickly upon juicing. Like I said, enjoy your juice.

SERVES 1; 30 MINUTES OR UNDER! GF/SF/GREEN

Lemon-Rosemary Home Fries

These are a very flavorful change of pace from the typical home fries we've all suffered through for most of our lives. This recipe does require cold, cooked potatoes, so you will need to plan ahead. One trick that works for me is to throw a few extra potatoes in the oven when I'm baking and remove them while they are still just a wee bit firm in the middle. That way, they won't become mushy when sautéed in this dish. Think "al dente," but for potatoes!

3 TABLESPOONS NON-HYDROGENATED MARGARINE*

¾ CUP THINLY SLICED OR CHOPPED WHITE OR YELLOW ONION

½ CUP THINLY SLICED SHALLOTS

2 LARGE POTATOES THAT HAVE BEEN BAKED AND COOLED, SKINS ON AND CHOPPED (4 CUPS CHOPPED POTATO PIECES)

1 TABLESPOON MINCED FRESH ROSEMARY LEAF

½ TABLESPOON MINCED FRESH SAGE LEAF

½ TEASPOON (OR TO TASTE) EACH: BLACK PEPPER AND SEA SALT

1 TABLESPOON FRESH LEMON JUICE

OPTIONAL GARNISH: FRESH LEMON SLICES AND/OR WEDGES

1. Sauté margarine, onion, and shallots over medium-high heat until they begin to brown (about 3-5 minutes) and are softened.
2. Add the potatoes, herbs, pepper, and salt. Cook, turning often, until potatoes are golden brown and crisp (about 5 minutes). Sprinkle evenly with the one tablespoon of fresh lemon juice.
3. If desired, garnish with lemon slices. If you like a little extra lemon kick, you can squeeze some juice from the lemon wedges on top of the potatoes. Enjoy!

SERVES 2-3

30 MINUTES OR UNDER! (WITH COOKED POTATOES) GF/SF (WITH OLIVE OIL SUBSTITUTION)/BLUE

*If you cannot eat soy, you may substitute olive oil for the margarine.

Magical Multigrain Pancake Mix

I credit the inspiration for this recipe to Alex Barrows, whose goal was to create the *ultimate* healthy pancake recipe. Before trying these, I associated pancakes with an unhealthy start to the day. However, because this mix is made with 100% whole grains and nutrient rich ingredients, I finally feel guilt-free and inspired to eat pancakes! Another pleasant surprise is that they aren't heavy like other whole grain pancakes I've tried. Keep in mind that this recipe makes fairly crunchy pancakes due to the millet and amaranth. If you prefer them less so, simply omit or reduce the millet (and amaranth if needed) or replace with equal parts rolled oats. Incidentally, this mix also makes fabulous waffles!

1 CUP EACH: WHOLE WHEAT FLOUR*, WHOLE WHEAT PASTRY FLOUR*, CORNMEAL, *AND* OATS*

⅓ CUP EACH: DRY MILLET, DRY AMARANTH, *AND* AMARANTH FLOUR (OR OTHER FLOUR OF CHOICE)

¾ TEASPOON SEA SALT

1 TABLESPOON BAKING POWDER

2 TABLESPOONS GROUND FLAX (FLAXSEED MEAL)

Mix all of the ingredients together very well and store in an airtight container for up to several months. If you live in a humid climate, you may need to store extra mix in the fridge or freezer. In an arid climate it will usually store just fine in the pantry.

MAKES 5 CUPS OF MIX (10 OR MORE SERVINGS); 30 MINUTES OR UNDER!

GF (WITH SUBSTITUTIONS)/SF/GREEN

*For a gluten-free option, substitute an all-purpose gluten-free flour for both of the wheat flours. If you like, you may also substitute quinoa flakes for the oats (see page 44).

TO MAKE A BATCH OF PANCAKES (THAT WILL SERVE 2-3):
Combine 1 cup of pancake mix with equal parts nondairy milk. Heat a large skillet over medium-high heat. Lightly oil or spray with oil. When the pan is hot, pour some batter onto the skillet. When bubbles form on top and the edges become dry, flip over and cook the other side. Remove when both sides are golden browned. Serve immediately.

♥Wanna buck the system? Try these Batter Up Buckwheat Pancakes for another option. Buckwheat enriches the blood, builds energy, and detoxifies the body. It's also high in calcium, protein, and vitamins!

1. COMBINE ¼ CUP FLAXSEED MEAL WITH ½ CUP BOILING WATER. LET IT SIT UNTIL GOOEY.

2. NEXT, MIX IN 2 CUPS NONDAIRY MILK AND ½ CUP OF APPLESAUCE.

3. IN A LARGE BOWL, COMBINE THE FOLLOWING INGREDIENTS WELL:
   - 1 CUP EACH: BUCKWHEAT FLOUR *AND* WHOLE WHEAT PASTRY FLOUR
   - 2 TEASPOONS BAKING POWDER
   - ¼ TEASPOON SEA SALT

4. MIX THE WET INGREDIENTS INTO THE DRY INGREDIENTS AND YOUR BATTER IS UP!

TROUBLESHOOTING NOTE: IF YOU HAVE ISSUES WITH THE PANCAKES STICKING, MAKE SURE YOUR SKILLET IS SUFFICIENTLY HOT (AND OILED IF IT ISN'T A NONSTICK PAN) BEFORE ADDING THE MIX. ALSO, IF YOU ARE USING AN EXCESSIVE AMOUNT OF FRUIT IN THE BATTER, THE PANCAKES CAN STICK A BIT BECAUSE OF THAT. THE PRICES WE PAY FOR FRUITY GOODNESS. . .

Sweet Banana Pancakes

Hellllooo, monkey! These are so delicious and nutritious that I could eat them every morning. They're even good plain, as they are very sweet when using really ripe bananas.

I VERY RIPE BANANA

¾ CUP EACH: "MAGICAL MULTIGRAIN PANCAKE MIX" (RECIPE PAGE 57) *AND* NONDAIRY MILK

I ⅛ TEASPOONS GROUND CINNAMON

SCANT ⅛ TEASPOON GROUND NUTMEG

I TABLESPOON PURE MAPLE SYRUP

OIL FOR FRYING (COCONUT, NON-VIRGIN OLIVE, SUNFLOWER, OR SAFFLOWER)

1. Peel the banana and mash it very well in a mixing bowl. Add the remaining ingredients and mix everything together thoroughly. Make sure there are no remaining bits of dry mix.
2. Heat a large skillet over medium-high heat. Pour about 1 teaspoon (or more if needed) oil onto the pan and distribute it evenly with a heat proof spatula.
3. When the pan and oil are sufficiently hot, pour the batter out in small amounts onto the skillet to make the pancakes. When they are browned on the bottom, flip them over. When they are browned on both sides, flip out. It's time to eat some crazy good pancakes. Serve them plain, with maple syrup, or cinnamon and sugar.

SERVES 2; 30 MINUTES OR UNDER! GF (WITH SUBSTITUTIONS)/SF/GREEN

Apple Cinnamon Flapjacks

These are delicious with a little maple syrup on top. However, to double the cinnamon apple goodness, these can also be topped with the "Easy Apple-Cinnamon Compote" (on page 200).

I CUP EACH: "MAGICAL MULTIGRAIN PANCAKE MIX" (PLEASE SEE PAGE 57) *AND* NONDAIRY MILK

½ CUP GRATED APPLE (SKINS ON IF ORGANIC)

2 TEASPOONS GROUND CINNAMON

2 TABLESPOONS ORGANIC SUGAR (OPTIONAL)

OIL FOR PAN-FRYING (COCONUT, NON-VIRGIN OLIVE, SUNFLOWER, OR SAFFLOWER)

1. Mix all of the ingredients together very well. Make sure there are no remaining bits of dry mix.
2. Heat a large skillet over medium-high heat. Pour about 1 teaspoon (or more if needed) of oil onto the pan and distribute it evenly with an heat proof spatula.
3. When the pan and oil are sufficiently hot, pour the batter out in small amounts onto the skillet to make the pancakes. When they are browned on the bottom, flip them over. When they are browned on both sides, remove to a plate. Serve with pure maple syrup. You may also top these with some of the apple compote (page 200) if you like your flaps jacked up.

SERVES 2-3; 30 MINUTES OR UNDER! GF (WITH SUBSTITUTIONS)/SF/GREEN

Raspberry Lemon Zest Pancakes

This is a very elegant, impressive, and delicious way to serve pancakes. The fact that they are also whole grain and *really* healthy makes them even more fabulous!

I CUP <u>EACH</u>: "MAGICAL MULTIGRAIN PANCAKE MIX" (PAGE 57) *AND* NONDAIRY MILK

I TEASPOON MINCED ORGANIC LEMON ZEST (PAGE 43)

¼ CUP RASPBERRIES (FROZEN OR FRESH)

OIL FOR PAN-FRYING (COCONUT, NON-VIRGIN OLIVE, OR SUNFLOWER)

TOPPING:

2 TABLESPOONS FRESH LEMON JUICE

¼ CUP ORGANIC POWDERED SUGAR

WAY OVER THE TOP:
- ADDITIONAL LEMON ZEST
- RASPBERRIES
- LEMON SLICES OR WEDGES

1. Combine the pancake mix with the milk. Stir very well to thoroughly combine, making sure there are no remaining bits of dry mix. Stir in the zest and the ¼ cup of raspberries.
2. Heat a large skillet over medium-high heat. If you don't have a truly nonstick pan, you will need to oil the skillet well so that the raspberries don't stick.
3. When the pan is hot, drop the batter onto it to form your pancakes. When they are very bubbly on top and browned on the bottom, flip over and cook the other side. Remove to a plate. Repeat until you've used all of the batter. Serve hot, sprinkled with the lemon juice and powdered sugar. If you are aiming for maximum fancy cuteness, garnish with additional lemon zest, raspberries, and lemon wedges.

SERVES 2-3; 30 MINUTES OR UNDER! GF (WITH SUBSTITUTIONS)/SF/GREEN

Blueberry Waffles

If you have a waffle maker, this recipe will provide you with some serious yumminess.
If you don't have a waffle maker, you can also make this recipe as pancakes. Either way, be sure to try these with some of the "Blueberry Citrus Sauce" (page 133) for serious blueberry business. Incidentally, I use dried blueberries here because they tend not to stick to a waffle maker that way. They also lend a little extra sweetness, due to their concentrated flavor. Of course, if you cannot find dried blueberries, you may substitute equal parts fresh or frozen.

½ CUP PLUS 2 TABLESPOONS "MAGICAL MULTIGRAIN PANCAKE MIX" (PLEASE SEE PAGE 57)

½ CUP NONDAIRY MILK

2 TABLESPOONS DRIED BLUEBERRIES

I TABLESPOON OIL (SAFFLOWER, SUNFLOWER, OR NON-VIRGIN OLIVE), OPTIONAL

2 TABLESPOONS ORGANIC SUGAR (NOT POWDERED), OPTIONAL

TOP IT: PURE MAPLE SYRUP, BROWN RICE SYRUP, OR "BLUEBERRY CITRUS SAUCE" (PAGE 133)

1. Combine the pancake mix with the milk and stir well to combine. Make sure there are no dry portions of the mix remaining. Add the blueberries, oil, and sugar and combine thoroughly.
2. Preheat your waffle maker according to the manufacturer's instructions.
3. Make the waffle according to those very same instructions.
4. Eat that waffle according to your inner guidance.

SERVES 1-2; 30 MINUTES OR UNDER! GF (WITH SUBSTITUTIONS)/SF/BLUE

Earth's Healthiest Waffles

These waffles are packed with whole grain loveliness and contain no added fats, sweeteners, or *anything* refined. Miraculously, they are still simple, quick, light, and completely delicious!

¾ CUP EACH: "MAGICAL MULTIGRAIN PANCAKE MIX" (PLEASE SEE RECIPE PAGE 57) AND NONDAIRY MILK

TOPPING OPTIONS:

♥"EASY APPLE-CINNAMON COMPOTE" (RECIPE ON PAGE 200), OR UNSWEETENED APPLESAUCE AND GROUND CINNAMON

♥"BLUEBERRY CITRUS SAUCE" (RECIPE ON PAGE 133)

♥BROWN RICE SYRUP OR PURE MAPLE SYRUP

♥SLICED STRAWBERRIES

1. Preheat your waffle maker according to the manufacturer's instructions.
2. Combine the multigrain mix and milk together very well with a spoon or fork. Make sure that there are no dry portions of the mix remaining.
3. Spray the waffle iron with nonstick spray or oil and cook the waffle according to the manufacturer's instructions.
4. To serve, you can use any of the following suggestions (or none, if you're a rebel):
   - Top with the "Easy Apple-Cinnamon Compote."
   - Top with a good amount of applesauce and a few sprinkles of cinnamon.
   - Top with the applesauce and cinnamon as previously suggested, but add a drizzle of brown rice syrup or maple syrup for extra sweetness.
   - Drizzle with some of the "Blueberry Citrus Sauce."
   - Simply eat them plain or pour a little brown rice syrup or maple syrup on top.
   - Top with strawberries and some brown rice syrup or maple syrup.

SERVES 2; 30 MINUTES OR UNDER! GF (WITH SUBSTITUTIONS)/SF/GREEN

FUN NOTE: IF YOU HAVE NEVER TRIED BROWN RICE SYRUP, YOU ARE IN FOR A TREAT! IT IS MADE FROM NOTHING BUT WHOLE GRAIN BROWN RICE, AND HAS A SUBTLE CARAMEL SWEETNESS THAT IS ABSOLUTELY DIVINE!

Chocolate-Chocolate Chip Waffles

I have always been the kind of person to totally reject the concept of dessert for breakfast, so I have actually surprised *myself* by including this recipe! However, I've decided that this recipe works for several reasons. Firstly, it's delicious! It also happens to be very easy to make, low in fat, and contains 100% whole grains. These waffles should also, incidentally, work nicely to change the attitude of anyone who thinks vegan breakfasts can't be totally delicious. Last, but not least, they need no syrup or additional toppings of any kind. For this reason, they work well as an energy-type snack on the run, just as many of the packaged bars do (that also frequently include chocolate…*so there*!).

¾ CUP <u>EACH</u>: "MAGICAL MULTIGRAIN PANCAKE MIX" (PLEASE SEE RECIPE PAGE 57) AND NONDAIRY CHOCOLATE MILK

1 TABLESPOON CHOCOLATE CHIPS (OR MORE IF YOU'RE REALLY GOING FOR IT!)

2 TABLESPOONS PURE MAPLE SYRUP

TOPTIONS:

RASPBERRY SYRUP OR CHOCOLATE SYRUP

MAPLE SYRUP OR BROWN RICE SYRUP

ORGANIC POWDERED SUGAR

1. Preheat your waffle maker according to the manufacturer's instructions.
2. Combine all of the ingredients together very well with a spoon or fork. Make sure there are no dry portions of the mix remaining.
3. Spray the waffle iron with nonstick spray or oil and cook the waffle according to the manufacturer's instructions.
4. Serve plain or with one of your many toptions.

SERVES 2

30 MINUTES OR UNDER! GF (WITH SUBSTITUTIONS)/SF/BLUE

Grandma's Favorite French Toast

When I last visited my lovely Grandma Pat, I told her not to buy her usual pre-made frozen French toast. I fed her this version instead, and she utterly loved it! Compared to the usual high cholesterol, nutrient poor, fiber-free French toast, this kind is quite healthy. It is naturally cholesterol-free and contains loads of potassium, fiber, and B-vitamins. I like to make more of the batter than I will use at one time, as I can continue using it to make French toast for the rest of the week.

2 VERY RIPE BANANAS

½ CUP PLUS 2 TABLESPOONS NONDAIRY MILK

1 TABLESPOON NUTRITIONAL YEAST POWDER (I USE RED STAR VEGETARIAN SUPPORT FORMULA)

¾ CUP ROLLED OATS*

1½ TEASPOONS GROUND CINNAMON

1 TABLESPOON ORGANIC SUGAR OR SUCANAT (OPTIONAL)

¾ TEASPOON VANILLA EXTRACT

⅛ TEASPOON SEA SALT

8 SLICES SPROUTED OR REGULAR WHOLE GRAIN BREAD*

3 TABLESPOONS OIL (SUNFLOWER, SAFFLOWER, NON-VIRGIN OLIVE, OR COCONUT) FOR FRYING

TOPPING OPTIONS:

PURE MAPLE SYRUP OR BROWN RICE SYRUP

ORGANIC POWDERED SUGAR

"BLUEBERRY CITRUS SAUCE" (PAGE 133) OR "EASY APPLE-CINNAMON COMPOTE" (PAGE 200)

1. In a blender, combine the bananas, milk, nutritional yeast, oats, cinnamon, sugar, vanilla, and salt until smooth.
2. At this point, I usually like to place the mixture directly into a storage container that is big enough to dip a slice of bread in. That way, any leftover mixture will be ready to go in the fridge.
3. Heat a medium sized skillet over medium heat. Add some oil to the pan (about 1 teaspoon per slice of bread).
4. If desired, cut the bread into triangular shapes. Dip your bread into the batter and get it nice and gooey on all sides.
5. Add the bread to the skillet when the pan is sufficiently hot, so that it doesn't stick. When the French toast is golden brown on the bottom, flip it over. When it is golden brown on both sides, remove to a plate.
6. Serve immediately with the topping(s) of your choice. The batter will keep in an airtight container, refrigerated, for several days. However, the longer the batter is stored, the thicker it will become. If it becomes overly thick, simply thin it with a little nondairy milk.

SERVES 8; 30 MINUTES OR UNDER! GF (WITH SUBSTITUTIONS)/SF/GREEN

*If you can't eat gluten, you may substitute quinoa flakes or gluten-free oats for the rolled oats (see page 44) and use a gluten-free bread.

Cranberry-Orange Granola

Few things are more homey than the smell of fresh granola baking in the oven. Enjoy the love!

4 CUPS ROLLED OATS

1 TEASPOON GROUND CINNAMON

½ TEASPOON GROUND NUTMEG

2 TABLESPOONS PLUS 2 TEASPOONS EACH: WHOLE FLAXSEEDS AND GROUND FLAX MEAL

1 ½ TEASPOONS SEA SALT (OR LESS IF YOU PREFER)

½ CUP PURE MAPLE SYRUP

¼ CUP EACH: ORGANIC SUGAR, ORANGE JUICE, AND ALL-PURPOSE OIL (SUCH AS COCONUT)

2 TEASPOONS VANILLA EXTRACT

4 TEASPOONS GRATED OR MINCED ORGANIC ORANGE ZEST

FINALE:
• ¾ CUP DRIED CRANBERRIES

1. Preheat the oven to 325° F. In a large bowl, mix everything very well, except for the cranberries. Give them a temporary time out.
2. Spread the mixture evenly onto cookie sheets. Try to keep the layer from being too thick, as it will bake more evenly if it is thinly spread out.
3. Place in the oven. While it is baking, remove every 10 minutes or so and stir well. Spread out evenly again and continue baking. Bake for about 25-35 minutes, or until the granola is lightly browned. Be careful not to overcook! Cool and then mix in the cranberries.
4. Once cooled, this will keep in an airtight container for several weeks or longer.

MAKES ABOUT 6 CUPS GRANOLA (10 SERVINGS); GF (CONTAINS OATS)/SF/BLUE

Googy Granola

My daughter, at age three, gave her favorite breakfast treat this serious, sophisticated name. This granola is delicious in the "Love Bug Parfaits" (page 53), plain, or topped with some nondairy milk.

1 CUP ROLLED OATS

¼ TEASPOON PLUS ⅛ TEASPOON (OR LESS IF YOU PREFER) EACH: SEA SALT AND CINNAMON

1 TEASPOON FLAXSEEDS (WHOLE)

2 TEASPOONS GROUND FLAXSEED (FLAX MEAL)

1 TABLESPOON EACH: RAW SUNFLOWER SEEDS, SHREDDED COCONUT, AND ORGANIC SUGAR

1 TABLESPOON ALL-PURPOSE OIL (SUCH AS COCONUT)

¼ TEASPOON VANILLA EXTRACT

3 TABLESPOONS PURE MAPLE SYRUP

FINALLY: ¼ CUP RAISINS

1. Preheat the oven to 325° F. In a large bowl, mix everything very well, except for the raisins.
2. Spread the mixture evenly onto cookie sheets. Try to keep the layer from being too thick, as it will bake more evenly if it is thinly spread out.
3. Place in the oven. While it's baking, remove every 10 minutes or so and stir well. Spread out evenly again and continue baking. Bake for about 25-35 minutes, or until the granola is lightly browned. Be careful not to overcook! Cool and then mix in the raisins until all googily-like.
4. Once cooled, this will keep in an airtight container for several weeks or longer.

MAKES ABOUT 1 ½ CUPS GRANOLA (3 SERVINGS); GF (CONTAINS OATS)/SF/BLUE

Yellow Tofu

Here is a dish that I enjoy and make frequently for my daughter who regularly requests it (and who came up with the name). It's very easy to make and full of antioxidants and B-vitamins from the turmeric and nutritional yeast. And, yes, very *yellow*.

1 CUP CRUMBLED* TOFU, FIRM OR SOFT (ABOUT ½ LB.)

4 TEASPOONS OIL (COCONUT, OLIVE, NON-VIRGIN OLIVE, OR SUNFLOWER)
½ TEASPOON DRIED TURMERIC

¼ TEASPOON SEA SALT
1 TEASPOON <u>EACH</u>: DRIED GRANULATED ONION, DRIED GRANULATED GARLIC, DRIED DILL, *AND* TAMARI (OR SHOYU OR SOY SAUCE)
1 ½ TABLESPOONS NUTRITIONAL YEAST POWDER
FRESHLY GROUND PEPPER TO TASTE

1. *Crumble the tofu over the sink, squeezing out the excess water with your hands. You should have one cup of crumbled tofu. Set it aside.
2. In a medium-large skillet set to medium heat, add the oil and turmeric and stir.
3. Add the other seasonings (salt, granulated onion and garlic, dill, tamari, nutritional yeast, and pepper) and stir well to combine with a heat proof spatula.
4. Add the tofu and mix it very well with the seasonings so that it's thoroughly combined.
5. Continue to cook, stirring often with the spatula, until the tofu becomes golden browned and slightly crusty (about 5-10 minutes). Serve immediately. This is good with a hefty dose of hot sauce on it, too!

SERVES 2-3; 30 MINUTES OR UNDER! GF/BLUE

FOR A YUMMY AND FILLING BREAKFAST BURRITO, YOU CAN PLACE ANY COMBINATION OF THE FOLLOWING INGREDIENTS IN A WARM TORTILLA (OR LARGE MULTIGRAIN PANCAKE): YELLOW TOFU, HOME FRIES OR HASH BROWNS, VEGAN BACON, CHOPPED ONIONS, CILANTRO, CHOPPED TOMATOES, SALSA OR HOT SAUCE, GREEN CHILI, CARROTS, STEAMED BROCCOLI, AND/OR SAUTÉED MUSHROOMS. GET CRAZY!

Chapter Seven: Sublime Starters

I must admit, this is my favorite recipe chapter. These are the kinds of foods I simply cannot live without! Fresh spring rolls are a staple in our house and we make main dishes out of many of these "starters" very often. Of course, these delectable morsels are also great for elevating a simple meal into an extra special feast!

Sourdough Bruschetta

This appetizer pairs wonderfully with pasta and a tossed salad for a quick, flavorful meal. Be sure to get the freshest, ripest tomatoes you can find, as well as a high quality sourdough bread. Often, bruschetta is made by topping bread with a tomato mixture, and *then* toasting it. However, I find it is much fresher in taste (and healthier) when the topping remains uncooked. Enjoy!

2 MEDIUM TOMATOES (RIPE)

4 MEDIUM CLOVES OF GARLIC, MINCED OR PRESSED

¾ TEASPOON BALSAMIC VINEGAR

10 MEDIUM BASIL LEAVES, FINELY CHOPPED

¼ TEASPOON SEA SALT

4 TEASPOONS OLIVE OIL (REGULAR OR EXTRA-VIRGIN)

•4-6 SLICES OF FRESH, CRUSTY SOURDOUGH BREAD

1. Chop the tomatoes and place them in a strainer. Allow them to drain over a bowl (or sink) for 5 minutes to remove the excess juices. You may wish to finger through them to assist this process.
2. Mix the garlic with the vinegar, basil, salt, and oil.
3. When the tomatoes have drained sufficiently, toss them with the basil mixture. Allow the tomato-basil mixture to marinate for about 15 minutes—or until the smell makes you a little crazy.
4. Grill or toast the sourdough bread and top with the mixture. Serve immediately.

SERVES 4-6; 30 MINUTES OR UNDER! SF/BLUE

Edamame Miso Dip with Black Sesame Crackers

This unusual, Asian take on hummus is visually stunning with the addition of orange carrots and black crackers against its powder-soft green color. It looks and tastes wonderful, yet it's quite a snap to make. Edamame (green soybean) has recently become popularized due to its very high fiber and nutritional content. Miso is detoxifying, cleansing, and an anticarcinogen. All in all, you can feel quite good about indulging in this healthy, delicious snack!

1¼ CUPS SHELLED EDAMAME, THAWED IF FROZEN

1 TABLESPOON PLUS 1 TEASPOON MELLOW WHITE MISO

¼ CUP EACH: RAW TAHINI *AND* ALL-PURPOSE OIL (SUCH AS COCONUT)

3 MEDIUM CLOVES GARLIC, PEELED

½ CUP BABY SPINACH, LIGHTLY PACKED

5 TABLESPOONS FRESH LIME JUICE

¾ TEASPOON SEA SALT (OR LESS IF YOU PREFER)

GARNISH (OPTIONAL):
•BLACK SESAME SEEDS

LIL' DIPPERS:
•CARROT SPEARS
•BLACK SESAME RICE CRACKERS

1. In a food processor, blend the edamame, miso, tahini, oil, garlic, and spinach very well until totally smooth. Be warned that this can take longer than you might think. Have faith and keep blending. All of the chunks *will* disappear! Blend in the lime juice and salt until the mixture is consistently smooth.
2. Remove the dip from the food processor, using a rubber spatula if necessary. Place it on your serving dish and scatter the sesame seeds on top. Serve with crackers and carrots for dipping.

MAKES ABOUT 1½ CUPS OF DIP; 30 MINUTES OR UNDER! GF/BLUE

Delectable Lowfat "Egg Rolls"

These "egg rolls" have been proven delicious in seven out of seven humans. However, they are not *just* yummy for the tummy. They are also very light, high in fiber and nutrients, and quite a snap to prepare once you realize you <u>are</u> a phyllo master.

I LB. PHYLLO, THAWED (SEE P. 42 FOR PHYLLO TIPS)*

FILLING:

I TABLESPOON TOASTED (DARK) SESAME OIL

I CUP <u>EACH</u>: SHREDDED CARROT *AND* THINLY SLICED SHIITAKE MUSHROOM CAPS

9 CUPS GRATED OR FINELY CHOPPED GREEN CABBAGE

½ TEASPOON GROUND BLACK PEPPER

⅛ TEASPOON GROUND WHITE PEPPER

2 TEASPOONS SEA SALT (OR LESS IF YOU PREFER)

6 MEDIUM CLOVES GARLIC, MINCED OR PRESSED

2 TABLESPOONS MINCED FRESH GINGER

FINISHING TOUCHES:
- 2-3 TABLESPOONS TOASTED SESAME OIL FOR THE BIG BRUSH OFF
- 2 TABLESPOONS UNTOASTED (RAW) SESAME SEEDS

1. Mix all of the filling ingredients together in a wok or very large pan. Stir well until everything is thoroughly combined, then cook over medium-high heat for about 5 minutes, or until the cabbage is *just* wilted. Remove from heat and set aside.

2. Spray or brush a large cookie sheet with oil. Set aside.

3. Gently remove the phyllo from its package. Lay it out flat on a clean surface. You may wish to cover it with a lightly dampened towel so that the phyllo doesn't dry out while you are working. This is a good time to preheat your oven to 375° F.

4. If your 1 lb. box of phyllo contains 20 large sheets, you will use one sheet per egg roll. If your box of phyllo contains 40 (smaller) sheets, you will use two sheets of phyllo per egg roll—one on top of another with double thickness. Remove one large (or two smaller) sheet(s) of phyllo from the stack and place on another clean, dry surface. Cover the main stash of phyllo with the damp towel again.

5. If you are using one large sheet of phyllo, fold it in half lengthwise. Next, place ¼ cup of the filling in the center of the lowest portion of the phyllo. Fold in the left and right sides to cover most of the filling, keeping parallel edges. Next, fold the bottom of the phyllo up and over the filling and continue to roll upwards (keeping parallel edges the whole time) until you have what actually resembles an egg roll. Yes!

6. Place the so-called egg roll on the cookie sheet and brush it lightly with some of the toasted sesame oil. Sprinkle with about ¼ teaspoon of the sesame seeds.

7. Finish by repeating steps 4, 5, and 6 (or see the tip below if you don't need all those egg rolls right now). Place the rolls in the preheated oven and bake until they are beautifully golden browned, about 10 minutes or so. Serve immediately. If you do have leftovers, simply store them in an airtight container in the fridge. They will keep for 1-2 days and can be reheated in a 375° F. oven.

MAKES ABOUT 20 ROLLS; SF/GF (WITH SUBSTITUTION)/GREEN

> *Tip*: Instead of rolling all of the egg rolls at once, you can store the filling and phyllo separately in the fridge for up to a week and just roll as you go.

*ARE YOU IN THE WHEATLESS PROTECTION PROGRAM?

INSTEAD OF PHYLLO, SIMPLY SUBSTITUTE RICE PAPER WRAPPERS. FIRST, GO THROUGH STEPS I AND 2 ON THIS PAGE. NEXT, PLEASE SEE PAGE 72 (STEPS 4-6), IGNORING THE PHYLLO MUMBO JUMBO IN STEPS 3-5 OF THIS RECIPE. CONTINUE WITH STEPS 6 AND 7 ON THIS PAGE, NOTING THAT THEY TAKE SLIGHTLY LONGER TO BAKE WHEN USING A RICE WRAPPER. ENJOY!

Vegetable Tempura with Ginger-Daikon Sauce

You will be pleasantly surprised at how easy it is to make high quality tempura right in your own kitchen! For a variation, you can change things up a little by substituting marinated tempeh or tofu cubes for some of the vegetables. Although tempura is best served fresh, it does reheat nicely in a 375°F oven. Simply place the pieces on an ungreased cookie sheet and bake until re-crisped.

GINGER-DAIKON SAUCE:

3 TABLESPOONS EACH: FINELY GRATED FRESH GINGER *AND* FINELY GRATED FRESH DAIKON (PEELED)

⅓ CUP TAMARI, SHOYU, OR SOY SAUCE

3 TABLESPOONS FRESH LIME JUICE

TEMPURA VEGETABLES:

4 CUPS VEGETABLE SPEARS (SUCH AS ZUCCHINI, CARROTS, ASPARAGUS, DAIKON, SCALLIONS, OR SHIITAKE MUSHROOM CAPS)*

TEMPURA BATTER:

I CUP FLOUR (WHOLE WHEAT PASTRY, UNBLEACHED WHITE, OR ALL-PURPOSE GLUTEN-FREE*)

2 TABLESPOONS ARROWROOT (OR CORNSTARCH)

¼ TEASPOON BAKING SODA

½ TEASPOON SEA SALT

I CUP ICE WATER

FRY IT OUT: PEANUT OR COCONUT OIL (ENOUGH TO MAKE A ½-INCH WELL IN YOUR SKILLET)

1. Place the grated ginger and daikon in a bowl along with the ⅓ cup of tamari and 3 tablespoons of lime juice. Stir to mix. If it looks too way too thick, that's excellent! You're right on track. Set aside.
2. *Prepare the vegetables by cutting them into spears or julienne strips (see page 41 for julienne tips). If you are using shiitake mushrooms, remove the stems and slice the caps thinly. Basically, you want uniformly sized veggies that are relatively thin so that they will cook quickly and evenly. An ideal size would be about ¼-inch thick and 2½ inches long. You should end up with about 4 cups of prepared vegetables.
3. To mix the tempura batter, combine the flour, arrowroot, baking soda, and salt. Stir well to combine, using a wire whisk or sifter if necessary. Next, add the ice water into the dry mix and stir *just* enough to mix the items together. It is better to have a few lumps than to over-mix.
4. Preheat the oil in a large heavy skillet over medium-high heat. Now, pay extra attention to this next part, as it is important to have your oil at just the right temperature. When you think the oil is getting hot, test it by dropping a pinch of batter into the oil. If it sizzles immediately, it is too hot. If it sinks and rises very slowly, it isn't quite hot enough. When it sinks and rises fairly quickly, it's perfect.
5. Now, it's time to rock and roll. Coat your vegetables in the tempura batter and place them one by one into the oil, being careful not to burn your fingers. Be sure to leave enough space so that no more than half of the pan is filled with tempura at any given time (to prevent greasy tempura).
6. When the tempura is golden brown on the underside, turn it over with a metal slotted spoon or spatula. When it is golden brown all over, remove with a metal slotted spoon or spatula and drain on paper towels. Continue to cook in batches until all of your veggies are used up. Serve immediately with the ginger-daikon sauce. Yummolicious!

SERVES 6-8; GF (WITH SUBSTITUTION)PURPLE

*If using an all-purpose gluten-free flour, please note that you may need to use an *extra* ¼ cup of flour to achieve the proper consistency. Also, don't be tempted to substitute rice flour—trust me.

Three Citrus Asparagus

This very simple starter is made elegant by its presentation. And pompous title.

16 MEDIUM SIZED ASPARAGUS SPEARS

1 TABLESPOON <u>EACH</u>: FRESH LIME JUICE *AND* ORANGE JUICE (THE FRESHER THE BETTER)

2 TABLESPOONS DRIED CRANBERRIES

2 TEASPOONS <u>EACH</u>: TAMARI (OR SHOYU OR SOY SAUCE) *AND* TOASTED (DARK) SESAME OIL

2 MEDIUM CLOVES GARLIC, MINCED OR PRESSED

1 TEASPOON <u>EACH</u>: ORGANIC SUGAR *AND* MINCED ORGANIC LEMON ZEST

½ TEASPOON ORANGE ZEST

<u>GARNISH</u>:

LONG STRIPS OF ORANGE ZEST

1 TEASPOON BLACK SESAME SEEDS (OR BROWN SESAME SEEDS)

1. Remove the tough bases from the asparagus spears (see page 39 for tips). Place the long spears along with the remaining ingredients (excluding garnish items) in a large skillet.
2. Set to medium-high heat and sauté for about 5 minutes, stirring often, until the asparagus is bright green and crisp-tender.
3. Tie each bundle of asparagus with one or more long strips of orange zest. Position artfully on two plates, making sure to include all of the cranberry-zest goodness from the pan. Sprinkle with the sesame seeds and serve immediately.

SERVES 2; 30 MINUTES OR UNDER! GF/GREEN

Green Bread

Many years ago, I was cooking for a family of four. Whenever I would make them this, their young son would do a happy dance and sing of his love for what he called "green bread." Needless to say, this is a big hit with kids! Also keep in mind that you do not need to use all of this spread right away. It freezes surprisingly well, and also keeps in the fridge for at least a week.

½ CUP (1 STICK) NON-HYDROGENATED MARGARINE

10 LARGE CLOVES GARLIC, PEELED (IF IT SEEMS LIKE TOO MUCH, IT'S ALMOST ENOUGH)

2 TABLESPOONS (LIGHTLY PACKED) *FRESH* PARSLEY

¼ CUP (TIGHTLY PACKED) *FRESH* BASIL

1 SCALLION (GREEN ONION), TRIMMED (USE BOTH WHITE AND GREEN PARTS)

¼ TEASPOON SEA SALT

<u>ZE BREAD</u>: ABOUT 10 LARGE SLICES OF CRUSTY MULTIGRAIN OR SOURDOUGH BREAD

1. Preheat the oven to 400° F. In a food processor, combine the margarine, garlic, parsley, basil, scallion, and salt until thoroughly "greenified" (and no chunks of garlic or scallion remain).
2. Spread this *generously* on the bread slices—don't be shy! Bake just until golden browned (be careful not to over-brown) and serve immediately.

SERVES ABOUT 10; 30 MINUTES OR UNDER! BLUE

Rosemary Mushroom Strudel

Mushroom lovers, this dish was made for you (us)! There is nothing like a medley of well flavored mushrooms to delight the palate and nourish the body. If you are gluten intolerant, you can substitute pan-fried polenta for the puff pastry. However you end up, this is a delicious, easy, and impressive way to begin a meal.

½ LB. FROZEN PUFF PASTRY DOUGH (THAWED ACCORDING TO THE PACKAGE DIRECTIONS)*

MUSHROOM MANIA:

1 CUP THINLY SLICED SHIITAKE MUSHROOM CAPS

1 ½ CUPS (3 OZ.) SLICED OR CHOPPED PORTABELLA MUSHROOM CAPS

1 ½ TEASPOONS FRESH ROSEMARY LEAF, CHOPPED

½ TEASPOON EACH: DRIED THYME AND FRESH LIME JUICE

¼ TEASPOON EACH: ORGANIC SUGAR AND GROUND BLACK PEPPER

5 LARGE CLOVES GARLIC, MINCED OR PRESSED

½ TEASPOON SEA SALT

1 TABLESPOON EACH: BALSAMIC VINEGAR, TAMARI (OR SHOYU OR SOY SAUCE), AND OLIVE OIL (OR ROSEMARY-INFUSED OLIVE OIL)

GARNISH:

1 TABLESPOON OLIVE OIL OR ROSEMARY INFUSED OLIVE OIL

1 TEASPOON EACH: DRIED MINCED ONION AND FRESH ROSEMARY LEAF, CHOPPED

1. Preheat the oven to 400° F. Sauté all of the ingredients for the mushroom mania medley (mmm...) over medium heat for 5-10 minutes, or until all of the liquid is absorbed.
2. Cut the puff pastry into 3-inch squares. Alternatively, you can opt for fun shapes, made using cookie cutters. Place the pastry pieces on lightly oiled cookie sheets, leaving just a little room in between so they can puff out. Top them evenly with the mushroom medley.
3. Drizzle the additional olive oil evenly on top of them and sprinkle with the dried onion and rosemary. Bake for about 10 minutes, or until the pastry is golden brown. Serve immediately.

SERVES 4; 30 MINUTES OR UNDER! GF (WITH POLENTA)/PURPLE

*To substitute polenta for the puff pastry, simply follow the directions for making polenta on page 94. When the polenta is firm (after chilling overnight), cut it into squares or shapes and pan-fry it until golden browned on both sides. Top the hot, pan-fried polenta pieces with the cooked mushroom mixture, sprinkle with the garnishes, and serve.

Artichoke, Kalamata, & Sun-Dried Tomato Mini-Pizzas with Garlic and Rosemary

Do I even need to give you the recipe after a title that long? Although these are quick and easy, they're *always* a huge hit! Absolutely divine and seemingly gourmet, this recipe takes less than 20 minutes, start to finish. I've left the measurements fairly loose, as it's sometimes nice to just make one of these (and sometimes nice to make twenty). Please don't be bashful with your toppings—just pile on the good stuff!

HIGH QUALITY CRUSTY SOURDOUGH BREAD, CUT INTO ½-INCH THICK SLICES

FRESH GARLIC, MINCED OR PRESSED (ABOUT 2 CLOVES PER SLICE OF BREAD)

TOPPINGS:

KALAMATA OLIVES, PITTED AND CHOPPED (ABOUT 4-5 OLIVES PER SLICE OF BREAD)

MARINATED ARTICHOKE HEARTS, DRAINED* (ABOUT 2-3 ARTICHOKE HEARTS PER SLICE OF BREAD)

MARINATED SUN-DRIED TOMATOES, JULIENNE CUT AND DRAINED* (1-2 TABLESPOONS PER SLICE OF BREAD)

FINISHING TOUCHES:

DRIED ROSEMARY LEAF, ABOUT ½ TO 1 TEASPOON PER SLICE

OLIVE OIL (REGULAR OR EXTRA-VIRGIN), ABOUT 2 TEASPOONS PER SLICE OF BREAD

SEA SALT (A LIGHT SPRINKLE PER SLICE OF BREAD)

1. Preheat the oven to 375° F.
2. For each slice of bread, spread the garlic evenly over the top with a knife. Arrange the olives, artichokes, and sun-dried tomatoes on top of the garlic. Sprinkle evenly with the dried rosemary. Drizzle with the olive oil and sprinkle lightly with sea salt.
3. Bake on an ungreased cookie sheet for about 10-20 minutes, or until the bread and toppings are lightly browned. Be careful not to overcook or the rosemary will become bitter.
4. Serve immediately.

SERVES: ANY NUMBER OF HUNGRY PEEPS; SF/PURPLE

*I usually place the artichoke hearts and sun-dried tomatoes in a strainer together to allow the excess marinade to fall away.

Fresh Thai Spring Rolls

These are one of the few "perfect" foods in life, in my opinion. They satisfy the craving for a treat that is crunchy and delicious, yet they are light and nourishing. These are best served immediately, but can be covered with wet paper towels and refrigerated in an airtight container for a few days. My trick for keeping a constant supply of these babies? I always keep the filling items on hand in the fridge, prepared and stored in airtight containers. That way, I can have freshly made spring rolls in no time, anytime!

ABOUT 1 CUP OF "THE PEANUT SAUCE" (PLEASE SEE PAGE 117)

1 "NEST" (1.76 OZ.) BEAN THREAD NOODLES (SEE PAGE 251)

TOFU STICKS:

½ LB. TOFU, EXTRA-FIRM (NOT SILKEN)

4 TEASPOONS TAMARI, SHOYU, OR SOY SAUCE

¾ TEASPOON EACH: DRIED GARLIC GRANULES AND DRIED ONION GRANULES

2 TEASPOONS TOASTED (DARK) SESAME OIL

FILLINGS, NOTHING BUT FILLINGS:

1 LARGE PEELED CARROT, CUT INTO 3-INCH PIECES AND JULIENNE SLICED (OR GRATED)

6 SCALLIONS (GREEN ONIONS), TRIMMED AND SLICED IN HALF TO FORM TWELVE 3-INCH PIECES

1 CUP FINELY CHOPPED (OR GRATED) RED CABBAGE

½ CUP (CHOPPED AND TIGHTLY PACKED) EACH: FRESH CILANTRO, FRESH BASIL, AND FRESH MINT

WRAP PARTY: 12 SPRING ROLL SKINS/RICE PAPER SHEETS

GARNISH: 2 TABLESPOONS TOASTED BROWN AND/OR BLACK SESAME SEEDS (SEE PAGE 42)

1. If you don't have "The Peanut Sauce" on hand, please make some according to the directions on page 117. Next, prepare the bean threads according to the instructions on their package. Rinse them in a strainer under cold water and cut them a few times so that they aren't quite as long. I usually keep these in the strainer the entire time I am preparing the spring rolls, as it is important to use well drained noodles.

2. Cut the tofu into four slabs and press them well with paper towels to remove most of the excess water (or press them according to the directions on page 43). Cut each slab into three long sticks. You should now have twelve tofu sticks. Marinate them in the tamari, garlic granules, and onion granules, gently turning the tofu so that all of the sides are coated. When most of the marinade has been absorbed into the tofu sticks, place them in a medium skillet in the sesame oil. Pan-fry the tofu in the oil over medium-high heat until they are nicely browned on both sides (about 2-4 minutes on each side). Set aside.

3. Prepare all of the fillings so that everything you need is now ready to go.

4. Find a pan or bowl large enough to put the rice paper wrappers in. Fill it two inches high with lukewarm or cool water. Place a sheet of rice paper in the water, making sure that it is covered entirely with the water. In a minute or so, it should be soft. Don't over-soak the wrapper, or it will tear more easily.

5. Remove the wrapper and allow any excess water to drip off of it. Lay it flat on a clean surface. Place a little of each filling ingredient (including one stick of tofu) in the middle of the wrapper. Don't overfill, or it will be tricky to roll. Roll the bottom of the rice paper wrapper up and over the fillings. Next, fold the left and right sides over the filling. If you can maintain parallel lines, it will produce a more even looking wrap. Finally, finish rolling it all of the way up. The rice paper will self-seal, so just set the spring roll aside and repeat this process until all of your fillings are used up.

6. Top each spring roll with some of the toasted sesame seeds. They should stick to the rice paper without any help, but you can always sprinkle a little water on top of your spring rolls to assist the process if necessary. Serve with the peanut sauce and enjoy the good stuff!

MAKES 12 SPRING ROLLS; GF/GREEN

Southwest Spring Rolls

This idea came to me when I was trying to create a fresh spring roll that would also double as a satisfying lunch. Because of the avocado and pine nuts, these did the trick! Although pairing southwest fillings with an Asian concept is a little "out there," so am I.

I CUP OF THE "9½ MINUTE GREEN CHILI" (PLEASE SEE PAGE 131)

SHEER MADNESS:

⅓ CUP PINE NUTS (RAW OR TOASTED)

I RIPE AVOCADO, PEELED, PITTED, AND CHOPPED

½ CUP GRATED (OR JULIENNE CUT) CARROT

½ CUP (PACKED) CHOPPED FRESH CILANTRO

4 SCALLIONS (GREEN ONIONS), TRIMMED AND CUT INTO EIGHT 3-INCH SPEARS

TALKIN' SHEET: 8 SPRING ROLL SKINS/RICE PAPER SHEETS (AVAILABLE IN ANY ASIAN MARKET AND MOST SUPERMARKETS)

1. If you don't have the green chili on hand, you will want to make that first. Please note that you may need to thicken the sauce with a little extra rice flour, so that it is thick enough to hold up in the spring rolls. Once the sauce is done, set it aside to cool.

2. If you have raw pine nuts, toast them in a dry pan over medium-low heat until they are lightly browned and aromatic. Watch them closely, as they brown very quickly and can burn easily. Remove them from the pan and set them aside to cool.

3. Prepare the other fillings and set them aside.

4. Find a pan or bowl large enough to put the rice paper wrappers in. Fill it two inches high with lukewarm or cool water. Place a sheet of rice paper in the water, making sure that it is covered entirely with the water. In a minute or so, it should be soft. Don't over-soak the wrapper, as it will tear more easily if you do.

5. Remove the wrapper and allow any excess water to drip off of it. Lay it flat on a clean surface. Place a little of each filling item in the middle of the wrapper. Top evenly with about 2 tablespoons of the green chili.

6. Roll the bottom of the rice paper wrapper up and over the fillings. Next, fold the left and right sides over the filling. If you can maintain parallel lines, it will produce a more even looking wrap. Finally, finish rolling it all of the way up. The rice paper will self-seal, so just set the spring roll aside and repeat this process until all of your fillings are used up.

7. These spring rolls can just be served plain, since the sauce is already in there! They will store for about one day refrigerated in an airtight container (especially if they are wrapped with damp paper towels first). However, they are much better when eaten immediately upon making them. Enjoy the delicious insanity!

MAKES 8 SPRING ROLLS; 30 MINUTES OR UNDER! GF/SF/GREEN

Mango-Cucumber Spring Rolls

When I eat these, I always feel like I'm basking in the summer sunshine of Thailand.
The flavor is subtle, but totally fresh and delightful. If you like a bit more heat, these are
wonderful with some chili-garlic sauce (available in most supermarkets in the Asian food section).
It can either be added to the sauce or into the roll along with the toppings.

ABOUT ¾ CUP OF THE "THAI SWEET CHILI SAUCE" (RECIPE PAGE 118)

1 "NEST" (1.76 OZ.) BEAN THREAD NOODLES

FILLING TROPICAL:

½ LARGE CUCUMBER, CUT INTO SPEARS (ABOUT ⅔ CUP)

1 RIPE MANGO, PEELED AND CUT INTO SPEARS

6 GREEN ONIONS, TRIMMED AND SLICED IN HALF LENGTHWISE TO FORM TWELVE 3-INCH PIECES

¾ CUP CRUSHED, DRY-ROASTED PEANUTS (SEE PAGE 41 FOR PEANUT CRUSHING TIPS)

½ CUP (TIGHTLY PACKED) FRESH MINT, CHOPPED

1 CUP (LIGHTLY PACKED) FRESH CILANTRO, CHOPPED

OPTIONAL FLAVOR BOMBS: CHILI-GARLIC SAUCE AND FRESH LIME WEDGES

WRAP IT UP RICE-LIKE: 12 SPRING ROLL SKINS/RICE PAPER SHEETS

OPTIONAL GARNISH: BROWN OR BLACK SESAME SEEDS, TOASTED (SEE PAGE 42)

1. If you do not have the "Thai Sweet Chili Sauce" on hand, you will first want to make some according to the directions on page 118. Set it aside.
2. Next, prepare the bean threads according to the instructions on their package. Rinse them in a strainer under cold water and cut them a few times so that they aren't quite as long. I usually keep these in the strainer the entire time I am preparing the spring rolls, as it is important to use well drained noodles.
3. Prepare all of the fillings so that everything you need is now ready to go.
4. Find a pan or bowl large enough to put the rice paper wrappers in. Fill it two inches high with lukewarm or cool water. Place a sheet of rice paper in the water, making sure that it is covered entirely with the water. Give it a nice little bath—but no bedtime story. There just isn't time. In a minute or so, it should be soft. Don't over-soak the wrapper, as it will tear more easily if you do.
5. Remove the wrapper and allow any excess water to drip off of it. Lay it flat on a clean surface. Place a little of each filling item in the middle of the wrapper. If you will be dropping the optional flavor bombs, you can add a little chili-garlic sauce to the fillings and squeeze some fresh lime juice on top.
6. Roll the bottom of the rice paper wrapper up and over the fillings. Next, fold the left and right sides over the filling. If you can maintain parallel lines, it will produce a more even looking wrap. Finally, finish rolling it all of the way up. The rice paper will self-seal, so just set the spring roll aside and repeat this process until all of your fillings are used up.
7. If you like, top each spring roll with some of the toasted sesame seeds. They should stick to the rice paper without any help, but you can always sprinkle a little water on top of your spring rolls to assist the process if necessary. Serve with the "Thai Sweet Chili Sauce."
8. These are best served immediately. However, you can wrap them in damp paper towels and refrigerate them in an airtight container for a few days.

MAKES 12 SPRING ROLLS; GF/GREEN

Vietnamese Spring Rolls

I first tried these in a Vietnamese Restaurant, long before fresh spring rolls were such a hot item. Ironically, at first I wasn't even sure if I liked them. However, only days later, I began to crave them to such an extent that I *had* to figure out how to make them for myself! I think the vibrantly healthy ingredients and unusual flavor are why I'm totally addicted. The sprouts, the fresh ginger and garlic—along with the greens—are absolute *power* foods!

½ LB. FIRM TOFU

4 TEASPOONS TAMARI, SHOYU, OR SOY SAUCE

¾ TEASPOON <u>EACH</u>: DRIED GARLIC GRANULES *AND* DRIED ONION GRANULES

2 TEASPOONS TOASTED SESAME OIL

SIMPLE SAUCE:

¼ CUP PLUS 2 TABLESPOONS <u>EACH</u>: HOISIN SAUCE (AVAILABLE IN MOST SUPERMARKETS AND ASIAN MARKETS) *AND* WATER

FILLIN' GOOD:

12 (YEAH, YOU HEARD ME!) MEDIUM CLOVES GARLIC, PRESSED OR MINCED

2 TABLESPOONS FINELY GRATED FRESH GINGER (OR MORE IF YOU PREFER)

I CUP BEAN SPROUTS (FRESH), LIGHTLY PACKED

¾ CUP (<u>PACKED</u>) CHOPPED CILANTRO

¾ CUP (LIGHTLY PACKED) CHOPPED ROMAINE (OR RED LEAF) LETTUCE

6 GREEN ONIONS, TRIMMED AND SLICED IN HALF LENGTHWISE TO FORM TWELVE 3-INCH PIECES

OH SHEET: 12 SPRING ROLL SKINS/RICE PAPER SHEETS

1. Cut the tofu into four slabs and press them well with paper towels to remove most of the excess water. Alternatively, you can press the tofu according to the directions on page 43. Cut each slab into three long sticks. You should now have twelve tofu sticks. Marinate them in the tamari, garlic granules, and onion granules, gently turning the tofu so that all of the sides are coated. When most of the marinade has been absorbed into the tofu sticks, place them in a medium skillet in the sesame oil. Pan-fry the tofu in the oil over medium-high heat until they are evenly browned (about 2-4 minutes on both sides). Set aside.
2. Combine the hoisin sauce and water until well mixed. Set aside. You're halfway there—good job!
3. Prepare all of the fillings so that everything you need is now ready to go.
4. Find a pan or bowl large enough to put the rice paper wrappers in. Fill it two inches high with lukewarm or cool water. Place a sheet of rice paper in the water, making sure that it is covered entirely with the water. In a minute or so, it should be soft. Don't over-soak the wrapper, as it will tear more easily if you do.
5. Remove the wrapper and allow any excess water to drip off of it. Lay it flat on a clean surface. Place a little of each filling item in the middle of the wrapper. Don't overfill, or it will become a salad.
6. Roll the bottom of the rice paper wrapper up and over the fillings. Next, fold the left and right sides over the filling. If you can maintain parallel lines, it will produce a more even looking wrap. Finally, finish rolling it all of the way up. The rice paper will self-seal, so just set the spring roll aside and repeat this process until all of your fillings are used up. Serve with the hoisin sauce. These are best served immediately. However, you can wrap them in damp paper towels and refrigerate them in an airtight container for a few days.

MAKES 12 SPRING ROLLS; GF/GREEN

Nori Rolls with Creamy Ginger-Wasabi & Lemon-Lime Soy Sauce

I have a good friend who flat out hated nori rolls...until she tried these! The secret is in the delicious sauces. I also find that people are surprised that they can use brown rice for making sushi. Just be sure to use *short* grain brown rice, as the other types will not "stick" properly. For a visual aid on the process of rolling nori, please see the step by step pictures on the last color insert page.

I CUP DRY SHORT GRAIN BROWN RICE

3 CUPS WATER

SCRUMPTIOUS SAUCES: "LEMON-LIME SOY SAUCE" (PAGE 125)
AND "CREAMY GINGER-WASABI SAUCE" (PAGE 124)

VEGGIES (FILLIN' THE LOVE):

½ AVOCADO, PEELED AND SLICED INTO SPEARS

I CARROT, JULIENNE SLICED OR GRATED

3 GREEN ONIONS, TRIMMED AND SLICED IN HALF LENGTHWISE TO FORM SIX 3-INCH PIECES

I CUP (LIGHTLY PACKED) BABY SPINACH

WRAP IT UP, PEOPLE: 3 SHEETS OF NORI

ON THE PREMISES:
- LARGE BOWL OF WATER
- SHARP KNIFE
- SUSHI MAT

---

1. Bring the rice and water to a boil over high heat in a covered pan. Reduce the heat to low and simmer, covered the entire time, until all of the water is absorbed and the rice is tender. Set the rice aside to cool.

2. Prepare your sauces and set them aside. Prepare all of your veggies and set them aside. Prepare yourself to be beside yourself with feelings of accomplishment and tummy love.

3. Now, it's sushi party time! Lay one sheet of nori on the sushi mat, shiny side down.

4. For this next step, you can dip your hands into the bowl of water to prevent the rice from sticking to your hands. Place ⅓ of the rice on the lower half of the nori, using your moistened hands to even the rice out and press it down. Make sure that the rice is evenly distributed over the entire portion of the lower half of the nori. Create a groove across the center of the rice (using the side of your hand) to place the groovy fillings into.

5. Place your desired fillings in the groove.

6. Get ready to roll. Using both of your hands, bring the bottom of the mat/nori roll up and over, using your fingers to secure the fillings.

7. Gently (yet firmly) squeeze the mat in order to make sure all of the fillings are stabilized.

8. Roll the rest of the way up. With your finger, spread a little of the water along the edge of the nori. This will seal the edge.

9. Place the nori, seam side down, on a cutting board. Dip your knife into the bowl of water and cut the nori roll across its length into several round pieces. Continue to dip the knife into the water bowl as often as necessary. If your knife remains wet and free of debris, your nori roll pieces will be much neater and less likely to tear.

10. Repeat this process with the remaining nori and fillings. Drizzle the nori pieces with the "Lemon-Lime Soy Sauce" and serve with the "Creamy Ginger-Wasabi Sauce" on the side. Drool.

MAKES 3 NORI ROLLS (SERVES 3 AS A MAIN DISH OR 6 AS AN APPETIZER); GF/BLUE

Tip: For inside-out (Uramaki-zushi) nori rolls, please see the directions on page 77. Fun!

Tempura Asparagus Nori Rolls

These inside-out (Uramaki-zushi) nori rolls are beautiful, fun to make, and a *serious* treat. Seriously.

WOULDN'T IT BE RICE:

I CUP DRY SUSHI RICE

2 CUPS WATER

1-2 TABLESPOONS RICE VINEGAR

I TABLESPOON AGAVE NECTAR OR ORGANIC "WHITE" SUGAR

½ TEASPOON SEA SALT

SWEET SOY SAUCE:

3 TABLESPOONS <u>EACH</u>: TAMARI (OR SHOYU OR SOY SAUCE)
AND BROWN RICE SYRUP

2 TEASPOONS TOASTED SESAME SEEDS (SEE PAGE 42)

CRUNCHY YUMNESS:

I 5 SPEARS ASPARAGUS

½ RECIPE TEMPURA BATTER (PLEASE SEE PAGE 68)

COCONUT OIL OR PEANUT OIL FOR FRYING

OPTIONAL FLAVOR BOOSTERS:

• 6 MANGO SPEARS (CUT PART OF A RIPE, PEELED MANGO INTO LARGE JULIENNE-STYLE STRIPS)

• ¼ CUP TOASTED SESAME SEEDS, PREFERABLY BOTH BLACK AND TAN

IN THE NEIGHBORHOOD:

• 3 SHEETS NORI

• PLASTIC WRAP

• LARGE BOWL OF WATER

• SHARP KNIFE

• SUSHI MAT

1. Bring the rice and water to a boil over high heat in a covered pot. Reduce the heat to low and simmer, covered the entire time, until all of the water is absorbed and the rice is tender. Stir in the rice vinegar to taste, along with the agave nectar (or sugar) and salt. Set the rice aside to cool.

2. In a small bowl, combine the tamari, brown rice syrup, and 2 teaspoons of sesame seeds until well mixed. Set aside. Wash the asparagus and remove their tough bases according to the tips on page 39.

3. Read through the tempura recipe on page 68. This will help you avoid errors while venturing into the unknown. Prepare the tempura batter according to the recipe on page 68. Pour enough oil into a large, heavy skillet to make a ½-inch well. Set to medium-high heat.

4. When the oil is hot, dip the asparagus spears in the batter and fry until golden brown on all sides. Remove with a slotted metal spoon or spatula and drain on paper towels. Continue this process until all of your asparagus spears are used up. At this point, you may find it helpful to taste one, just in case.

5. Cut or tear a sheet of nori in half (parallel to lines marked on its rough side) and lay it on the sushi mat.

6. Dip your hands into the bowl of water to prevent the rice from sticking to them. Press a layer of rice onto the entire surface of the nori, using your moistened hands to even out the rice and press it down. Make sure that the rice is evenly distributed out to the edges as well.

7. Cover with plastic wrap. Gently flip it all over (everything but the sushi mat). Now, the sushi mat will be at the bottom with the plastic next, then the rice, then the nori on top. You will be working with the longest side horizontal to you (the same as with regular nori rolls, as shown in the insert after page 198).

8. Place about five of the asparagus spears width-wise along the middle of the nori. If using the mango, place 2 spears alongside the asparagus. Using both of your hands, bring the bottom of the mat/rice up and over the fillings, until the rice has enclosed the whole roll. Squeeze firmly in order to stabilize the fillings.

9. Spread the ¼ cup of sesame seeds on a plate and gently coat all sides of the nori roll with them (saving some for the other rolls), so that the entire outer portion of the rice is coated in seeds. Pretty cute, no?

10. Place the nori roll on a cutting board. Dip your knife into the bowl of water and cut the nori roll across its length into several round pieces. Continue to dip the knife into the water bowl as often as necessary. If your knife remains wet and free of debris, your nori roll pieces will be much neater and less likely to tear.

11. Repeat with the remaining nori and asparagus, then serve immediately with the sauce. Get serious.

MAKES 3 TEMPURA ROLLS (SERVES 6 AS AN APPETIZER); GF (WITH GLUTEN-FREE FLOUR)/PURPLE

Asian Asparagus Wraps

What an easy way to impress guests! These crunchy munchies will have people thinking you went all out, when actually they take only about 15 minutes to prepare. The key is to make sure you have very flavorful asparagus spears before wrapping them. In fact, they should taste a bit *too* flavorful as is, since wrapping them in the phyllo will "dilute" their flavor a bit.

3 LARGE (OR 6 SMALL)* SHEETS PHYLLO DOUGH, THAWED (SEE PAGE 42 FOR PHYLLO TIPS)

OVERLY FLAVORFUL ASPARAGUS:

12 THIN (OR 6 FAT) ASPARAGUS SPEARS, TRIMMED (SEE PAGE 39 FOR TIPS)

2 TEASPOONS TOASTED (DARK) SESAME OIL

1 TABLESPOON EACH: FRESH LIME JUICE *AND* TAMARI, SHOYU, OR SOY SAUCE

6 CLOVES GARLIC, MINCED OR PRESSED

THE END (HAPPILY EVER AFTER):

NON-HYDROGENATED MARGARINE (OR TOASTED SESAME OIL) FOR BRUSHING**

2 TABLESPOONS RAW SESAME SEEDS (PREFERABLY BLACK)

1. Place the asparagus, sesame oil, lime juice, tamari, and garlic in a medium-large skillet. Sauté over medium heat, stirring often, *just* until the asparagus is bright green and barely tender. You will want them to be slightly underdone, as they will cook a little more in the oven. Remove from heat and set aside.
2. Preheat the oven to 400° F. Gently remove three large (or six small)* sheets of phyllo and set them aside. Immediately roll up the remaining phyllo dough in plastic. Place in another airtight plastic bag and put it back in the fridge.
3. If you are using three large sheets of phyllo, cut them in half width-wise to make six sheets.
4. Place one sheet of phyllo on a clean dry surface and brush it with margarine or toasted sesame oil (or spray it with oil**). Place two thin asparagus spears (or one fatty) at the bottom of the phyllo sheet, making sure to scrape some of the garlic and flavorings from the pan onto the asparagus. Roll the phyllo up and over the asparagus. Continue rolling up until you have a phyllo "cigar."
5. Place it on a lightly oiled cookie sheet. Brush the top with more margarine or toasted sesame oil (or spray with oil). Sprinkle with some raw sesame seeds. Repeat this process with the remaining asparagus and phyllo.
6. Bake until golden brown, about 5-10 minutes. Be careful not to over-brown, as phyllo cooks very quickly. Serve immediately.

MAKES 6 ASPARAGUS WRAPS; 30 MINUTES OR UNDER! SF (IF USING OIL)/BLUE

*If your 1 lb. package of phyllo dough contains twenty large sheets of phyllo, you'll need to use three sheets. However, if your 1 lb. package of phyllo contains forty smaller sheets, you'll need six sheets.

**You may instead *spray* the phyllo with oil, as it's quicker and lower in fat. Of course, the more "buttery" and time consuming approach of brushing the phyllo yields a more intense, rich flavor.

Creamy Hummus with Variations

I fell in love with the flavor of this thinner, lemony hummus in college. The favorite lunch spot of everyone I knew was a café that served just this sort of hummus. I spent years trying to recreate it and finally discovered that the secret was to add enough lemon juice, tahini, and olive oil so that the end result would be unusually creamy and light tasting. Of course, if you prefer a thicker hummus you can simply omit the olive oil (or use less of it). If possible, refrigerate this for several hours (or overnight) before serving. This will give the raw garlic a chance to mellow and allow the flavors to become happily married.

15 OZ. CAN (1½ CUPS) GARBANZO BEANS (CHICKPEAS), RINSED & DRAINED*

2-3 MEDIUM CLOVES GARLIC, PEELED

¼ CUP RAW TAHINI (SESAME PASTE)

¼ CUP PLUS 2 TABLESPOONS *FRESH* LEMON JUICE

1 TEASPOON SEA SALT (OR LESS IF YOU PREFER)

¼ CUP PLUS 2 TABLESPOONS OLIVE OIL (REGULAR OR EXTRA-VIRGIN)*

In a food processor, blend the garbanzo beans and garlic cloves very well. Add the tahini, lemon juice, salt, and oil and process until fully emulsified and creamy. Refrigerate in an airtight container for up to ten days. For best results, allow to warm to room temperature before serving.

MAKES ABOUT 2 CUPS OF HUMMUS; 30 MINUTES OR UNDER! GF/SF/BLUE

*For a lower fat hummus, reserve the liquid when you drain the beans. Use ¼ cup bean liquid (and 2 tablespoons oil) instead of the full amount of oil.

Serving Suggestions:

CLASSIC: SPRINKLE THE HUMMUS WITH A LITTLE PAPRIKA AND PARSLEY. IF YOU WISH, DRIZZLE SOME EXTRA-VIRGIN OLIVE OIL OVER THE TOP. SERVE WITH WARMED PITA WEDGES OR CRUSTY BREAD. KALAMATA OLIVES CAN ALSO MAKE AN APPEARANCE HERE.

HUMMUS WRAP: SPREAD A TORTILLA GENEROUSLY WITH HUMMUS. TOP WITH ALL OF YOUR FAVORITE FIXINGS. I LIKE TO USE CHOPPED TOMATO, PICKLES, THINLY SLICED RED ONION, LETTUCE OR SPINACH, FRESH BASIL, KALAMATA OLIVES, AND CUCUMBERS.

GREEK HUMMUS "PIZZA:" PLEASE SEE THE RECIPE ON PAGE 135 FOR "FRESH GREEK DELIGHT." YOU WON'T REGRET IT.

HUMMUS WITH ZATAR: ZATAR IS A TANGY, UNIQUE, AND DELIGHTFUL COMBINATION OF SUMAC, THYME, AND SPICES, AND CAN BE FOUND IN MANY HEALTH FOOD STORES (OR ONLINE). YOU MAY SPRINKLE IT OVER THE HUMMUS FOR A LOVELY AND SURPRISING FLAVOR ADDITION.

Olive Oil with Crispy Garlic and Rosemary (with Sourdough)

Have you ever gone to an Italian restaurant and been served fresh bread with a bowl of olive oil and garlic to dip it in? Do you agree that there is *never* enough garlic in said bowl? This recipe solves that problem, and solves it well. Another flavor booster I have added is rosemary-infused olive oil. However, if you haven't planned enough in advance to make the oil, simply add a little crushed, dried rosemary to the end product.

½ OZ. FRESH ROSEMARY SPRIGS

¾ CUP PLUS 2 TABLESPOONS EXTRA-VIRGIN OLIVE OIL

10 MEDIUM-LARGE CLOVES GARLIC, PRESSED OR MINCED

¼ TEASPOON SEA SALT

LOTS OF FRESHLY GROUND PEPPER TO TASTE

FOR SERVING: CRUSTY ARTISAN BREAD (SOURDOUGH OR MULTIGRAIN)

1. Place the rosemary in a glass container with a tight fitting lid. If necessary, cut the rosemary so that it is low enough in the container to be completely covered by the oil. Pour the oil on top of the rosemary and cover tightly with the lid. Set aside (out of sunlight) for several days.

2. Remove the rosemary from the oil and discard it. Set aside ¾ cup of the rosemary olive oil (which should basically be what is left after discarding the oily rosemary).

3. In a medium skillet, sauté the garlic and the ¾ cup of oil over low heat. It should gently sizzle for about eight to ten minutes, or until the garlic just begins to turn golden. Don't over-brown, or the garlic can become bitter.

4. Stir in the salt and pepper and serve as a dip for the bread. This will store in an airtight container for several days.

SERVES 8; 30 MINUTES OR UNDER! SF/PURPLE

TRY ADDING THE FOLLOWING YUMMIES TO

THE OIL FOR A DELICIOUS VARIATION:

ORGANIC LEMON RIND, KALAMATA AND OTHER GREEK OLIVES, MULTI-COLORED PEPPERCORNS, AND A PLETHORA OF FRESH HERBS. ALLOW THEM TO MARINATE IN THE OIL FOR AT LEAST SEVERAL HOURS BEFORE SERVING, THEN REMOVE.

Thai Spinach Nests

Here is an unusually flavorful dish that looks and tastes like something really special. However, it is very simple and quick to prepare. Yet another opportunity to fool your lucky guests into eating something healthy, yet smashtastic.

"THAI SWEET CHILI SAUCE" (PLEASE SEE RECIPE ON PAGE 118)

TANTALIZING TOPPING:

½ CUP FINELY GRATED COCONUT

¼ CUP DRY-ROASTED, UNSALTED PEANUTS

2 TABLESPOONS VERY FINELY DICED FRESH GINGER (DICED INTO PIECES THE SIZE OF PEPPERCORNS USING A SHARP, NON-SERRATED KNIFE)

¼ CUP PEELED AND VERY FINELY DICED LIME (DICED INTO PIECES THE SIZE OF PEPPERCORNS USING A SHARP, NON-SERRATED KNIFE)

1 TABLESPOON VERY FINELY DICED RED ONION (DICED INTO PIECES THE SIZE OF, YES, PEPPERCORNS)

⅛ TEASPOON SEA SALT

1- 2 CUPS OF SPINACH LEAVES (REGULAR OR BABY), WASHED WELL AND PATTED DRY

1. Prepare the sauce and set it aside.
2. In a dry skillet, toast the coconut over low heat until it becomes aromatic and very lightly browned. This should only take a few minutes. Be careful not to overcook. Remove the coconut from the pan as soon as it browns (to avoid scorching).
3. If your peanuts are whole, crush them. Crush them now. Please see page 41 for peanut crushing tips if necessary. Don't overdo it though, as it is nice to retain some of the crunch of the peanuts.
4. Mix the coconut and peanuts together in a small bowl. Stir in the ginger, lime, onion, and salt and combine well.
5. Place the spinach artfully on plates, seam side up (so as to make it easiest to hold the toppings). Place a little of the topping in each leaf. Drizzle with the sauce and serve.

SERVES ABOUT 4

30 MINUTES OR UNDER! GF/BLUE

Do-ahead tip:
You can prepare the filling in advance—just create two mixtures. First, combine the crushed peanuts and toasted coconut. Then, combine the remaining ingredients separately. Before showtime, simply mix them together and proceed with step five.

Lemon-Cilantro Pakoras

Hold on to your socks, this one has flavor that will knock them off! I have made these many times for catering events and they never fail to disappear immediately. Pakoras are a traditional part of an Indian meal and are usually served with a chutney. However, these are so tasty that I usually just serve them plain. If you do prefer your pakoras to have a dipping sauce, I would especially recommend the "Cilantro Chutney Elixir" (page 125).

DRY INGREDIENTS:

½ CUP PLUS 2 TABLESPOONS GARBANZO (CHICKPEA) FLOUR

1 TABLESPOON RICE FLOUR

⅛ TEASPOON <u>EACH</u>: GROUND CAYENNE PEPPER *AND* BAKING SODA

¼ TEASPOON <u>EACH</u>: DRIED TURMERIC *AND* GROUND CORIANDER

1 ½ TEASPOONS <u>EACH</u>: CUMIN POWDER, CUMIN SEEDS, *AND* SEA SALT

VEGETABLE MIXTURE:

½ CUP FINELY CHOPPED CAULIFLOWER (CUT INTO VERY, VERY SMALL PIECES)

½ CUP (PACKED) CILANTRO, WASHED WELL AND CHOPPED

¼ CUP (4 TABLESPOONS) FRESH LEMON JUICE

1 ½ CUPS CHOPPED YELLOW (OR WHITE) ONION*

OIL FOR FRYING: PEANUT OR COCONUT

1. Mix the dry ingredients together very well in a small bowl. Set aside.
2. Combine the vegetable mixture (cauliflower, cilantro, lemon juice, and onion) together in a large bowl, stirring very well.
3. Add the dry mixture to the vegetable mixture in the large bowl and stir to combine thoroughly.
4. Place enough oil in a large, heavy skillet to form a ½-inch well. Set to medium-high heat.
5. To test the oil for the correct temperature, drop a small amount of the batter into it. If it sizzles immediately and begins to brown soon after, it is ready. If it takes a while to sizzle and brown, it is not yet hot enough.
6. To form the pakoras, you have two options. You can either use a small cookie scoop or your hands to gather small amounts of the batter. You will want each pakora to be about one tablespoon in size. Gently drop the pakora into the oil. Continue to put as many pakoras into the oil as will fill about half of the skillet. If you put in too many at once, the oil temperature will drop.
7. Cook for about 1-2 minutes (or until nicely browned on the underside) and flip over. Cook for another 1-2 minutes, or until nicely browned on all sides. Remove with a metal slotted spoon or spatula and drain on paper towels.
8. Serve immediately. If you do have leftovers, these reheat very nicely in a 400° F. oven.

SERVES 4; 30 MINUTES OR UNDER! GF/SF/PURPLE

*<u>NOTE</u>: It is best to chop the onions by hand for this recipe, as chopping them in a food processor can make them overly wet, causing the pakoras to fall apart.

Asparagus, Portabella, and Kalamata Triangle Puffs

Talk about a decadent way to eat your veggies! These only take about 25 minutes to make and are always impressive. This filling may also be served over polenta for a gluten-free treat.

½ LB. PUFF PASTRY DOUGH, THAWED ACCORDING TO PACKAGE INSTRUCTIONS

1 ½ CUPS CHOPPED PORTABELLA MUSHROOM CAPS

1 CUP CHOPPED ASPARAGUS

(TRIMMED AND CUT INTO 1-INCH PIECES)

5 LARGE CLOVES GARLIC, MINCED OR PRESSED

¼ CUP WHITE WINE OR COOKING WINE

1 TABLESPOON EXTRA-VIRGIN OLIVE OIL

(OR REGULAR OLIVE OIL)

LAST ADDITIONS:
- ½ TABLESPOON FRESH LEMON JUICE
- 10 KALAMATA OLIVES, PITTED & CHOPPED
- ¼ TEASPOON EACH: SEA SALT AND GROUND BLACK PEPPER

1. Preheat the oven to 400° F. In a large skillet over medium-high heat, sauté the mushroom caps, asparagus, garlic, wine, and oil for 5 minutes, stirring often.
2. Stir in the lemon juice, olives, salt, and pepper. Remove from heat and set aside.
3. Cut the pastry dough into three long rectangles, then cut each rectangle into three squares.
4. Place a little of the vegetable mixture in the center of each square. Next, fold the pastry dough over the filling to form a triangle. Pinch the dough in front to close each triangle. You should end up with nine triangle puffs (unless you're really bad at math).
5. Place the triangles on a lightly oiled cookie sheet. Bake for about 15 minutes, or until golden browned. Serve immediately.

SERVES ABOUT 4; 30 MINUTES OR UNDER! SF/PURPLE

Sun-Dried Tomato Hummus with Sourdough

This is a quick and easy version of the raw "Triple Omega Dip" (page 182). As a non-raw item, it can then be paired with some crusty sourdough bread for a special treat. Yum!

¾ CUP COOKED CHICKPEAS

¼ CUP PLUS 2 TABLESPOONS RAW WALNUTS

2 TABLESPOONS (PACKED) MARINATED SUN-DRIED TOMATOES, DRAINED

3 LARGE CLOVES OF GARLIC, PEELED

- 5 TABLESPOONS EXTRA-VIRGIN OLIVE OIL
- 3 TABLESPOONS RAW TAHINI
- ¼ CUP FRESH LEMON JUICE
- 1 ⅛ TEASPOONS SEA SALT
- ⅛ TEASPOON PAPRIKA (OPTIONAL)

GARNISH: ¼ CUP (LIGHTLY PACKED) FRESH BASIL, SLICED INTO THIN RIBBONS.

ONE LOAF OF CRUSTY SOURDOUGH (OR MULTIGRAIN) BREAD

1. In a food processor, blend the chickpeas, walnuts, tomatoes, and garlic. If necessary, add in a little of the olive oil. Blend until smooth. Add in the remaining olive oil, tahini, lemon juice, salt, and paprika. Puree until the dip is as smooth as possible. Be a smooth operator.
2. Remove to a serving bowl and scatter the basil ribbons over the top. Serve with the crusty bread for dipping. This will store in an airtight container for up to a week.

MAKES ABOUT 1 ½ CUPS OF DIP; 30 MINUTES OR UNDER! GF/SF/BLUE

Indian Papadams

Admittedly this is not *really* a recipe. It is only an instructional guide to flash frying papadams. However, once I finally learned how to do this, it added a whole new dimension to the Indian meals I prepared. With some freshly fried papadams on the table, your guests will feel like they are in the finest Indian restaurant!

1 PACKAGE PAPADAMS (BLACK PEPPER AND CUMIN ARE TWO POPULAR VARIETIES)

OIL FOR FRYING (PEANUT, CORN, OR COCONUT)

ON HAND:

THE LARGEST HEAT-PROOF SPATULA YOU OWN

A TABLE FORK

PAPER TOWELS

1. Please read through the instructions before you begin. Once the oil becomes hot, you will need to be very efficient, as this process goes extremely quickly! First, lay out some paper towels on your counter. Traditionally, papadams are drained standing on end. If you can rig a setup for this, go for it!
2. Pour enough oil into a large, heavy skillet to make a ½-inch well.
3. Allow the oil to become very hot over medium-high heat. This should take about 4-5 minutes. If you have any crumbled bits of papadam, they work great for testing the oil. When they sizzle and expand immediately after being placed in the oil, you are ready for the big show.
4. To fry the papadams, place one in the oil and immediately push it down with the flat side of a large, heat-proof spatula. The papadam should sizzle and expand immediately. If it doesn't, your oil is not yet hot enough.
5. As soon as the papadam expands, it is done. Using the spatula and fork, *immediately* remove the papadam and allow the excess oil to drain off by holding it over the skillet for a few seconds.
6. Drain it on the paper towels.
7. Repeat with the remaining papadams. Once completely cooled, you can place them in an airtight container and they will remain crisp for one or more days (depending on your climate).

SERVING SIZE: VARIABLE; 30 MINUTES OR UNDER! GF/SF/PURPLE

PAPADAMS ARE AVAILABLE IN INDIAN GROCERIES (AND OFTEN OTHER ETHNIC MARKETS) PACKAGED ON THE SHELF. IF YOU CANNOT FIND THEM IN A STORE NEAR YOU, THEY ARE AVAILABLE ONLINE FROM INDIAN FOOD COMPANIES.

Dolmadas

Here is a little goody that is much easier to make than you might think. Unfortunately, these are often served dripping with oil in many restaurants, which I find to be rather unnecessary. Alternatively, this version is flavorful, light, and nutritious. This makes quite a few dolmadas, but they are so easy to nibble on as leftovers that you may end up wishing you had made more! These are delicious along with some "Creamy Hummus" (p. 79), "Quick and Delightful Zatar Wedges" (p. 200), and a "Greek Salad" (p. 106).

I CUP DRY LONG GRAIN BROWN RICE

2 CUPS WATER

3 TABLESPOONS EXTRA-VIRGIN OLIVE OIL

½ CUP COOKED CHICKPEAS, RINSED AND DRAINED

2 TABLESPOONS (PACKED) MINCED PARSLEY

2 ROMA TOMATOES, FINELY CHOPPED

¼ CUP EACH: FRESH LEMON JUICE AND FINELY MINCED ONION

2 TEASPOONS DRIED DILL

½ TEASPOON SEA SALT (OR TO TASTE)*

56 GRAPE LEAVES (THESE CAN BE FOUND PRESERVED IN A JAR IN MANY ETHNIC MARKETS)

1. Place the rice and water in a covered pot. Bring to a boil over high heat. Reduce the heat to low and simmer until the rice is tender and all of the water is absorbed. Don't lift the lid or stir the rice while it is cooking. When the rice is done, set it aside and allow it to cool slightly.
2. Add the oil, chickpeas, parsley, tomatoes, lemon juice, onion, and dill to the rice and stir until well combined. Add the sea salt and mix well. *Since the salt content in grape leaves will vary, it is best to make the rice mixture less salty than you would normally prefer. The grape leaves will add a fair bit of salty flavor to the dolmadas, so it is crucial not to over-salt the rice. Indeed.
3. It isn't a bad idea to let this mixture sit in the fridge and marinate for a few hours before wrapping it in the leaves, if yoos got the time. If yoos don't, no worries. Proceed.
4. Place a vegetable steamer insert into a large pot that has a tight fitting lid. Add a little water to the pot, being careful not to bring the water level above the bottom of the insert. Set aside.
5. Gently remove a cluster of leaves from the jar. Don't be intimidated, you can do this!
6. Place one grape leaf on the counter, smoothest side down, with the stem base closest to you. Place one tablespoon of the filling in the center of the leaf. Fold the bottom of the grape leaf up and over the filling. Next, fold the sides in. Finally, roll up from the bottom to form a nice little package. Place your cigar-shaped dolmada inside the vegetable steamer.
7. Do this 55 more times.
8. Cover the pan with the lid and allow your dolmadas to steam over medium heat for about 20 minutes, or until the grape leaves become tender.
9. Congratulations! Enjoy your little newborn creations.

MAKES 56 DOLMADAS (SERVES ABOUT I0-I5 PEOPLE AS A STARTER); GF/SF/GREEN

Indian Phyllo "Samosas"

Although phyllo isn't exactly traditional Indian fare, this version of samosas is easy
to make, low in fat, and *ridiculously* scrumptious!

½ LB. PHYLLO, THAWED (SEE PAGE 42 FOR PHYLLO TIPS)

2¾ CUPS PEELED AND DICED POTATOES

OIL AND SEEDS:

2 TABLESPOONS OIL (COCONUT, SUNFLOWER, NON-VIRGIN OLIVE, OR SAFFLOWER)

1 TEASPOON BLACK MUSTARD SEEDS

SPICES, NOT VICES:

¾ TEASPOON EACH: CUMIN POWDER, AMCHUR, *AND* ASAFETIDA

1¼ TEASPOONS CORIANDER POWDER

¼ TEASPOON GROUND CAYENNE PEPPER

ADDITIONS:

½ CUP FROZEN PEAS

1 TABLESPOON FRESH LIME JUICE

3-4 LARGE CLOVES GARLIC, MINCED OR PRESSED

1 TEASPOON EACH: SEA SALT *AND* ORGANIC SUGAR

¼ CUP (LIGHTLY PACKED) CHOPPED FRESH CILANTRO

FOR BRUSHING (OR IN A SPRAYER): SUNFLOWER, SAFFLOWER, OR NON-VIRGIN OLIVE OIL

OPTIONAL CUTIFICATION (GARNISH): CUMIN SEEDS AND/OR BLACK SESAME SEEDS

OPTIONAL (BUT HIGHLY RECOMMENDED) SAUCES: "SPICY ONION CHUTNEY" (PAGE 126), "CILANTRO CHUTNEY ELIXIR" (PAGE 125), AND/OR "TAMARIND-DATE CHUTNEY" (PAGE 126)

1. Boil the potatoes in enough water to cover for about 20-30 minutes, or until tender. Drain and mash them with a potato masher, leaving in some of the lumps. Set aside.

2. In a medium skillet, heat the oil and seeds over medium-high heat for about a minute, or just until the seeds begin to pop. Stir in the spices and sauté another minute. Remove from heat and stir in the additions (peas, lime juice, garlic, salt, sugar, and cilantro). Next, stir the mashed potatoes into the mixture until the filling is thoroughly combined. Set aside.

3. Preheat the oven to 400° F. Lightly oil a large cookie sheet and set it aside.

4. If your ½ lb. of phyllo equals ten large sheets, cut them in half (width-wise) as you will want to end up with twenty sheets of phyllo. Set the twenty sheets of phyllo aside on a clean, dry surface and cover with a damp towel. Wrap the remaining phyllo in airtight plastic and place it back into the fridge for future fun.

5. Gently remove one sheet of phyllo and lay it flat on a clean, dry surface. Place the damp towel back on the other stack of phyllo. Spray (or brush) the sheet of phyllo with a little oil. Fold it into thirds, the long way. You want to create a long, skinny, rectangular shape. Spray (or brush) the phyllo rectangle with oil again.

6. Scoop a rounded tablespoon of the filling out and onto the base of the phyllo rectangle. Fold the phyllo up and over the filling. Continue to fold, working your way up to the top, forming it into a triangular shape as you go. Place the small, wrapped triangle onto the oiled cookie sheet and spray (or brush) it with oil again. Remember to phyllo your inner strength—you *can* do this!

7. Repeat this process with the remaining phyllo and filling until you have twenty samosas.

8. Sprinkle the top of each samosa with a few cumin seeds and/or sesame seeds if you like. Bake for about 10 minutes, or until they are beautifully golden browned. Serve with chutney if desired.

MAKES 20 SAMOSAS; SF/BLUE

Chapter Eight: Simple Sides

These dishes are all about simplicity and goodness. Although they are technically side dishes, many of these also work very well as quick and easy entrées.

Moroccan Quinoa

This is a fairly unusual take on a Moroccan dish, as couscous would be a more traditional choice. However, I prefer quinoa as it is a highly nutritious whole food that gives vitality and is very high in nutrients, including calcium. I often make a meal of this dish, as it is tasty, satisfying, and contains no added fat. For a serious treat, this can be topped with the "Moroccan Pomegranate Sauce" (page 130).

½ cup dry quinoa

¾ cup water

¼ cup plus 2 tablespoons orange juice (the freshah the bettah)

½ teaspoon (packed) minced organic lemon or orange zest (see page 43)

3 medium cloves garlic, pressed or minced

1 ⅛ teaspoons EACH: ground cumin AND ground cinnamon

⅛ teaspoon ground paprika

1 tablespoon EACH: dried cranberries (or raisins) AND pure maple syrup

Almondzo:

2 tablespoons sliced (or slivered) almonds

Fresh Finale:

¼ teaspoon sea salt

1 teaspoon fresh lemon juice

1 tablespoon (PACKED) fresh mint, minced

1. Rinse the quinoa and drain it (this removes any bitter taste present in quinoa).
2. Place the quinoa in a medium sized pot along with the water, orange juice, zest, garlic, cumin, cinnamon, paprika, cranberries or raisins, and maple syrup. Bring to a boil over medium-high heat.
3. Reduce the heat to low and cover the pot with a tight fitting lid. Allow the mixture to simmer for about 30 minutes, or until the liquids are absorbed and the quinoa is tender. While it is cooking, you may need to occasionally remove the lid to keep the liquids from overflowing.
4. While the quinoa is cooking, toast the almonds in a dry pan over low heat. Shake the pan often in order to evenly brown the almonds. When they are aromatic and golden browned, immediately remove them from the pan and set aside. You may also see page 38 for more details on toasting almonds if you need some entertainment while the quinoa is cooking.
5. When the quinoa is done, stir in the salt, lemon juice, and mint. Serve topped with the almonds. Drizzle with the "Moroccan Pomegranate Sauce" if you've chosen absolute greatness.

Serves 2; GF/SF/Green

You may notice that the garlic gets cooked in this recipe, whereas I normally add it last to retain more of its nutrients. However, uncooked garlic would be an overwhelming contrast to the delicate flavors of this dish. It's all about the balance!

Zesty Kale with Cranberries

If you have a proper citrus zester (see page 43), you can pull this impressive dish together in no time. Once you begin eating this, you may have to remind yourself that it's actually good for you! However, with the immune-boosting properties of kale, garlic, citrus zest, and lemon, there's no way your body will forget. Eat up and feel the love.

2 TABLESPOONS SLIVERED OR SLICED ALMONDS, TOASTED (SEE PAGE 38)

4 CUPS (LIGHTLY PACKED) LACINATO (BLACK) KALE RIBBONS (SEE DIRECTIONS FOR PREPARATION)

2 TABLESPOONS EACH: DRIED CRANBERRIES AND ORANGE JUICE (THE FRESHER THE BETTER)

I TABLESPOON EACH: FRESH LEMON JUICE AND CHOPPED ORGANIC ORANGE ZEST

2 TEASPOONS EACH: TAMARI (OR SHOYU OR SOY SAUCE) AND OLIVE OIL (OR COCONUT OIL)

I TEASPOON PURE MAPLE SYRUP

⅛ TEASPOON (OR MORE TO TASTE) DRIED RED CHILI PEPPER FLAKES

3 MEDIUM-LARGE CLOVES GARLIC, PRESSED OR MINCED

1. If you need to toast the almonds, you'll want to do that first (please see the toasty tips on page 38). Next, wash the kale well. Lay it on a cutting board and cut about two inches off of the base (this will include the toughest portion of the stems). I don't remove the stems above this point, as they are tender enough to eat when cooked if they are finely chopped. Next, cut the kale into fine ribbons. You should end up with a total of 4 cups of lightly packed kale ribbons.

2. Place the kale along with the remaining ingredients (except for the almonds) in a medium-large skillet. Cook over medium-high heat for about 5 minutes or so, until the kale is wilted but still dark green. Remove and top with the toasted almonds. Serve immediately.

SERVES 2-4; 30 MINUTES OR UNDER! GF/GREEN

Cilantro-Lime Rice

I have had so many versions of this simple, tangy rice and loved them all. I especially like this version, as it is made with whole grain rice and lots of healthy, fresh ingredients! Enjoy.

I CUP LONG GRAIN BROWN RICE

2 CUPS WATER

2 TABLESPOONS EACH: FRESH LIME JUICE AND FINELY MINCED ONION (WHITE OR YELLOW)

¼ CUP (PACKED) FINELY CHOPPED FRESH CILANTRO

I MEDIUM-LARGE CLOVE GARLIC, MINCED OR PRESSED

2 TEASPOONS OIL (COCONUT, OLIVE, SUNFLOWER, OR SAFFLOWER)

½ TEASPOON SEA SALT (OR LESS IF YOU PREFER)

1. Place the rice and water in a medium sized covered pot and bring to a boil over medium-high heat. Reduce the heat to low and simmer (covered) until the rice is tender and all of the water is absorbed. This should take about 35-45 minutes.

2. Mix all of the remaining ingredients into the rice and stir well to combine. Serve immediately.

SERVES 3; GF/SF/GREEN

Ful Mudhamas

I first tried this dish at a wonderful Mid-Eastern restaurant. Although they used fava beans for authenticity, I've found that pinto beans can ful almost anyone. This dish makes a tasty, quick meal when served alongside a green salad, hummus (page 79), and zatar wedges (page 200).

3 CUPS (OR TWO 15 OZ. CANS) COOKED AND DRAINED FAVA OR PINTO BEANS (UNSALTED)

4 TEASPOONS EXTRA-VIRGIN (OR REGULAR) OLIVE OIL

3 TABLESPOONS PLUS 1 TEASPOON FRESH LEMON JUICE

2 TABLESPOONS (PACKED) MINCED FRESH CILANTRO OR PARSLEY

¾ TEASPOON SEA SALT (OR LESS IF YOU PREFER)

2 SMALL-MEDIUM CLOVES GARLIC, MINCED OR PRESSED

Toss everything together and mix well. Serve at room temperature or cold. This will store refrigerated in an airtight container for several days.

SERVES 4; 30 MINUTES OR UNDER! GF/SF/GREEN

Cucumber-Dill Toss

This is the perfect solution to a summertime abundance of cucumbers and fresh dill. It is also very light, fat-free, and quite tasty. Of course, it's quite nutritious as well—cucumbers are renowned for their cleansing properties and dill is a wonderful aid to digestion.

2 MEDIUM-LARGE CUCUMBERS, *VERY* THINLY SLICED

1 MEDIUM RED ONION, *VERY* THINLY SLICED

¼ CUP FRESH DILL (OR MORE TO TASTE), FINELY CHOPPED

4 TEASPOONS ORGANIC "WHITE" SUGAR

½ CUP APPLE CIDER VINEGAR

½ TEASPOON SEA SALT

1. Place all of the ingredients in a large, airtight container and stir well to combine.
2. Refrigerate (tightly covered) for several hours or overnight to marry the flavors. You may want to occasionally take the container out and shake it a bit to make sure the marriage lasts. This will store for a week or more refrigerated in an airtight container.

SERVES ABOUT 4; GF/SF/GREEN

Anna's Zucchini

My friend Anna Royer introduced me to this ultra simple and delicious way of preparing zucchini. The thing I like best is the feeling that I am eating "fried" zucchini while using only a minimum of oil. Feigned decadence shall prevail!

I TEASPOON OIL (COCONUT, OLIVE, OR SUNFLOWER)

I MEDIUM ZUCCHINI, SLICED IN ¼-INCH ROUNDS

⅛ TEASPOON GARLIC GRANULES, OPTIONAL

SEA SALT AND GROUND BLACK PEPPER (OR LEMON-PEPPER) TO TASTE

1. Heat the oil in a large skillet over medium-high heat. Distribute the oil evenly over the pan.
2. Place the zucchini rounds individually onto the pan in a single layer, so as not to overlap. Cook until the undersides are golden browned.
3. Flip each one over individually and brown the other side. Remove to a plate when both sides are fabulously golden browned. Season with the garlic, salt, and pepper. Serve immediately.

SERVES I; 30 MINUTES OR UNDER! GF/SF/GREEN

TO MAKE ANNA'S SIMPLE ZUCCHINI WRAP:

HEAT A SOFT, WHOLE GRAIN TORTILLA AND TOP IT WITH THE HOT ZUCCHINI SLICES. ADD GRATED SOY CHEESE, DICED ONIONS, AND NUTRITIONAL YEAST—SO EASY! AS THIS IS SO SIMPLE AND UNUSUAL, KEEP IN MIND THAT IT'S NOT EXACTLY ONE TO IMPRESS YOUR NEW IN-LAWS WITH. SAVE IT FOR WHEN YOU AREN'T IN THE MOOD TO COOK BUT WANT SOMETHING HEALTHY AND LIGHT.

Krazy Kale Chips

Want to get addicted to something that's ka-*razy* good for you? Glad I could help.

4 TEASPOONS OLIVE OIL (REGULAR OR EXTRA-VIRGIN)

3 TABLESPOONS APPLE CIDER VINEGAR

¼ TEASPOON EACH: GARLIC GRANULES *AND* SEASONED SALT

4 CUPS (LIGHTLY PACKED) KALE, CHOPPED INTO PIECES ABOUT 2 x 3-INCHES IN SIZE

1. Preheat the oven to 375° F. In a small bowl, mix the oil, vinegar, garlic, and salt until well combined.
2. Place the kale in a very large bowl and pour the mixture over it. Combine very well, using your hands if necessary. Spread the kale evenly over a large nonstick cookie sheet, pouring any extra liquid from the bowl on top of the kale pieces. Bake for 10 minutes. Remove and turn the pieces over. Bake for another 10-20 minutes, or until all of the kale is crispy. However, please note that not all of the kale will crisp at the same time. Feel free to remove pieces that are crisp even if the whole batch isn't quite there yet.
3. Remove immediately from the cookie sheet and serve—you will *not* have leftovers.

SERVES 2; 30 MINUTES OR UNDER! GF/SF/GREEN

Oven "Fries"

Believe it or not, these actually taste *better* than typical French fries! Obviously, they're a nice change of pace because they are so much lower in fat. However, the unique blend of seasonings make these genuinely scrum-dilly. These are especially popular with children (of all ages).

2 MEDIUM POTATOES, WASHED WELL (SKINS ON)

1 TABLESPOON OIL (OLIVE, COCONUT, OR SUNFLOWER)

1 TEASPOON ORGANIC SUGAR OR SUCANAT

OPTIONAL: A DASH OF GROUND CAYENNE PEPPER

4 MEDIUM CLOVES FRESH GARLIC, PRESSED (OR ¾ TEASPOON DRIED GRANULATED GARLIC)

½ TEASPOON EACH: SEASONED SALT, LEMON-PEPPER, DRIED ONION GRANULES, *AND* PAPRIKA

¼ TEASPOON SEA SALT (OR LESS IF YOU PREFER)

1. Cut the potatoes into ½-inch thick slices. Next, cut each slice into sticks that resemble the shape of French fries. Keep them as uniformly sized as possible so that they cook evenly.
2. Preheat the oven to 400° F. Place the potatoes along with all of the other ingredients in a large bowl. Using a rubber spatula, toss everything together very well so that the potatoes are evenly coated with the seasonings and oil.
3. Place the potatoes on a nonstick (or lightly oiled) cookie sheet, scraping all of the seasonings onto them with the spatula. Spread the potatoes out over the pan so that none are overlapping. Bake for about 10-15 minutes. Turn them over with a heat proof spatula, then bake for another 10-15 minutes or so (or until they are delectably browned on both sides). Serve immediately with any dip that makes you flip.

SERVES 1-2; 30 MINUTES OR UNDER! GF/SF/BLUE

Kid's Kale

When children first see this, they often proclaim that they will have nothing to do with it. However, when they finally try it, they invariably scarf it down and ask for seconds! You can feel like a champion eating this, as kale is one of the most immune boosting, energizing, and strengthening vegetables around. It is also ridiculously high in calcium, iron, and vitamins. Admittedly, I belong to the elitist cult that prefers the lacinato variety (also called black kale).

½ LB. (2 CUPS PACKED) LACINATO KALE RIBBONS

2 TABLESPOONS LIQUID VEGETARIAN BROTH

1 TEASPOON OIL (COCONUT, OLIVE, OR SUNFLOWER)

2 MEDIUM CLOVES GARLIC, MINCED OR PRESSED

2-3 TEASPOONS TAMARI, SHOYU, OR SOY SAUCE

LAST ADDITIONS:
• 2-3 TEASPOONS FRESH LEMON JUICE
• 1 TEASPOON NUTRITIONAL YEAST POWDER

1. Wash the kale well. Lay it on a cutting board and cut off the ends (about two inches off of the base), which will include the toughest portion of the stems. I don't remove the stems above this point, as they are tender enough to eat when cooked (if they are finely chopped).
2. Cut the kale into thin ribbons. You should have 2 cups (packed) of kale ribbons. Next, place the kale along with the broth, oil, garlic, and two teaspoons of the tamari into a medium-large skillet. Cook over medium-high heat for 5-10 minutes, stirring often. I prefer to cook my kale less, more toward the 5 minute end, although many people like theirs more well done. You make the choice.
3. Toss with two teaspoons of the lemon juice and the nutritional yeast powder. If desired, add the additional tamari and lemon juice to taste. Enjoy the brilliant flavor and powerful antioxidants!

SERVES 2; 30 MINUTES OR UNDER! GF/GREEN

Apple Pie Acorn Squash

Here is a dish that works well either as an entrée or as a side. It is delicious, easy to prepare, and promises to fill your home with the aroma of cinnamon goodness. Because this is such a great dish for Thanksgiving and other gatherings, I have made this recipe suitable for a large crowd. However, you can easily reduce the amounts given to serve this to a smaller group. Be sure to roast the seeds for an extra treat that is both healthy and delicious!

5 ACORN SQUASHES

GRAND GRAIN:

1 CUP WATER

⅓ CUP DRY AMARANTH

DOWN-HOME APPLE GOODNESS:

3 CUPS DICED APPLE

1 CUP RAISINS

½ CUP PURE MAPLE SYRUP

2 TEASPOONS GROUND CINNAMON

1 TEASPOON PUMPKIN PIE SPICE

5 TABLESPOONS NON-HYDROGENATED MARGARINE, MELTED

¼ TEASPOON SEA SALT

OPTIONAL GARNISH:
- 4 TEASPOONS PINE NUTS
- GROUND CINNAMON TO TASTE

1. Preheat the oven to 400° F. Cut each squash in half and scoop the seeds out.* With a spoon, remove as many of the goopy strands as possible from the inside of each squash.
2. Place all of the squash halves face down in one or more large baking pan(s). Pour enough water into the pan(s) to make a ½-inch well. Cook, uncovered, for about 45-55 minutes, or until the flesh is almost fully tender. To test for doneness, poke a fork into the flesh of the squash. If it is still very firm, it will need to cook longer.
3. Meanwhile, bring the 1 cup of water to a boil in a small saucepan over high heat. Add the amaranth and turn the heat down to medium-low. Simmer until the amaranth is tender, about 10-15 minutes. Drain off the excess water.
4. Toss the drained amaranth with the diced apple, raisins, maple syrup, cinnamon, pumpkin pie spice, margarine, and sea salt.
5. Turn each squash right side up in the baking pan(s). Distribute the amaranth filling evenly into each of the squash centers. If desired, top with the pine nuts and dust with cinnamon. Bake uncovered for another 15 minutes or so, or until the acorn flesh and apples are very tender. Serve.

SERVES 10; GF/BLUE

To roast the squash seeds:
While scooping out the seeds, place them in a strainer. Separate the seeds from the stringy pulp and rinse them in the strainer under cold water. Toss the seeds with a little oil and seasoned salt and lay them flat on a baking sheet. Roast at 400° F., turning every 10 minutes, until they are golden brown (about 30 minutes total). Once cooled, they will store in an airtight container at room temperature for several days.

TIP: IF AN ACORN SQUASH HALF WON'T SIT UPRIGHT, SIMPLY CUT A LITTLE NUBBIN' OFF OF ITS BASE TO MAKE A FLAT SURFACE.

Creamy Polenta

This is a very quick and simple version of the Italian classic. Granted, this is a *major* shortcut compared to the traditional method which takes an hour or more to cook. However, this version is still delicious and makes homemade polenta accessible for people who wouldn't otherwise try it. As this is also a kid pleaser, many parents I know (including myself) have made this a staple in their repertoire. There are several ways to serve this, so you will want to read through this recipe entirely before you begin. A delicious variation (if you will be serving it as firm, pan-fried polenta) is to stir additions into the polenta while it is still creamy. Rosemary, fresh or roasted garlic, organic lemon zest, and sautéed, sliced mushrooms all work beautifully for this.

1 CUP DRY POLENTA MEAL

3¼ CUPS WATER

2 TABLESPOONS NON-HYDROGENATED MARGARINE

3 TABLESPOONS NUTRITIONAL YEAST POWDER

¾ TEASPOON SEA SALT (OR LESS IF YOU PREFER)

1. Place the polenta and water in a medium saucepan and whisk (with a wire whisk or fork) to remove lumps. Cook over medium heat, whisking continually, until it begins to thicken. Stirring the polenta constantly will prevent it from spattering, clumping, and other forms of disorderly conduct.
2. Once it begins to thicken a bit, turn the heat down to the lowest setting your burner can manage. Continue to cook, whisking very often, until it is thick (usually about 5-10 minutes).
3. Stir in the margarine and allow it to melt. Once it has melted, mix it in well. Finally, add the nutritional yeast and salt. Stir the mixture until everything is well combined.

SERVES 4-6; 30 MINUTES OR UNDER! GF/BLUE

To serve creamy style:

If serving the polenta immediately, it is delicious just plain. However, you can top it with tomato sauce or soy cheese. If desired, you may add just a little more water to the portion you will be eating as creamy polenta. If you are reserving some polenta to make "firm style," do not add any extra water to that part.

To serve firm style:

Option 1: Place the cooked, warm polenta in plastic wrap and roll it up into a log formation (like you see in stores). After it has chilled in the fridge for several hours (or overnight) and become firm, it can then be cut into rounds. Sauté the firm polenta rounds in a little oil or margarine over medium heat until golden on both sides (about 3-5 minutes on each side).

Option 2: You can press the creamy polenta into a pan. Cover and refrigerate for several hours (or overnight). Once it has chilled and become firm, you can cut it into squares (or fun shapes using cookie cutters). Finally, pan-fry the shapes in a little oil or margarine until golden on both sides.

Perfect Pinto Beans

What *is* a perfect pinto bean? I thought I knew. Originally, I had lime, garlic, and every kind of Mexican spice you could think of in this recipe. Then, I received a little education from a friend who was raised in New Mexico. His family prided themselves on cooking up the best beans possible, relying on their cleanliness and texture to make them "perfect." Additions were added later as a matter of personal preference. So, after taking Authentic Beans 101, I pared this recipe down to include only the absolute essentials. The kombu was spared because of its ability to add nutrients and transform the beans into a more digestible state. Also, both the kombu and the bay leaves enhance the natural flavor of the beans. If you have a pressure cooker in your kitchen, it will make whipping up these tasty beans an especially quick task. Soaking the beans greatly improves their digestibility and reduces their cooking time. Personally, I like to begin soaking the beans in the morning so that I can cook them for dinner that evening.

1 CUP DRY PINTO BEANS

2¼ -3½ CUPS WATER

2-INCH PIECE OF KOMBU (SEE PAGE 252 FOR MORE SEA TALES)

2 BAY LEAVES

LAST ADDITION: 1 TEASPOON SEA SALT (OR LESS IF YOU PREFER)

1. First, sort through the beans to remove any undesirable items such as stones, debris, bad beans, or nerd candy. Next, cover the pinto beans with plenty of water (about 4 cups or so). Allow them to soak overnight (or for 8-12 hours). However, if you don't have time to soak your beans, have no fear! You can still proceed confidently with this recipe.
2. Drain the soaked beans. Rinse them well. If you are using unsoaked beans, rinse them well and then drain them.
3. Place the beans in a pressure cooker (or pot with a tight fitting lid). If you are using soaked beans, use the 2¼ cups of water. If you are using unsoaked beans, use the full 3½ cups of water. Place the kombu and bay leaves in the pot along with the water and beans.
4. Cover and bring to a boil over high heat. Reduce the heat to low and simmer until the beans are tender. For *soaked* beans, this takes about 45 minutes in a pressure cooker or 1½ hours in a regular pot. For *un*soaked beans, this will take about 70 minutes in a pressure cooker and two hours or more in a regular pot.
5. When your beans are tender, simply discard the kombu and bay leaves. As if they meant nothing to you. If you have too much liquid in the pot at this point, you may pour it out. Personally, I *like* to have a little bit of liquid left as much of it gets absorbed into the beans over time. Stir in the salt and there you have it!

MAKES ABOUT 3 CUPS OF BEANS; GF/SF/GREEN

Yummy Fat-Free Refried Beans

After discovering how easy it was to make refried beans at home, I haven't gone near the canned variety. If you like things a little spicy, feel free to shake some cayenne pepper into the mix. As is, this recipe is usually a hit with children and other people who normally "don't care for beans."

I BATCH OF "PERFECT PINTO BEANS" (RECIPE ON PAGE 95)

I TEASPOON EACH: DRIED GARLIC GRANULES, DRIED ONION GRANULES, AND CUMIN POWDER

¾ TEASPOON PAPRIKA

3 TABLESPOONS EACH: WATER AND FRESH LIME JUICE

1. Prepare the "Perfect Pinto Beans" as directed in the previous recipe, making sure to discard the bay leaves and kombu. Drain off any excess water as well.
2. In a food processor, blend all of the ingredients until thoroughly creamy and well combined. Serve these velvety beans as the main ingredient in tacos, tostadas, burritos, or anything else your lovely heart desires. However, please do not confuse them with actual velvet. Trust me.
3. Place leftovers in an airtight container—they freeze well and will also keep in the fridge for one week.

SERVES 4-6; 30 MINUTES OR UNDER! (WITH COOKED BEANS) GF/SF/GREEN

Mexican Fiesta Rice

This is an extremely flavorful and very addictive version of traditional Mexican rice. I could literally eat this every single day! Hey, lay off. It's way healthier than crack. This rice is ideal with "Perfect Pinto Beans" (page 95) and a tossed green salad for a simple, lowfat, nutritious, and satisfying meal.

2 TABLESPOONS OIL (OLIVE, SUNFLOWER, OR COCONUT)

I CUP DRY LONG GRAIN BROWN RICE (OR BROWN BASMATI RICE)

¾ CUP DICED ONION

2 CUPS WATER

½ CUP CHOPPED TOMATOES (PREFERABLY FRESH)

3 TABLESPOONS TOMATO SAUCE (NOT TOMATO PASTE)

I TEASPOON EACH: CUMIN SEEDS AND CUMIN POWDER

½ TEASPOON MEXICAN OREGANO (OR REGULAR OREGANO)

I TABLESPOON "CHICKY BABY" SEASONING (PAGE 194)

(OR OTHER POWDERED VEGAN CHICKEN FLAVORING)

OPTIONAL: ½ CAYENNE PEPPER, MINCED (SEE PAGE 39 FOR TIPS)

FINAL ADDITIONS:
- 3 TABLESPOONS FRESH LIME JUICE
- 3 LARGE CLOVES GARLIC, MINCED OR PRESSED
- I TEASPOON SEA SALT

GARNISH: ½ CUP CHOPPED CILANTRO

1. For this dish, you will want to use a large pot with a tight fitting lid. In this very same pot, sauté the oil, rice, and onion over medium heat (stirring often) for 5 minutes, or until the onion just begins to brown.
2. Add the water, tomatoes, tomato sauce, cumin seeds and powder, oregano, Chicky Baby seasoning, and cayenne (if using). Cover the pot tightly and bring to a boil.
3. Turn the heat down to low. Simmer, covered, for about one hour (or until all of the liquid is absorbed and the rice is tender). While the rice is cooking, do not lift the lid or stir the mixture. Rice likes its privacy while cooking.
4. Once the rice is done, stir in the lime juice, garlic, and salt. Sprinkle with cilantro and party down!

SERVES 4-6; GF/SF/BLUE

Whibbs

That's right. You heard me right. *Whibbs.* Thank you, Wendy Krucina, for coming up with such a fun name for these little buddies! The secret of these yummy, gooey morsels is to find a really good, flavor-packed barbecue sauce and use *way* more of it than you think is proper. There is nothing worse than a bland whibb. Notably, these are much less "fancy" than if they required a made-from-scratch sauce. However, their simplicity and great flavor make these one of those recipes that tend to get used constantly. Incidentally, any time I bring these to a potluck, they disappear in under five minutes!

I LB. EXTRA-FIRM TOFU (NOT SILKEN)*

I TABLESPOON OIL (COCONUT, SAFFLOWER, SUNFLOWER, OR NON-VIRGIN OLIVE)

I ½ CUPS VEGAN BARBECUE SAUCE

1. Cut the tofu into eight slabs. Press the tofu according to the master plan on page 43. Let it press for as long as possible (anywhere from 30 minutes up to several hours).
2. Preheat the oven to 375° F. Cut each slab in half (lengthwise). You will now have 16 naked whibbs.
3. Set a large skillet (or wok) over medium-high heat and add the oil. Place the tofu into the pan in a single layer so that all of the pieces are flat against the oil in the pan. However, if your pan is not large enough, you can do this step in multiple batches. Cook the tofu for about 3-5 minutes on each side, or until the tofu is golden brown on both sides. Remove from heat and set aside.
4. Place some of the barbecue sauce in a large baking pan. Place the tofu on top of the sauce in a single layer. Cover the tofu with the remaining sauce, making sure every tofu stick is well coated on all sides. At this point, you should be thinking: "This is *waaaaay* too much sauce. Can this be right?" Trust me, it is better to have too much sauce than too little when it comes to this dish. It is the difference between a totally delectable whibb and a "just o.k." whibb.
5. Bake the whibbs for about 15 minutes and then turn them over with a spatula, continuing to keep them in a single layer. At this time, take some of the stray sauce from the pan and place it on the whibbs (a small spoon works well for this). This will ensure that the sauce cooks into the tofu instead of onto the pan. Continue to bake for about 15 more minutes. Turn again, spooning the stray sauce onto the whibbs. Continue to bake for about 10 more minutes. You should have them in the oven for a total of about 40 minutes.
6. When they are browned and gooey, remove them from the oven and enjoy the good eats.

MAKES 16 WHIBBS (SERVES ABOUT 4); GF/BLUE

*Frozen and thawed tofu would also work well in this dish. Simply freeze one pound of tofu (place the whole container in the freezer) for at least twelve hours. Then, allow it to thaw in the fridge overnight. Gently squeeze out the excess water and then proceed with the recipe as given.

SERVING SUGGESTION: WHIBBS WORK WELL AS A SIDE DISH OR AS A SIMPLE MAIN DISH. THEY ALSO MAKE A TRULY DELICIOUS SANDWICH (OR WRAP) FILLING ALONG WITH SOME VEGAN MAYONNAISE, PICKLES, ONIONS, GRATED CABBAGE, AND LETTUCE. OH YES.

Kid's Favorite Veggie Fried Rice

If you have cold, leftover rice and pre-washed baby spinach on hand, this dish takes only ten minutes from start to finish. I recently served this to a group of five-year-olds who happily gobbled it down (even after some of them had proclaimed they didn't like vegetables). One vegetable "hater" even asked me if I could make it again for her very soon! For adults, you can toss in some sliced mushrooms, green onions, and/or chili-garlic sauce for some added kick. Either way, it's a great reason to keep extra rice on hand!

2 TABLESPOONS <u>EACH</u>: OIL (SAFFLOWER, SUNFLOWER, OR COCONUT) *AND* TAMARI (OR SHOYU OR SOY SAUCE)

1 TABLESPOON TOASTED (DARK) SESAME OIL

1 ½ TABLESPOONS ORGANIC SUGAR OR SUCANAT

1 ½ TEASPOONS <u>EACH</u>: DRIED GARLIC GRANULES *AND* DRIED ONION GRANULES

¼ TEASPOON SEA SALT (OPTIONAL)

<u>OPTIONAL</u>: 1 TABLESPOON TOASTED SESAME SEEDS

KID-FRIENDLY GOODIES:
- 1 SMALL CARROT, DICED
- 2 CUPS (LIGHTLY PACKED) BABY SPINACH, WASHED WELL
- ½ CUP FROZEN CORN KERNELS
- 3 CUPS <u>COLD</u>, COOKED (LEFTOVER) BROWN RICE

1. Place the oil, tamari, toasted sesame oil, sugar, garlic and onion granules, and sea salt (if using) in a large skillet or wok and stir to combine. Set the heat to medium-high.

2. Add the goodies (the carrot, spinach, corn, and rice). Cook, stirring, just until the spinach is wilted and the rice is heated through. Serve plain or topped with the toasted sesame seeds.

SERVES 4; 30 MINUTES OR UNDER! (WITH COOKED RICE) GF/BLUE

Easy and Addictive Eggplant "Chips"

It is slightly disturbing how this dish can make it possible—even likely—for an entire eggplant to be consumed by one person (that would be me) in one sitting. These "chips" are one of my standby favorites as they are delicious and require a prep time of only five minutes. It should be noted, however, that these are soft and gooey, rather than crispy. With that said, I hope you enjoy this healthy, unusual snack!

ONE 1 LB. EGGPLANT, SLICED IN ¼-INCH THICK ROUNDS

4 TABLESPOONS <u>EACH</u>: OLIVE OIL *AND* LIQUID BROTH (VEGETABLE OR "CHICKEN" BROTH, P. 194)

2 TABLESPOONS PLUS 2 TEASPOONS TAMARI, SHOYU, OR SOY SAUCE

2 TEASPOONS DRIED GARLIC GRANULES

1 TEASPOON ORGANIC SUGAR OR SUCANAT

OPTIONAL HEAT:
- ⅛ TEASPOON CAYENNE

1. Preheat the oven to 400° F. Place the eggplant rounds in a single layer on a large cookie sheet. Whisk together all of the other items and pour over the eggplant. Turn the slices over so that the marinade can soak into the other side of the eggplant as well.*

2. Allow the eggplant to marinate briefly while the oven is preheating. Turn the slices over again, keeping them in a single layer. Bake them for about 10-15 minutes, or until the underside is very nicely browned.

3. Flip the slices over with a spatula and bake for another 5-10 minutes, or until the eggplant is *very* tender and looks caramelized (gooey and well browned) on both sides. Serve immediately.

SERVES 2-3; 30 MINUTES OR UNDER! GF/BLUE

*You will have some sauce that doesn't quite absorb into the eggplant. It will bake onto the pan, but if you soak the pan for at least 10 minutes, it will wash off easily.

Garlic Mashers

These yummy mashed potatoes make for a lovely yet simple meal along with some "Kid's Kale" (page 92) and seasoned beans. Of course, they're also ideal for Thanksgiving or any special occasion, especially topped with the insanely delectable "Scrumptious Shiitake Gravy" (page 122).

4 cups peeled and chopped potatoes (cut into uniformly sized pieces)
¼ cup non-hydrogenated margarine
¾ cup nondairy milk (plain and unsweetened)
1 teaspoon sea salt (or less if you prefer)
2 medium cloves garlic, minced or pressed

1. Place the potatoes in a large pot. Pour plenty water over them (so that they will be under the water the *entire* time they are cooking, as some of the liquid will cook off).
2. Cover and bring to a boil over high heat. Reduce the heat to low and simmer for about 20 minutes, or until a fork inserted into one of the pieces proves them to be very tender.
3. Drain the potatoes and place them back in the pot (or in a mixing bowl). Bury the margarine under the potatoes (in order to melt the margarine quickly and easily). Once melted, stir well to mix. Stir in the remaining ingredients until thoroughly combined.
4. Do you desire a very fluffy, puffy, cloud-like mashed potato product? If so, give them a good long swirl with some electric beaters as well. Serve immediately.

Serves 4; 30 minutes or under! GF/Blue

Zen Rice with Seaweed Gomasio

This is one of those dishes that I make frequently and really rely on. It is such the essence of lovely simplicity that I feel like I should be wearing a Zen monk's robe when I eat it!
Both children and adults enjoy this dish, with or without the gomasio. Or robe.

1½ cups dry long grain brown rice (or brown basmati rice)
3 cups water
4 teaspoons (or more to taste) "Seaweed Gomasio" (see page 194 for recipe)

8 teaspoons oil (coconut or olive)
4 teaspoons tamari, shoyu, or soy sauce
2 teaspoons nutritional yeast powder

1. Place the rice and water in a rice cooker, pressure cooker, or regular pot with a tight fitting lid. Bring to a boil over high heat. Reduce the heat to low and simmer until the water is absorbed and the rice is tender. In a rice cooker or regular pot, this will take about 45 minutes. In a pressure cooker, this will take about 15 minutes or so once the top begins to shake and shimmy.
2. While the rice is cooking, make the gomasio. Set it aside.
3. Drizzle the rice with the oil and tamari. Top with the nutritional yeast and gomasio and serve.

Serves 4-6; GF/Green

Oven Roasted Cauliflower with Rosemary and Garlic

This dish is so yummy that I've been known, in moments I'm not proud of, to eat an entire batch of this at one time! Don't be like me…*share* the goodness. Incidentally, this is a great side dish for Thanksgiving (or any special occasion) and can be prepared in advance. Simply toss all of the ingredients together and marinate overnight. Pop it into the oven half an hour before dinner, and there go you! *Simple elegance.*

2 TEASPOONS FRESH ROSEMARY LEAF, STEMS REMOVED AND CHOPPED

4 TEASPOONS OLIVE OIL, EXTRA-VIRGIN OR REGULAR

6 MEDIUM CLOVES GARLIC, MINCED OR PRESSED

½ TEASPOON SEA SALT (PLUS UP TO ⅛ TEASPOON MORE IF YOU LIKE)

¼ TEASPOON EACH: ORGANIC SUGAR (OR SUCANAT) *AND* GROUND BLACK PEPPER

½ TEASPOON BALSAMIC VINEGAR

3½ CUPS CHOPPED CAULIFLOWER (CUT INTO BITE SIZED PIECES)

1. Preheat the oven to 400° F. Place everything but the cauliflower in a large bowl and stir to mix. Next, add the cauliflower and combine well with the seasonings using a rubber spatula. At this point you can allow the mixture to marinate for up to 24 hours (refrigerated in an airtight container) if you like.
2. Spread the mixture onto a large ungreased cookie sheet, using the rubber spatula to scrape all of the herbs and spices onto the cauliflower. Bake for about 15 minutes.
3. Turn the cauliflower over with a heat proof spatula and bake for another 10-15 minutes, or until lightly browned and *very* tender. Remove and serve. Feel impressed with yourself for as long as you like.

SERVES 2; 30 MINUTES OR UNDER! GF/SF/GREEN

Coconut-Lime Rice

Yum. That's all I have to say on the matter.

½ CUP FINELY MINCED ONION (WHITE, YELLOW, OR RED)

4 TEASPOONS TOASTED (DARK) SESAME OIL

I CUP EACH: JASMINE (OR WHITE BASMATI) RICE, WATER, *AND* COCONUT MILK

2 TEASPOONS ORGANIC LIME ZEST, FINELY CHOPPED (ZEST OF ONE LIME)

¼ TEASPOON DRIED TURMERIC

FINAL FRESHLINGS:

2 TABLESPOONS MINCED FRESH CILANTRO

3 TABLESPOONS FRESH LIME JUICE

½ TEASPOON SEA SALT

ONE SCALLION (GREEN ONION), TRIMMED AND CHOPPED

2 TEASPOONS GRATED FRESH GINGER

2 LARGE CLOVES GARLIC, MINCED OR PRESSED

Combine the onion, oil, rice, water, coconut milk, zest, and turmeric in a covered pot or rice cooker. Stir well and bring to a boil. Reduce the heat to low and simmer (covered) for about 15 minutes, or until all of the liquid has been absorbed. Stir in the remaining ingredients and serve. Hello, flavor party!

SERVES 3; 30 MINUTES OR UNDER! GF/SF/PURPLE

Joe's Guacamole

Joe Gilbert introduced me to this unconventionally chunky and spicy guacamole. He says that it's a crying shame to add anything but *fresh* items to guacamole. Therefore, it contains no cumin. I can't say I disagree—I love the clean flavor of this addictive dip. You can serve this in a number of ways: It is the filling for the "Funky Chunky Guacamole Wrap" (page 189). It's also delicious paired with the "Spiced Lime Tortilla Chips" (page 206). Of course, you can also just buy some organic tortilla chips to serve this with. For a color splash, try a combination of yellow, blue, and red (naturally colored) tortilla chips.

2 RIPE AVOCADOS

½ CUP CHOPPED TOMATOES (RIPE, FLAVORFUL TOMATOES SUCH AS CHERRY OR GRAPE ARE IDEAL)

⅓ CUP FINELY MINCED WHITE, YELLOW, OR RED ONION

2 LARGE CLOVES GARLIC, MINCED OR PRESSED

3 TABLESPOONS MINCED FRESH JALAPENO (SEE PAGE 39 FOR SPICY DETAILS)

2 TABLESPOONS EACH: *FRESH* LIME JUICE *AND* FRESH CHOPPED CILANTRO

½ TEASPOON SEA SALT

1. Place the flesh of one avocado in a medium bowl. Mash it well with a fork. Chop the flesh of the other avocado into small or medium sized chunks. Add the chopped avocado to the bowl and gently mix it into the mashed avocado. This will lend you a creamy base with lots of chunky (and funky) avocado pieces remaining.
2. Gently stir in the additional items until well combined and serve. Although this is best served immediately, it will store for a day or two, refrigerated in an airtight container.

SERVES 4; 30 MINUTES OR UNDER! GF/SF/Blue

NOTE: FOR CILANTRO-HATERS (YOU KNOW WHO YOU ARE), THE CILANTRO CAN SIMPLY BE OMITTED FROM EITHER OF THESE RECIPES.

Kid's Choice Guacamole

Here is a creamy, non-spicy guacamole that is often first choice for adults as well! It is simple, quick, and tastes fresh and delightful. This guacamole is great served with chips (see page 206 for homemade chips), in a wrap, on a burrito, or any other fling that flaps your fancy.

I AVOCADO, RIPE AND READY

I TABLESPOON EACH: FRESH LIME JUICE *AND* MINCED FRESH CILANTRO

I MEDIUM CLOVE GARLIC, MINCED OR PRESSED

⅛ TEASPOON SEA SALT

1. Remove the avocado flesh from its skin and place it in a bowl. Mash it very well with a fork.
2. Stir in the lime juice, cilantro, garlic, and salt until very well combined. Although this is best served immediately, it will store for a day or two, refrigerated in an airtight container.

SERVES 2-4; 30 MINUTES OR UNDER! GF/SF/Blue

Quick and Healthy Herbed Garlic Bread

This bad boy has always been a hit with my weight loss clients as it satisfies the craving for garlic bread in a *very* healthy way. Although I would opt for the "Green Bread" (page 69) when choosing a garlic bread for fancier events, this is the *perfect* choice for everyday eating!

4 SLICES SPROUTED OR WHOLE GRAIN BREAD (SUCH AS EZEKIEL 4:9 BREAD)

4 TEASPOONS OLIVE OIL (PREFERABLY EXTRA-VIRGIN)

4 MEDIUM CLOVES GARLIC, MINCED OR PRESSED

½ TEASPOON <u>EACH</u>: DRIED BASIL *AND* DRIED OREGANO

⅛ TEASPOON SEA SALT

1. Preheat the oven (or toaster oven) to 375° F.
2. Evenly drizzle each piece of bread with 1 teaspoon of oil. Spread each slice with one clove of garlic. Really distribute the oil and garlic evenly over the entire piece of bread.
3. Sprinkle the spices and salt evenly over the bread slices. Place the bread directly on an oven rack for about 10-15 minutes, or until the garlic and bread begin to brown. Remove and serve immediately.

SERVES 4; 30 MINUTES OR UNDER! SF/GREEN

Seasoned Indian Basmati Rice

This traditional Indian rice is very easy to prepare and pairs well with just about any Indian curry or soup. Usually the whole spices are left in when the rice is finished, but you may wish to remove them. Although it is traditional to use white basmati rice, brown basmati is a healthier substitute. Either way, it's lovely and makes your kitchen smell divine!

1½ CUPS DRY BROWN BASMATI RICE (OR WHITE BASMATI FOR A MORE TRADITIONAL DISH)

3 CUPS WATER

2 CINNAMON STICKS

5 WHOLE CLOVES

5 WHOLE CARDAMOM PODS (PREFERABLY GREEN)

½ TABLESPOON CUMIN SEEDS

1. To prepare, simply place all of the ingredients in a large pot with a tight fitting lid (or in a rice cooker). Bring to a boil over high heat.
2. Reduce heat to low and simmer, covered, until all of the water is absorbed. Fluff and serve. That's it!

MAKES ABOUT 5 CUPS OF RICE; 30 MINUTES OR UNDER! GF/SF/GREEN (WITH BROWN BASMATI RICE)

Chapter Nine: Scrumptious Salads

Who doesn't love a healthy, life enhancing salad—especially when it tastes amazing? Many of these salads can actually stand in for a main course, while others are the perfect accompaniment. They are all very fresh, full of nutrients, and incredibly delicious!

Spinach-Strawberry Salad

I have made this easy, elegant salad for more catering events than I can remember and it has never failed to garner rave reviews (and requests for the recipe!). If you have access to sorrel, it's a terrific addition. Simply substitute it for some of the spinach.

DELECTABLE DRESSING:

2 TABLESPOONS EACH: OIL (SUNFLOWER, SAFFLOWER, OR NON-VIRGIN OLIVE), APPLE CIDER VINEGAR, AND ORGANIC SUGAR

1 TABLESPOON EACH: SESAME SEEDS, TAMARI (OR SHOYU OR SOY SAUCE), AND ORANGE JUICE

½ TABLESPOON POPPY SEEDS

⅛ TEASPOON PAPRIKA

SALAD:

ONE 5 OZ. BAG OF BABY SPINACH, ORGANIC AND PRE-WASHED

1 PINT STRAWBERRIES, TRIMMED AND THINLY SLICED

TOPPING: ½ CUP SLICED ALMONDS, TOASTED (SEE PAGE 38)

1. Whisk the oil, vinegar, sugar, sesame seeds, tamari, orange juice, poppy seeds, and paprika together to make the dressing. Set aside.
2. Place the spinach (and sorrel, if using) and strawberries in a large bowl. Top with the dressing and toss to combine.
3. Top with the almonds just before serving. Warn your tummy about the overly intense fabulousness it is about to experience.

SERVES ABOUT 4; 30 MINUTES OR UNDER! GF/GREEN

Baby Greens with Light Ginger-Miso Dressing

This is a very simple and light salad, yet full of flavor, nutrients, and good juju.

TO TASTE: "LIGHT GINGER-MISO DRESSING" (PLEASE SEE PAGE 129)

4 CUPS BABY GREENS

1 SMALL CARROT, JULIENNE CUT, GRATED, OR MINCED

½ CUCUMBER, CUT IN HALF LENGTHWISE AND THINLY SLICED CROSSWISE

¼ CUP EACH: GRATED RED CABBAGE AND SHELLED EDAMAME

½ RED ONION, THINLY SLICED

OPTIONAL GARNISH: ¼ CUP WASABI PEAS (AVAILABLE IN MOST HEALTH FOOD STORES)

1. Whisk the dressing together and set it aside.
2. Wash the greens well and dry them with a towel (or in a salad spinner). Prepare the other veggies. Place the greens and veggies in bowls and top them with the desired amount of dressing. If you like to be kicked in a good way, garnish with some wasabi peas. Serve immediately.

SERVES 4; 30 MINUTES OR UNDER! GF/GREEN

Asian Salad with Peanut Dressing

This salad is not fooling around. It will nourish you, fill up your belly, and keep your taste buds on your team. If you want it to totally function as a meal, simply toss in some marinated, pan-fried tempeh or tofu cubes.

TO TASTE: "THE PEANUT SAUCE" (PLEASE SEE PAGE 117)

SALAD DAYS:

4 CUPS BABY GREENS OR BABY SPINACH

1 CUP BEAN SPROUTS

½ CUCUMBER, CUT IN HALF LENGTHWISE AND THINLY SLICED CROSSWISE (INTO THIN HALF-MOONS)

SMALL CARROT, JULIENNE CUT, GRATED, OR CHOPPED

2 SCALLIONS (GREEN ONIONS), TRIMMED AND CHOPPED

OPTIONAL: 1 CUP PEA PODS (ENDS SNIPPED)

GARNISH: 2 TABLESPOONS TOASTED BROWN OR BLACK SESAME SEEDS (SEE PAGE 42)

1. Make the peanut sauce and set it aside. *Aside.* Best not to drink it like a smoothie at this point.
2. Wash your green babies well and dry them with paper towels (or using a salad spinner).
3. Place the greens in bowls. Top them with the bean sprouts, cucumber, carrot, and scallions. If using the pea pods (and/or tempeh or tofu cubes), bring them on!
4. Drizzle with the peanut sauce and top with the toasted sesame seeds. Serve immediately.

SERVES 2 AS A MAIN DISH; SERVES 4 AS A SIDE SALAD; 30 MINUTES OR UNDER! GF/BLUE

MY STANDARD TOFU TOSS-IN (THAT ALSO WORKS WITH TEMPEH)?
CUBE UP SOME FIRM TOFU AND SPRINKLE IT WITH A LITTLE TAMARI
OR SHOYU, NUTRITIONAL YEAST, ONION GRANULES, AND GARLIC GRANULES.
NEXT, SAUTÉ IT IN SOME OLIVE OR SESAME OIL UNTIL IT IS BROWNED
ON ALL SIDES. SO GOOD, SO EASY, AND SO SIMPLE. PLUS, IT'S A GREAT
WAY TO SERVE KIDS SOMETHING THEY LOVE THAT IS HEALTHY AND QUICK!

Greek Salad

Please don't tell any non-vegetarian Greek people about this. Anyone who has an intimate love for feta cheese will simply accept no substitutes. However, I've found that most people *really* love this salad despite the absence of feta. The dressing is so flavorful that it gives quite a bit of oomph to the tofu. Be sure to use high quality olives, such as kalamatas, instead of canned ones. In my experience, canned black olives generally taste more like a tin can than an olive.

To Taste: "Classic Vinaigrette" (please see page 120)

¼ cup crumbled firm tofu*

4 cups chopped romaine lettuce or baby greens, washed well and patted dry

¼ cup very thinly sliced red onion

¾ cup each: chopped ripe tomato *and* chopped cucumber

16 kalamata olives (or other good Greek olives)

1. Make the "Classic Vinaigrette" and set it aside.
2. *To crumble the tofu, simply squeeze the water out of it and then crumble it with your hands. At this point, you can toss the tofu with a little of the vinaigrette if you like. Set it aside.
3. Place the lettuce in bowls and top with the onion, tomato, cucumber, olives, and crumbled tofu. Drizzle each salad with some of the vinaigrette and serve immediately. If you are using non-pitted, whole olives, be sure to warn your guests! Enjoy.

Serves 4-6; 30 minutes or under! GF/Blue

Princess Salad

There is no logical reason to call this a princess salad, other than that it makes my daughter like it even more. That, and the fact that I tell her any self-respecting horse would love it! This salad is the essence of simplicity and is a quick, easy way to get children to eat carrots frequently. You could toss in some crushed pineapple as well, but the short list of ingredients here make this easy enough to throw together in under five minutes. Carrots are very high in beta carotene, and the vitamin C in the orange juice helps the iron in the raisins absorb into the body.

2 medium carrots, grated

¼ cup raisins

¼ cup orange juice (the fresher the better)

You, my friend, have just stumbled across the simplest directions in this book! Congratulations. Here goes: Toss ingredients together and serve.

Serves 2; 30 minutes or under! GF/SF/Green

Thai Tofu & Tropical Fruit Salad

This is fairly unusual, yet strangely addictive. A meal in a bowl, this satisfying salad will make you sing!

½ LB. FIRM OR EXTRA-FIRM TOFU (NOT SILKEN)

SPUNKY SPARKLE DRESSING:

¼ CUP *FRESH* LIME JUICE

¼ TEASPOON SEA SALT

4 TEASPOONS ORGANIC SUGAR

2 TEASPOONS <u>EACH</u>: TOASTED (DARK) SESAME OIL *AND* TAMARI (OR SOY SAUCE OR SHOYU)

½ TEASPOON (OR MORE TO TASTE) RED CHILI FLAKES

I TABLESPOON (PACKED) MINCED FRESH MINT

I TEASPOON BLACK, BROWN, OR WHITE SESAME SEEDS (PREFERABLY TOASTED)

2 TABLESPOONS (PACKED) MINCED FRESH CILANTRO

TOFU MARINADE:

2 TEASPOONS *FRESH* LIME JUICE

I TABLESPOON TAMARI, SHOYU, OR SOY SAUCE

ALTERNATIVE TOFU BUSINESS:

2 LARGE SHALLOTS, VERY THINLY SLICED

I TABLESPOON OIL (COCONUT, SUNFLOWER, SAFFLOWER, OR NON-VIRGIN OLIVE)

¼ TEASPOON SEA SALT

GET FRESH:

2 CUPS CHOPPED FRESH PINEAPPLE

I KIWI, PEELED AND SLICED

I MANGO, PEELED AND CHOPPED

2 CUPS (PACKED) BABY SPINACH

GARNISH:

2 TEASPOONS FINELY SHREDDED COCONUT (RAW OR LIGHTLY TOASTED)

2 TABLESPOONS CRUSHED DRY-ROASTED (UNSALTED) PEANUTS (SEE PAGE 41 FOR TIPS)

1. Slice the tofu into four slabs and press between paper towels (see page 43) for about ten minutes. While the tofu is pressing, whisk the dressing together and set it aside.
2. Cut the tofu into cubes. Sprinkle them evenly with the 2 teaspoons of lime juice and 1 tablespoon of tamari. Gently toss to coat and set aside.
3. In a medium skillet over medium-high heat, sauté the shallots in the 1 tablespoon of oil for about 3-5 minutes (until the shallots are soft and are beginning to brown). Add the tofu and the ¼ teaspoon of salt and continue to sauté, turning the tofu cubes often with a heat proof spatula, until the tofu is nicely browned on all sides. Set aside.
4. Prepare the pineapple, kiwi, mango, and spinach and set them aside.
5. *To serve*: Place the baby spinach in large salad bowls. Top with the fruit and tofu-shallot mixture. Drizzle with the desired amount of dressing (you may wish to use just half of the dressing and see if that is the right amount for your taste buds). If you don't wish to add the rest of dressing, it will keep refrigerated (in an airtight container) for about a week.
6. Garnish with the coconut and peanuts. Serve immediately.

SERVES 2-4 (2 IF USING AS A MEAL); 4 IF USING AS A SIDE SALAD); GF/BLUE

Thai Spring Roll Salad with Peanut Sauce

Want the glorious taste of a fresh Thai spring roll, but not in a rolling kind of mood? Look no further. This version is easy to make and still delicious. It is purposely heavy on the veggies and light on the noodles. However, if you prefer a more substantial feel, double the noodles and add more peanut sauce.

TO TASTE: "THE PEANUT SAUCE" (PLEASE SEE PAGE 117)

CANOODLING: 1 "NEST" (1.76 OZ.) OF BEAN THREAD NOODLES (SEE PAGE 251)

VEG OUT:

1 CUP (LIGHTLY PACKED) ROMAINE LETTUCE, WASHED AND PATTED DRY

2 TABLESPOONS (PACKED) EACH: MINCED FRESH BASIL AND MINCED FRESH MINT

¼ CUP (LIGHTLY PACKED) MINCED FRESH CILANTRO

2 SCALLIONS (GREEN ONIONS), TRIMMED AND FINELY CHOPPED

1 CARROT, JULIENNE SLICED OR GRATED

1 CUP GRATED OR FINELY CHOPPED RED CABBAGE

GARNISH:

1 TABLESPOON TOASTED BLACK AND/OR BROWN SESAME SEEDS (SEE PAGE 42 FOR TOASTY TIPS)

2 TABLESPOONS CRUSHED DRY-ROASTED, UNSALTED PEANUTS (SEE PAGE 41 FOR TIPS)

1. Prepare the peanut sauce and set it aside.
2. Prepare your noodles according to the instructions on their package. When they are tender, place them in a strainer and rinse them under cold water. Allow them to drain, then cut the noodles into fourths with a sharp knife, kitchen scissors, or sword.
3. Place all of your veggies and herbs in a large bowl and toss to mix. Add the noodles and pour in the desired amount of peanut sauce. Stir everything gently, yet thoroughly, to combine. Garnish with the sesame seeds and peanuts. Serve immediately (or within an otherwise reasonable time lapse).

SERVES 4; 30 MINUTES OR UNDER! GF/BLUE

Indian Kuchumber Salad

Here is the boom-boom that I love to pile on my plate at Indian buffets. Except all organic-like.

1¾ CUPS DICED CUCUMBER (ONE MEDIUM CUCUMBER), PEEL LEFT ON IF ORGANIC

½ CUP CHOPPED TOMATO (OR HALVED GRAPE OR CHERRY TOMATOES)

¾ CUP DICED RED ONION (OR WHITE OR YELLOW)

2 TABLESPOONS EACH: FRESH LIME JUICE AND NON-VIRGIN OLIVE OIL (OR SUNFLOWER OIL)

½ TEASPOON EACH: SEA SALT AND GROUND BLACK PEPPER

3 TABLESPOONS CHOPPED FRESH CILANTRO

OPTIONAL: 1 TEASPOON UNTOASTED (RAW) BLACK SESAME SEEDS

Gently toss all of the ingredients together until very well combined. Serve cold or at room temperature.

SERVES 4; 30 MINUTES OR UNDER! GF/SF/GREEN

Fatoush Salad

After eating this for years in restaurants, I finally came up with a recipe of my own for this fresh and delightful salad. This version is lower in fat and slightly more minty than the other kinds I've tasted. If you don't care for mint, simply replace it partially (or fully) with parsley. This makes for a delicious, satisfying, and light meal when served with some "Creamy Hummus" (page 79), "Dolmadas" (page 85), and wedges of warm pita bread.

4 TORTILLAS (OR PITA ROUNDS), CUT INTO 1½-INCH PIECES

1-2 TABLESPOONS OLIVE OIL, REGULAR OR EXTRA-VIRGIN

DRESSING:

3 TABLESPOONS OLIVE OIL

THE FRESH JUICE OF 1 LARGE LEMON

½ TEASPOON SEA SALT

FRESH GROUND PEPPER TO TASTE

1 TABLESPOON ZATAR (SEE PAGE 253)

SALAD:
• 1 LB. CHERRY TOMATOES, HALVED
• 2 CUPS DICED (OR VERY THINLY SLICED) CUCUMBER
• ½ CUP MINCED FRESH MINT
• ¼ CUP CHOPPED SCALLIONS (GREEN ONIONS)

1. Preheat the oven to 400°F. Spread the tortilla or pita strips in a single layer onto a lightly oiled cookie sheet. Brush them with the 1-2 tablespoons of oil.
2. Bake the strips until they are golden brown and crisp. Set them aside.
3. Whisk the dressing together and set it aside.
4. Next, place the tomatoes, cucumber, mint, and scallions in a medium-large bowl.
5. Add the tortilla or pita strips to the salad and top with the dressing. Gently combine everything until thoroughly mixed and serve.

SERVES 3-4; 30 MINUTES OR UNDER! GF (WITH GLUTEN-FREE TORTILLAS)/SF/BLUE

Spinach, Orange, and Toasted Almond Salad

This salad is the essence of simplicity and good taste. Additionally, the vitamin C in the orange helps the body to assimilate the iron in the spinach. A great example of how the best flavor companions often make ideal nutrition partners!

½ CUP OF THE "LIGHT BALSAMIC DRESSING" (PLEASE SEE RECIPE ON PAGE 129)

4 CUPS BABY SPINACH

1 CUP FRESH MANDARIN OR CLEMENTINE ORANGE SEGMENTS (PEELED)

VERY THIN SLICES OF RED ONION TO TASTE

¼ CUP TOASTED ALMONDS (SEE PAGE 38)

1. Whisk or stir all of the dressing ingredients together. You may have a little of the dressing left over after making the salads, but never fear! It lasts for several weeks in the fridge.
2. Place the spinach, orange segments, and onion together in a large bowl and drizzle with the dressing. Toss to mix. Scatter the almonds on top and serve immediately.

SERVES 4; 30 MINUTES OR UNDER! GF/GREEN

Avocado and Grapefruit Salad with Chili-Roasted Almonds

This salad (a.k.a. love on a plate) is refreshing, unusual, pretty, and delicious. It is perfect either by itself as a light lunch, or served alongside a Mexican meal as a side salad. Nutritionally, it's very high in fiber, vitamins, calcium, iron, and potassium. What a *seriously* fun way to eat your veggies!

CHILI-ROASTED ALMONDS:

4 TABLESPOONS SLIVERED ALMONDS

¼ TEASPOON CUMIN POWDER

½ TEASPOON GROUND PAPRIKA

⅛ TEASPOON CAYENNE POWDER

1 ½ TEASPOONS ORGANIC SUGAR OR SUCANAT

2 TEASPOONS TAMARI, SHOYU, OR SOY SAUCE

LIME-ORANGE DRIZZLE DRESSING:

1 TABLESPOON OIL (SUNFLOWER, SAFFLOWER, FLAX, OR NON-VIRGIN OLIVE)

½ TEASPOON SEA SALT

4 TEASPOONS ORGANIC SUGAR OR SUCANAT

1 TEASPOON EACH: BLACK (OR BROWN) SESAME SEEDS *AND* TAMARI, SHOYU, OR SOY SAUCE

2 TABLESPOONS EACH: FRESH LIME JUICE *AND* FRESH ORANGE JUICE

SEXY SALAD:

1 RIPE AVOCADO

1 LARGE RED GRAPEFRUIT

2 CUPS (PACKED) BABY SPINACH

1. To yummify the almonds: Mix all of the ingredients for the chili-roasted almonds together in a small, dry skillet. Set the pan to low heat and toast the almonds, turning very often with a spatula. Cook for about 5 minutes, or just until they become lightly browned and aromatic. Be careful not to overcook, as they can burn very quickly (trust me, I know). They will be a little sticky, which is fine. As soon as the almonds are cool enough to touch, remove them from the pan and break them apart with your fingers. If you wait too long, they will stick to the pan and be more difficult to break apart. Set the almonds aside.
2. Whisk the dressing ingredients together and set aside.
3. Peel and chop the avocado. Set it—you guessed it—aside.
4. To prepare the grapefruit, slice it in half and cut out the segments with a knife or grapefruit spoon. This method is a bit more time consuming, but ensures that you end up with only the juicy red segments. If you don't mind tasting the bitter white portion under the peel of the grapefruit, you can simply peel the grapefruit like an orange and cut it into segments.
5. Place the spinach in large salad bowls and top with the grapefruit and avocado. Whisk the dressing again (the sugar tends to settle at the bottom) and then drizzle it over the salads. Top with the almonds and serve immediately.

SERVES 2 AS A MAIN COURSE (OR 4 AS A SIDE SALAD); 30 MINUTES OR UNDER! GF/BLUE

Baby Greens with Arugula, Apples, and Caramelized Pecans

This salad is all at once elegant, very easy to prepare, delectable, and nourishing! I have often relied on this bad boy as a way to impress guests when I'm short on time. The raspberry dressing comes together very quickly, but you can substitute a bottled raspberry vinaigrette (such as Annie's) if you prefer.

PECANS:

½ CUP PECANS

¼ CUP PURE MAPLE SYRUP

QUICK 4-INGREDIENT RASPBERRY DRESSING:

6 TABLESPOONS RASPBERRY FRUIT SPREAD OR JAM

1 TABLESPOON EACH: BALSAMIC VINEGAR AND OIL (NON-VIRGIN OLIVE OR SUNFLOWER)

2 TABLESPOONS WATER (OR MORE IF YOU PREFER)

SALAD:

3 CUPS (PACKED) BABY GREENS

1 CUP (PACKED) ARUGULA (OR ADDITIONAL BABY GREENS)*

¼ CUP VERY THINLY SLICED RED ONION

1 CUP DICED RED DELICIOUS APPLE (OR OTHER SWEET APPLE—PEARS ARE TERRIFIC TOO!)

1. Preheat the oven to 350° F. Stir the pecans and maple syrup together and spread them out in a single layer onto a lightly oiled baking pan. Bake them for about 10 minutes.
2. Remove the gooey lovelies from the oven and stir them well. Place them back into the oven and bake for about 10 more minutes.
3. Scrape the candied pecans onto waxed paper and allow them to cool. Be sure to remove any maple syrup from the pan and scrape it onto the pecans—don't let the elixir of tree go to waste on the pan!
4. Whisk or stir the ingredients for the raspberry dressing together and set aside.
5. *To assemble the salad*: Toss the greens and arugula together. Top with the onion and apple. Drizzle the vinaigrette on top and toss to mix. Top with the pecans and serve immediately.

SERVES 4; 30 MINUTES OR UNDER! GF/SF/BLUE

*If you don't have any arugula on hand, you can substitute additional baby greens, although the taste will be much milder. If you want a little more kick, you can also increase the amount of arugula (and decrease the amount of baby greens accordingly). Either way, it's delicious!

French Lentil Salad with Sourdough Croutons and Pomegranate Balsamic Dressing

This "salad" is really more of an entrée, but it can also be served in smaller portions alongside a main dish. It is elegant, flavorful, and really satisfying. If you like that sort of thing.

SAUCE:

¼ CUP PLUS 2 TABLESPOONS "POMEGRANATE BALSAMIC MOLASSES" (PAGE 130)

3 TABLESPOONS OLIVE OIL (EXTRA-VIRGIN OR REGULAR)

3 LARGE CLOVES GARLIC, MINCED OR PRESSED

¼ TEASPOON PLUS ⅛ TEASPOON EACH: SEA SALT AND DRIED ONION GRANULES

¼ CUP ORANGE JUICE (THE FRESHER THE BETTER)

2 TABLESPOONS TAMARI, SHOYU, OR SOY SAUCE

1 TEASPOON FRESH LIME OR LEMON JUICE

FRESHLY GROUND BLACK PEPPER TO TASTE

LE LENTILS:

1 CUP DRY FRENCH LENTILS (LE PUY LENTILS)

2¼ CUPS WATER

4 BAY LEAVES

2 TEASPOONS DRIED ROSEMARY LEAF

OPTIONAL FOR GARNISH:
•¼ CUP POMEGRANATE SEEDS

GET YOUR CROUT ON:

2 TABLESPOONS OLIVE OIL (EXTRA-VIRGIN OR REGULAR)

4 CUPS CRUSTY SOURDOUGH BREAD CUBES (CUT INTO BITE-SIZED PIECES)

¼ TEASPOON EACH: SEA SALT, DRIED GARLIC GRANULES AND DRIED ONION GRANULES

¾ TEASPOON DRIED ROSEMARY

GROUND BLACK PEPPER, TO TASTE

SALAD:

4 CUPS (LIGHTLY PACKED) CHOPPED BABY SPINACH OR ARUGULA (OR A MIXTURE OF BOTH)

¾ CUP DICED CARROT

½ CUP VERY THINLY SLICED RED ONION

1. To make the sauce: Whisk all of the sauce ingredients together and set aside.
2. To make the lentils: Place the lentils, water, bay leaves, and rosemary in a pressure cooker or regular pot with a tight fitting lid. Bring to a boil over high heat. Reduce heat to low and simmer until the water is absorbed and the lentils are tender, yet still firm. This will take about 45 minutes in a regular pot or 15 minutes in a pressure cooker. Remove the bay leaves and set the lentils aside.
3. To make the croutons: In a large pan or wok, heat the oil over medium-high heat. When the oil is hot, toss in the bread, salt, garlic and onion granules, rosemary, and pepper. Immediately stir the mixture so that the bread cubes are evenly coated with the oil and seasonings. Cook for about 5-10 minutes, stirring often, until they are evenly golden browned. Remove from heat.
4. *To assemble your masterpieces*: Distribute the spinach into four bowls and top evenly with the French lentils. Place the carrots, onion, and croutons on top of the lentils and drizzle with the sauce. If you are using the pomegranate seeds, add them last. Serve immediately. *Mmmmm…..now that's good eats!*

SERVES 4; BLUE

Chili-Ginger Cabbage

This one has a serious kick, so I don't necessarily recommend serving it to your great Aunt Millie. However, for the bold of buds, this dish is extremely addictive, nourishing, and delightful! Aside from the time it takes to marinate, it comes together very quickly.

6 CUPS (PACKED) FINELY CHOPPED GREEN CABBAGE

¼ CUP WATER

¼ CUP EACH: THINLY JULIENNED* (NOT GRATED) FRESH GINGER AND FRESH LIME JUICE

3 TABLESPOONS ORGANIC "WHITE" SUGAR

¾ TEASPOON SEA SALT

½ - 1 FRESH CAYENNE PEPPER, SEEDED AND MINCED (SEE PAGE 39)

2 TABLESPOONS RICE VINEGAR (OR ADDITIONAL LIME JUICE)

1. Sauté the cabbage in the water over medium-high heat, stirring often, *just* until it becomes slightly wilted. This should take well under 5 minutes, so be careful not to overcook.
2. Place the ginger in a large mixing bowl. Stir in the lime juice, sugar, salt, cayenne, and vinegar and mix well to combine.
3. Add the cabbage to the bowl and stir everything together thoroughly. Place in an airtight container and allow to marinate in the refrigerator for several hours (or overnight). Stir or shake the mixture every so often to assist the marinating process. Serve chilled.

SERVES 6; GF/SF/GREEN

*Part of the appeal of this dish is that it contains tangible pieces of ginger. Hence, the anti-grating remark. To prepare the ginger, slice it first into thin rounds, and then slice each round into "sticks." Of course, if you have a mandolin, you can use that instead.

Shiitake, Walnut, and Dried Cranberry Salad

This salad is *super* nutritious, delicious, and easy to prepare. But don't let that stop you—try it anyway!

1 CUP SLICED SHIITAKE MUSHROOM CAPS

4 MEDIUM CLOVES GARLIC, MINCED OR PRESSED

2 TEASPOONS EXTRA-VIRGIN OLIVE OIL

¼ CUP EACH: WALNUTS AND DRIED CRANBERRIES

¼ TEASPOON GROUND BLACK PEPPER

3 TABLESPOONS BALSAMIC VINEGAR

2 TABLESPOONS EXTRA-VIRGIN OLIVE OIL

• 2 TEASPOONS CHOPPED ORANGE ZEST

• 1 TABLESPOON PURE MAPLE SYRUP

• ½ CUP VERY THINLY SLICED RED ONION

• ½ TEASPOON SEA SALT

ADD LAST: 4 CUPS (PACKED) MIXED BABY GREENS

1. In a medium skillet, sauté the mushrooms and garlic in the 2 teaspoons of oil over medium-high heat for 5 minutes, or until the mushrooms are tender. Remove from heat and set aside.
2. In a large bowl, combine all of the remaining ingredients (aside from the baby greens). Toss very well to combine. Add the greens and shiitakes to the bowl and toss everything together until thoroughly combined. Serve immediately.

SERVES 4; 30 MINUTES OR UNDER! GF/SF/GREEN

Italian Bread Salad with Tangy Basil Vinaigrette

I always associate this one with potlucks. Maybe that's because I have so many vivid memories of people, in said potluck setting, *raving* about this salad. However, be warned—it makes no excuses for its totally bold, intense flavor! Anyway, a salad giving you excuses would be pathetic and just a little creepy.

8 OZ. LOAF OF SLIGHTLY STALE CRUSTY SOURDOUGH BREAD, CUT INTO CUBES (6 CUPS OF BREAD CUBES)*

DELIRIOUSLY DELECTABLE DRESSING:

4 *LARGE* CLOVES GARLIC, PEELED

⅓ CUP (TIGHTLY PACKED) FRESH BASIL LEAVES

¼ CUP EXTRA-VIRGIN OLIVE OIL

⅓ CUP NON-VIRGIN OLIVE OIL (OR ADDITIONAL EXTRA-VIRGIN OLIVE OIL IF YOU PREFER)

⅓ CUP RED WINE VINEGAR

¾ TEASPOON SEA SALT

¼ TEASPOON GROUND BLACK PEPPER

SALAD STUFF:

½ LB. RED LEAF OR ROMAINE LETTUCE (ONE MEDIUM SIZED HEAD)

ONE MEDIUM-LARGE CUCUMBER, VERY THINLY SLICED

ONE SMALL RED ONION, VERY THINLY SLICED

THREE ROMA TOMATOES, SEEDED AND CHOPPED

¼ CUP KALAMATA OLIVES, PITTED AND CHOPPED IN HALF

1. *Cut or tear the bread into bite sized cubes or pieces. You should end up with six cups of bread cubes. Allow them to sit overnight in a partially open bag. The purpose of this is to make the bread slightly stale so that it does not become soggy when the dressing is added to the salad. Of course, if you already have stale bread, you can pretend like this step never happened.

2. Place the garlic, basil, and a little of the olive oil in a blender. Blend on low to emulsify the ingredients. Add the remaining olive oil and other dressing ingredients and blend on high for a minute or so, until very smooth and thick.

3. Wash the lettuce. Dry it with paper towels or in a salad spinner to remove all of the excess water. This step is important, as too much water on the lettuce will dilute the dressing. Prepare the other vegetables at this point as well.

4. Put the bread cubes in the largest bowl you can get your hands on. Place the lettuce, cucumber, onion, tomatoes, and olives on top of the bread. Pour all of the dressing on top, making sure to get every last drop with a rubber spatula. Using the same spatula, stir the salad very well to mix the dressing evenly.

5. Cover the salad bowl and refrigerate it for an hour or so. This will allow the dressing time to work its magic. Stir again and serve, either at room temperature or chilled. Enjoy having the most popular item at the potluck! You will never live this down.

SERVES ABOUT 6; 30 MINUTES OR UNDER! (WITH SLIGHTLY STALE BREAD) SF/PURPLE

Japanese Salad with Ginger Magic Dressing

This is a very simple salad to prepare if you have the dressing on hand. To make this salad a meal, you can toss in some marinated, sautéed tofu or tempeh cubes (page 105).

¼ CUP "GINGER MAGIC DRESSING" (PLEASE SEE PAGE 121)

2 CUPS (LIGHTLY PACKED) BABY GREENS

¼ CUP EACH: FINELY CHOPPED RED CABBAGE, FINELY GRATED CARROTS, AND VERY THINLY SLICED CUCUMBER

2 TABLESPOONS SHELLED EDAMAME, THAWED IF FROZEN

1 TABLESPOON MINCED OR VERY THINLY SLICED ONION (YELLOW OR WHITE)

OPTIONAL: 2 TABLESPOONS WASABI PEAS

1. Prepare the dressing and set it aside.
2. Place the greens in bowls and top equally with the cabbage, carrots, cucumber, edamame, and onion. Drizzle with the dressing and serve topped with the wasabi peas if you're feeling frisky.

SERVES 2; 30 MINUTES OR UNDER! GF/GREEN

Black Bean, Cilantro, and Apricot Salad

This is a hearty (yet light) salad that can function either as a main dish or side. It is aesthetically beautiful and has an unusual, yet very appealing, blend of flavors. Although it needs to be marinated for several hours, the actual preparation time is under thirty minutes.

15 OZ. CAN OF BLACK BEANS, DRAINED AND RINSED (1 ½ CUPS COOKED BEANS)

½ CUP EACH: CHOPPED DRIED APRICOTS, MANGO JUICE, AND CHOPPED CILANTRO

¼ CUP EACH: DICED CARROTS AND CORN KERNELS

2 SCALLIONS (GREEN ONIONS), TRIMMED AND FINELY CHOPPED

2 MEDIUM-LARGE CLOVES GARLIC, MINCED OR PRESSED

2 TABLESPOONS EACH: OLIVE OIL (OR OTHER OIL OF CHOICE) AND FRESH LIME JUICE

½ TABLESPOON EACH: TAMARI (OR SHOYU OR SOY SAUCE) AND GRATED FRESH GINGER

¾ TEASPOON SEA SALT

ADD LAST: 4 CUPS (LIGHTLY PACKED) CHOPPED BABY SPINACH

1. Mix all of the ingredients (except for the spinach) together very well and place in an airtight container. Marinate for several hours or overnight in the refrigerator. While it is marinating, stir the mixture several times to make sure all of the ingredients get to know each other really well. Intimately.
2. Bring the salad to room temperature and toss with the spinach. Serve and savor the goodness.

SERVES 4; GF/GREEN

Chapter Ten: Sauces & Dressings that Will Change Your Life!

These liquid lovelies are great to have on hand as they make meals flavorful in a snap. As you may notice from the long list of recipes here, I love me some sauces—I hope you do too!

Quick, Creamy, and Dreamy Miso Dressing

This decadently delish dressing is perfect on green salads, pasta salads, sandwiches, or as a bath.

½ CUP "VEGENAISE" VEGAN MAYONNAISE

2 TABLESPOONS MELLOW WHITE MISO (DO NOT USE A DARK MISO FOR THIS RECIPE)

4 TEASPOONS FRESH LEMON JUICE

I TEASPOON TAMARI, SHOYU, OR SOY SAUCE

I MEDIUM CLOVE GARLIC, MINCED OR PRESSED

Combine the mayonnaise and miso very well until no lumps remain. Stir in the remaining items. If you desire a thinner dressing, add just a *little* more water or lemon juice. This will store in an airtight container, refrigerated, for at least two weeks.

MAKES ABOUT ¾ CUP OF DRESSING; 30 MINUTES OR UNDER! GF/Purple

The Peanut Sauce

This freakishly delicious concoction is the counterpart to the "Fresh Thai Spring Rolls" (page 72). However, it makes a great topping for just about anything—noodles, stir-fries, veggies, tofu, tempeh, satay, and salads. I don't actually *cook* with this sauce, however, as it tends to become too thin if heated. Instead, if I am using this with a stir-fry, for example, I'll prepare my stir-fry first and then top it with the sauce afterward. The sauce warms up by contact, but still remains thick this way. No matter how you use it, though, this scrumptious sauce can change your life. For the better. It's *that* good. Try it.

4 CLOVES GARLIC, PEELED

½ CUP NATURAL PEANUT BUTTER (SMOOTH)

I-INCH SEGMENT OF GINGER, CHOPPED

⅛ CUP (2 TABLESPOONS) CHOPPED WHITE OR YELLOW ONION

⅓ CUP WATER, PREFERABLY FILTERED

I CUP COCONUT MILK

⅛ CUP (2 TABLESPOONS) TAMARI, SHOYU, OR SOY SAUCE

I ½ TEASPOONS SEA SALT (OR LESS IF YOU PREFER)

¼ CUP APPLE CIDER VINEGAR OR FRESH LIME JUICE

½ CUP ORGANIC SUGAR OR SUCANAT

2 TABLESPOONS DARK MOLASSES (DO NOT USE BLACKSTRAP AS IT IS OVERPOWERING)

2 TABLESPOONS TOASTED (DARK) SESAME OIL

OPTIONAL:
• I TABLESPOON BLACK BEAN PASTE
• I TABLESPOON (OR MORE, HOTTIE!) SRIRACHA HOT CHILI SAUCE

1. In a large blender, place the garlic cloves, peanut butter, ginger, onion, and water. Blend until as smooth as is humanly possible.
2. Add all of the remaining ingredients and process very well—until smooth. Place in a glass container with a tight fitting lid. This will keep for about two weeks in the refrigerator. If you have will power.

MAKES ABOUT 3 CUPS OF SAUCE; 30 MINUTES OR UNDER! GF/Blue

Thai Sweet Chili Sauce

Here is a sauce that takes only five minutes to prepare but works nicely with a wide variety of applications. It is used with the "Thai Spinach Nests" (page 81), "Mango-Cucumber Spring Rolls" (page 74), and "Sesame Tofu with Fresh Basil and Thai Sweet Chili Sauce" (page 164). This also works well as a sauce for just about any kind of spring roll. Thai sweet chili sauces are traditionally very light and thin. However, if you prefer a thicker sauce, simply whisk in a bit of arrowroot and heat until thickened.

½ CUP ORGANIC "WHITE" SUGAR

2 TABLESPOONS TAMARI, SHOYU, OR SOY SAUCE

½ CUP PLUS 1 TABLESPOON RICE VINEGAR

3 TABLESPOONS VERY FINELY GRATED CARROT

½ - 1 TEASPOON (OR MORE) DRIED RED CHILI FLAKES

Combine all of the ingredients and store in a glass jar. This will keep, refrigerated, for at least a week. Shake this sauce very well just before you use it as the sugar tends to settle at the bottom.

MAKES ABOUT 1 CUP OF SAUCE; 30 MINUTES OR UNDER! GF/Blue

Rich Tomato Sauce

I spent several fun hours with my cooking buddy, Stacey Groth (who is also my cousin and fabulous in general) perfecting this recipe. I still remember the moment when she took a final taste and said, "Perrrrrfect." It's very easy to prepare and goes great with pasta, polenta, and pizza. Enjoy!

15 OZ. CAN TOMATO SAUCE (PLAIN)

15 OZ. CAN DICED TOMATOES WITH ONION AND GARLIC

3 TABLESPOONS EXTRA-VIRGIN OLIVE OIL

¼ CUP WHITE COOKING WINE OR WHITE WINE

1 TABLESPOON BALSAMIC VINEGAR

2 TABLESPOONS ORGANIC SUGAR OR SUCANAT

1 TEASPOON EACH: DRIED ROSEMARY LEAF, SEA SALT, AND NUTRITIONAL YEAST POWDER

1 ½ TEASPOONS EACH: DRIED BASIL AND DRIED THYME

2 TEASPOONS EACH: DRIED OREGANO AND DRIED ONION GRANULES

6-8 MEDIUM CLOVES GARLIC, PRESSED OR MINCED

¼ TEASPOON RED PEPPER FLAKES

1. Place all of the ingredients in a medium saucepan and bring to a boil, stirring, over high heat.
2. Reduce the heat to low and simmer uncovered, stirring occasionally, for about 30 minutes. This will marry the flavors and also allow the alcohol sufficient time to cook off. This sauce will store in an airtight container in the fridge for up to two weeks (or in the freezer for several months).

MAKES ABOUT 4 CUPS OF SAUCE; GF/SF/Green

Creamy Mayo To Play Dead For

I would have said this freakishly yummy mayo was "to die for," but that seemed a bit unnecessary. However, it *is* so good that four out of five people admit that they'd routinely fake their own deaths for a bit of this on their sandwich! Keep in mind, however, that this is a savory, *garlicky* mayo and therefore not one for fruit salads and the like. It is best used as a sandwich or wrap spread. Many thanks to Marilyn Diamond, who graciously shared her recipe for almonnaise (from her lovely *Fit For Life* cookbook) which inspired this version. Hope you enjoy!

First:

½ cup raw almonds (peeled and slivered)*

Next:

3 medium cloves garlic, peeled

1 ½ teaspoons nutritional yeast powder

¾ teaspoon sea salt

3 tablespoons *fresh* lemon juice

Grand Finale:

¾ cup plain and unsweetened nondairy milk

1 cup olive oil

1. In a food processor, blend the almonds for *far* longer than you think is necessary. Go ahead and take a nap or walk the dog while you are waiting. Yes, I jest, but you really do want them to be very, *very* finely ground. At this point, you are paving the way for either smooth, creamy, glorious mayo or somewhat gritty "beach" mayo.

2. Next, add the garlic to the food processor and blend until finely chopped. Add in the yeast, salt, and lemon juice and blend very well. Here you will want to use a rubber spatula to scrape all of the mixture off the sides and bottom so that every little bit is blending evenly.

3. Once you have a consistent, smooth mixture, slowly blend in the milk. Again, you may need to use your spatula to make sure none of the mixture is being left out of the happy dance.

4. Next, slowly drizzle the oil in, pulsing the food processor gradually as you do so. Once all of the oil has been added, blend everything for up to a minute (or until very smooth and nicely thickened). Again, make sure that there are no lingering bits of the mixture left behind.

5. This will become thicker once it has been refrigerated overnight, so go ahead and place it in an airtight container and pop it into the fridge. This will keep for at least a week.

Makes about 2 cups of mayo; 30 minutes or under! GF/SF/Blue

*The best type of almonds for this recipe are the kind that are already peeled. They're available in most stores as slivered almonds. However, if you cannot find them, simply buy whole, raw almonds and cover them with boiling water. Allow them to sit for ten minutes, then peel them.

Tahini-Lemon Dressing

This recipe is why I cannot tolerate bottled tahini dressings. I'm too spoiled on the fresh flavor of this version! It's hearty enough to make a meal out of a salad and is also perfect as a sauce for a falafel wrap.

½ CUP RAW TAHINI

¼ CUP WATER, PREFERABLY FILTERED

1 TABLESPOON TAMARI, SHOYU, OR SOY SAUCE

JUICE OF 1 LARGE LEMON

2 SMALL CLOVES GARLIC, MINCED OR PRESSED

½ TABLESPOON MINCED FRESH PARSLEY

1 TEASPOON MINCED FRESH CHIVES

1½ TABLESPOONS MINCED FRESH DILL

½ TEASPOON DRIED ONION GRANULES

2 TABLESPOONS OLIVE OIL (REGULAR OR EXTRA-VIRGIN), SUNFLOWER OIL, OR FLAX OIL

Whisk the tahini with the water to remove all of the lumps. Whisk in the remaining ingredients until well combined. This will store, refrigerated in an airtight container, for about a week.

MAKES ABOUT 1 CUP OF DRESSING; 30 MINUTES OR UNDER! GF/BLUE

Classic Vinaigrette

This is a quick and yummy dressing that stores for at least a month in the fridge if you use dried herbs. However, if you plan to use it up more quickly, it's even better with fresh herbs. It makes a great dressing for the "Greek Salad" (page 106), or any other salad for that matter!

1 CUP OLIVE OIL, REGULAR OR EXTRA-VIRGIN

½ CUP APPLE CIDER VINEGAR (OR SLIGHTLY MORE TO TASTE)

8 MEDIUM CLOVES GARLIC, MINCED OR PRESSED

2 TEASPOONS EACH: DRIED BASIL AND DRIED OREGANO (OR 2 TABLESPOONS EACH IF USING FRESH, MINCED HERBS)

FRESH GROUND PEPPER AND SEA SALT TO TASTE (DON'T BE SHY, THESE ARE IMPORTANT!)

Whisk or stir all of the ingredients together until well combined. If using fresh herbs, this will store, refrigerated in an airtight container, for up to a week. If you are using dried herbs, this will keep for a month or more (refrigerated in an airtight container as well).

MAKES ABOUT 1½ CUPS OF DRESSING; 30 MINUTES OR UNDER! GF/SF/BLUE

> *Tip*: Certain herbs lose more flavor than others when dried. Some examples of herbs that taste relatively the same dried as they do fresh are rosemary and oregano. Basil, dill, chives, and parsley are examples of herbs that taste *much* better fresh.

Simple Sesame-Miso Sauce

This sauce is *crazy* simple! Although it may not bowl you over, it's extremely nutritious and has a subtle flavor that many people really enjoy. Supremely healthy, it includes the nutritional benefits of both miso and raw sesame. It is perfect served over grains, tofu, or potatoes for a simple yet nourishing meal. For a little extra somethin-somethin, you can add 2 teaspoons of lemon or lime juice to this as well.

3 TABLESPOONS <u>EACH</u>: RAW TAHINI *AND* MELLOW WHITE MISO (DO NOT USE DARK MISO HERE)

2 TABLESPOONS DRIED ONION GRANULES

½ CUP WARM WATER

Whisk all of the ingredients together until very smooth. Serve at room temperature or lightly warmed. Do not allow this sauce to boil at any point, as many of miso's nutrients are destroyed when boiled. This will keep in an airtight container in the fridge for a month or more.

MAKES ABOUT 1 ¼ CUPS OF SAUCE; 30 MINUTES OR UNDER! GF/GREEN

Ginger Magic Dressing

What can I say about this dressing? My good friend Jennie likes to buy this by the gallon! She puts it on everything from salads, to rice, to veggie wraps. At one point, she told me that her young daughter would eat *anything* if it had this sauce on it. My original inspiration when creating this recipe was to include every healthful thing I could imagine and see if it tasted good in the end. Luckily, it did. This dressing is like my philosophy in general: Food should be a celebration of what is nutritious *and* delicious!

⅓ CUP CHOPPED ONION (WHITE OR YELLOW)

3 MEDIUM-LARGE CLOVES GARLIC, PEELED

2 TABLESPOONS <u>EACH</u>: DICED CELERY *AND* DICED FRESH GINGER

1 TABLESPOON <u>EACH</u>: TOMATO PASTE *AND* ORGANIC SUGAR OR SUCANAT

¼ CUP <u>EACH</u>: WATER *AND* APPLE CIDER VINEGAR

½ CUP OIL (NON-VIRGIN OLIVE, SUNFLOWER, LIGHT UNTOASTED SESAME, OR FLAX)

2 TEASPOONS FRESH LEMON JUICE

1 TEASPOON NUTRITIONAL YEAST POWDER

½ TEASPOON <u>EACH</u>: GROUND BLACK PEPPER *AND* SEA SALT

2 TABLESPOONS TAMARI, SHOYU, OR SOY SAUCE

1. Place the onion, garlic, celery, ginger, tomato paste, and sugar in the blender. Add just enough of the water and vinegar to blend. Continue to blend until all of the chunky items have become emulsified.
2. Add the remaining water and vinegar along with all of the other ingredients and blend until as smooth as possible. You may need to use a spatula to scrape down the sides (and inside of the lid) of your blender, so that everything is well combined. This should keep, refrigerated, for two weeks or more.

MAKES ABOUT 2 CUPS; 30 MINUTES OR UNDER! GF/GREEN

Scrumptious Shiitake Gravy

Oooohh…how decadent and delicious is this gravy? Very. The last time I included this in a cooking class, the students were actually eating it by the cupful! This is divine served over baked or mashed potatoes, crunchy tempeh, noodles, grains, pan-fried tofu, or an empty cup. Don't let the long list of ingredients fool you—this is actually quite simple to make. And soooooo worth it!

1 CUP THINLY SLICED SHIITAKE MUSHROOM CAPS

ONE MEDIUM YELLOW ONION, MINCED

½ CUP NON-HYDROGENATED MARGARINE (1 STICK)

¼ CUP TAMARI, SHOYU, OR SOY SAUCE

8 LARGE CLOVES GARLIC, MINCED OR PRESSED

½ CUP <u>EACH</u>: WHITE WINE OR SHERRY, RICE FLOUR, *AND* NUTRITIONAL YEAST POWDER

1 CUP WATER

¼ CUP BALSAMIC VINEGAR

1 TEASPOON DRIED SAGE

2 TEASPOONS DRIED ROSEMARY LEAF

3 CUPS NONDAIRY MILK, PLAIN AND UNSWEETENED

4 TEASPOONS DRIED ONION GRANULES

2 TEASPOONS ORGANIC SUGAR OR SUCANAT

2 TABLESPOONS "CHICKY BABY SEASONING" (P. 194) OR VEGETARIAN CHICKEN SEASONING

1½ TEASPOONS SEA SALT (OR LESS IF YOU PREFER)

1 TEASPOON GROUND BLACK PEPPER (OR FRESHLY GROUND TO TASTE)

1. In a large saucepan, sauté the mushrooms and onion in about 3 tablespoons of the margarine over medium-high heat until the onions are soft and just beginning to brown. Be sure to stir often during this process. If the pan becomes dry, add more margarine as needed.
2. Add the tamari, garlic, and wine and stir well. Sauté for another 2-3 minutes, stirring often.
3. Reduce the heat to medium-low. Add the rice flour and nutritional yeast and stir well to make a smooth base (aside from the lumpy mushrooms and onions, that is). This is your "roux." Add the water slowly, stirring constantly, until the base is as smooth as possible.
4. Add the remaining items, one at a time, stirring well to combine. Simmer gently over medium-low heat to marry the flavors for about 15-20 more minutes. You will want to stir the gravy often during this time to make sure that nothing sticks to the bottom of your pan. Serve hot or warm. Enjoy your gravy, you lucky baby.

MAKES ABOUT 6 CUPS; 30 MINUTES OR UNDER! GF/PURPLE

Tip: If you crush and crumble the sage and rosemary with your hands before adding them, it will help release their flavors and aromas.

Delicious & Quick Asian Brown Sauce

Here is a quick and fully delectable sauce that should induce even the pickiest of eaters to eat their veggies! Use it to dress up a stir-fry or drizzle it over rice, tofu, or tempeh.

¼ CUP TAMARI, SHOYU, OR SOY SAUCE

¾ CUP WATER

½ CUP ORGANIC SUCANAT

(OR PACKED BROWN SUGAR)

¼ CUP OIL (SESAME OR NON-VIRGIN OLIVE)

5 LARGE CLOVES GARLIC, MINCED OR PRESSED

1 TABLESPOON ARROWROOT (OR CORNSTARCH)

(OR SLIGHTLY MORE IF DESIRED)

1. Place the tamari, water, sucanat, oil, and garlic in a medium saucepan and set heat to medium-high. Cook for 2-3 minutes or until hot. Next, add the arrowroot to the mixture by sprinkling it in very slowly. If you lightly dust the arrowroot evenly over the sauce and whisk it in immediately, it will dissolve and refrain from lumping.

2. Reduce the heat to medium-low and continue to cook, whisking constantly, until it is just thickened. This should take well under 5 minutes. If you allow it to cook too long with the arrowroot in it, the sauce can become overly thick and gummy. Alternatively, if the sauce is too thin, adding a little more arrowroot will thicken it up. As always, the arrowroot needs to be heated in order to activate its thickening superpowers. This will keep in the fridge stored in an airtight container for two weeks or more.

MAKES ABOUT 1 ½ CUPS OF SAUCINESS; 30 MINUTES OR UNDER! GF/Blue

Chunky Ginger-Pineapple Sweet & Sour Sauce

This is a very bold, healthy, and flavorful version of sweet and sour sauce. It's great to have on hand as it makes a delicious, quick dinner out of sautéed tofu (or tempeh) and vegetables. I have found that ketchup, pedestrian as it may be, works perfectly to bring about a subtle tomato flavor and rosy red color.

2 TABLESPOONS OIL (NON-VIRGIN OLIVE, COCONUT, OR SUNFLOWER)

¼ TEASPOON ASAFETIDA (SEE PAGE 251)

2½ CUPS CHOPPED FRESH PINEAPPLE

(CUT INTO VERY SMALL CHUNKS)

1 TABLESPOON <u>EACH</u>: APPLE CIDER VINEGAR, GRATED FRESH GINGER, *AND* TAMARI (OR SHOYU OR SOY SAUCE)

¼ CUP PLUS 2 TABLESPOONS ORANGE JUICE

• ¼ TEASPOON SEA SALT

• ¼ CUP KETCHUP

• JUICE OF 1 LIME

• 2 MEDIUM CLOVES GARLIC, PRESSED

• ¼ CUP PLUS 1 TABLESPOON SUCANAT OR SUGAR

• 2 TABLESPOONS <u>EACH</u>: WATER *AND* ARROWROOT (OR CORNSTARCH)

1. Sauté the oil and asafetida over medium heat in a large skillet for about 3 minutes, stirring often, until the asafetida becomes aromatic and you begin to swoon.

2. Add all of the other ingredients to the pan except for the arrowroot. Stir well to combine.

3. Next, add the arrowroot to the mixture by sprinkling it in very slowly. I find that if I lightly dust the arrowroot evenly over the sauce and whisk it in immediately, it will dissolve and refrain from lumping. Heat, stirring constantly, until the sauce begins to thicken. Remove from heat and serve. This sauce will keep in an airtight container, refrigerated, for a week or more.

MAKES ABOUT 3 CUPS OF SAUCE; 30 MINUTES OR UNDER! GF/Blue

Toasted Sesame-Orange Teriyaki Sauce

This sauce is perfect for topping stir-fries, tofu, tempeh, and Asian noodle dishes. My original intention when creating this recipe was to make a very flavorful Asian sauce that was high in nutrients and very low in fat. If you like a serious orange kick, be sure to toss in the orange zest. If you want even *more* orange kicking you, go ahead and substitute additional orange juice for the water.

2 TABLESPOONS ARROWROOT (OR CORNSTARCH)

1 CUP PLUS 1 TABLESPOON WATER

1½ CUPS FRESH ORANGE JUICE

¼ CUP PLUS 2 TABLESPOONS EACH: MAPLE SYRUP AND TAMARI (OR SHOYU OR SOY SAUCE)

3-4 TABLESPOONS GRATED FRESH GINGER

9 LARGE CLOVES GARLIC, MINCED OR PRESSED

2 TABLESPOONS EACH: MOLASSES (DO NOT USE BLACKSTRAP) AND TOASTED SESAME OIL

3 TABLESPOONS TOASTED SESAME SEEDS (SEE PAGE 42)

OPTIONAL: 1 TABLESPOON (OR MORE TO TASTE) MINCED ORGANIC ORANGE ZEST

1. Place the arrowroot and just a little of the water in a small bowl and whisk together (using a wire whisk or fork) until all of the lumps are removed. Set aside.
2. In a medium saucepan, place the remaining water, juice, maple syrup, tamari, ginger, garlic, molasses, oil, and zest (if using). Cook over medium-low heat, stirring often, for about 5 minutes.
3. Increase the heat to medium-high and whisk in the arrowroot-water mixture. Continue to cook *just* until the sauce is thickened. If you prefer a slightly thicker sauce, you may sprinkle in a little more arrowroot (whisk it into the sauce immediately to prevent lumps). Stir in the sesame seeds and serve hot. This will keep for two weeks or more in an airtight container, refrigerated.

MAKES ABOUT 3½ CUPS OF SAUCE; 30 MINUTES OR UNDER! GF/BLUE

Creamy Ginger-Wasabi Sauce

The idea for this sauce came to me when I was making nori rolls one day. I was out of pickled ginger, and also didn't feel like mixing up several different sauces. So, I combined many of the flavors that complement nori rolls into this one sauce. It is absolutely delicious! If you like more bite, do feel free to increase the amount of wasabi powder. Do.

½ CUP "VEGENAISE" VEGAN MAYONNAISE

2 TEASPOONS ORGANIC "WHITE" SUGAR

1 TEASPOON TAMARI, SHOYU, OR SOY SAUCE

1 TABLESPOON EACH: GRATED FRESH GINGER, TOASTED SESAME SEEDS (PAGE 42), AND WASABI POWDER (DON'T USE PRE-MIXED WASABI PASTE OR WASABI POWDER WITH CORNSTARCH IN IT)

⅛ TEASPOON SEA SALT

1. Whisk or stir all of the ingredients together until well mixed. Serve as a dip for nori rolls, on sandwiches, or in any other way you can think of. Well, *almost* any way you can think of.
2. This will store for 2-3 days, refrigerated in an airtight container.

MAKES ABOUT 6 SERVINGS OR ¾ CUP OF SAUCE; 30 MINUTES OR UNDER! GF/PURPLE

Lemon-Lime Soy Sauce

This is the simplest of sauces (obviously) and really livens up nori rolls. It also makes a quick, light sauce for fresh spring rolls. Be sure to use fresh juice for this recipe as it makes all the difference.

I TABLESPOON EACH: FRESH LIME JUICE *AND* FRESH LEMON JUICE

3 TABLESPOONS TAMARI, SHOYU, OR SOY SAUCE

Mix the ingredients together and serve cold or at room temperature. This will store, refrigerated in an airtight container, for up to two weeks.

MAKES ABOUT ⅓ CUP OF SAUCE; 30 MINUTES OR UNDER! GF/GREEN

Cilantro Chutney Elixir

When I first discovered that I could throw together an authentic-tasting Indian cilantro chutney, I was elated! I was finally liberated from the "need" to get this at a restaurant. I then proceeded to go through my "chutney phase," during which I ate this on everything. Well, not everything. I recall my breakfast cereal being spared. I love the way this combination of ingredients *feels* as well…I get such an immediate boost from all of these powerfully healthy ingredients that I actually consider this a form of medicine!

I CUP (PACKED) FRESH CILANTRO

3 TABLESPOONS FINELY SHREDDED COCONUT

2 TABLESPOONS EACH: CHOPPED FRESH GINGER *AND* DRY-ROASTED PEANUTS

3 MEDIUM CLOVES GARLIC, PEELED

½ JALAPENO, SEEDED (SEE PAGE 39 FOR HOT TIPS, BABY)

I TEASPOON CUMIN SEEDS

½ TEASPOON SEA SALT

2 TABLESPOONS *FRESH* LIME JUICE

½ CUP WATER

1. In a food processor, place the cilantro, coconut, ginger, peanuts, garlic, and jalapeno. Blend very well, using a rubber spatula if needed to scrape down the inside of the food processor.
2. Add all of the remaining ingredients and blend again until very well mixed. Serve cold or at room temperature. This will keep in the fridge for one or two weeks when stored in an airtight glass container.

MAKES ABOUT I CUP OF CHUTNEY; 30 MINUTES OR UNDER! GF/SF/GREEN

Spicy Onion Chutney

This recipe is a very healthy version of one of my favorite Indian condiments. This uniquely flavored chutney gives a kick to samosas, flat breads, papadams, bean burritos, or rice.

¾ CUP PLUS 1 TABLESPOON FINELY DICED ONION (YELLOW OR WHITE)

1 TABLESPOON *FRESH* LEMON JUICE

1 TEASPOON EACH: OIL (SUNFLOWER, NON-VIRGIN OLIVE, OR FLAX), PAPRIKA, *AND* KETCHUP

¼ TEASPOON EACH: SEA SALT, CUMIN POWDER, CAYENNE POWDER, *AND* CORIANDER POWDER

Mix all of the ingredients together very well. Serve cold or at room temperature (do not heat, especially if using flax oil). This will store in an airtight container in the fridge for several weeks.

MAKES ABOUT 1 CUP OF CHUTNEY; 30 MINUTES OR UNDER! GF/SF/GREEN

Tamarind-Date Chutney

This irreplaceable chutney represents the perfect balance of sweet and tart and contains the glorious tamarind fruit. This is delicious on the "Aloo Gobi Chole" (page 163) or as a dipping sauce for any of the Indian appetizers from the starters chapter.

2 OZ. TAMARIND (ALSO CALLED "WET" TAMARIND); SEE PAGE 253 FOR MORE INFO

1 ½ CUPS HOT WATER

¾ CUP PITTED, CHOPPED DATES

½ TEASPOON CUMIN POWDER

½ TABLESPOON ORGANIC "WHITE" SUGAR

¾ TEASPOON SEA SALT

¾ CUP WATER

> OPTIONAL HEAT: ⅛ TEASPOON CAYENNE POWDER (OR TO TASTE)

1. Break the tamarind into chunks and soak it in the 1½ cups of hot water for about 30 minutes.
2. After it has soaked, mush the tamarind up with your fingers until no longer mushable. Don't be alarmed if the mixture seems too thin—this story *will* have a very happy ending.
3. Place a strainer (with standard sized holes) over a bowl. Don't use a fine mesh strainer, as the holes will be too small for this purpose. Press the tamarind mixture through the strainer and into the bowl using the back of a spoon. Some of the tamarind goodness will cling to the underside of the strainer, so make sure to scrape that into the bowl as well. When you can no longer extract any tamarind from the strainer, discard the pulp and rinse the strainer out.
4. Place the strained tamarind mixture into a saucepan. Add the chopped dates and bring to a boil over medium-high heat. Reduce the heat to medium-low and simmer until slightly thickened, about 5-10 minutes (stirring often). Using a fork, mash this mixture very well.
5. Add the remaining ingredients and simmer for another 5 minutes, stirring often.
6. Place the strainer over a bowl again. Pour this mixture through the strainer and into the bowl, using the back of a spoon to extract as much of the sauce from the pulp as you can. Discard any remaining pulp that is left in the strainer and…you got it goin' on! Your chutney is in the bowl. Serve cold or at room temperature. This will store for several weeks or more in the fridge (in an airtight container).

MAKES ABOUT 1 ½ CUPS OF CHUTNEY; GF/SF/GREEN

Thai Green Curry Sauce

This sauce is scrumptious over vegetables, tofu, tempeh, noodles, and rice. If you're fortunate enough to have access to traditional Thai ingredients such as kaffir lime leaves and fresh lemongrass, they make delicious, authentic additions. However, as many of us aren't so lucky, I have given a basic recipe that includes widely accessible ingredients. No matter what you do with this sauce, however, you will find it is *unreasonably* delicious.

2 TABLESPOONS THAI GREEN CURRY PASTE ("THAI KITCHEN" MAKES A GOOD VERSION)

3-4 LARGE CLOVES GARLIC, MINCED OR PRESSED (OR TO TASTE)

3 TABLESPOONS GRATED FRESH GINGER (OR GALANGAL) ROOT

14 OZ. CAN COCONUT MILK (PREFERABLY REGULAR, NOT REDUCED FAT)

2 TABLESPOONS EACH: ORGANIC "WHITE" SUGAR AND ARROWROOT (OR CORNSTARCH)*

1 TABLESPOON SEA SALT (OR LESS IF YOU PREFER)

¼ CUP PLUS 1 TABLESPOON FRESH LIME JUICE

¼ CUP (PACKED) FRESH BASIL (OR FRESH THAI BASIL)

Puree all of the ingredients in a blender until the consistency is very smooth and uniform. To serve, simply cook in an uncovered pot over medium heat, whisking often, until warm and thickened. This will keep for a week or more in the fridge, stored in an airtight container.

MAKES ABOUT 3 CUPS OF SAUCE; 30 MINUTES OR UNDER! GF/SF/Purple

*The arrowroot will thicken the sauce when it becomes heated. Personally, I prefer a thicker sauce, as it is ensures that none of the goodness gets left behind in the pan! However, if you like a thinner, more traditional sauce, you can omit the arrowroot.

Got Dressing!

This dressing has *got* it all: powerfully nutritious ingredients (including **g**inger, **o**range, and **t**ahini), a very quick prep time, and a taste that will make you want to eat salads every day! However, this yummy concoction is also divine over noodles for a cold Asian dish. Simply put, it's got it goin' on.

3 TABLESPOONS TAHINI (PREFERABLY RAW)

½ CUP ORANGE JUICE (THE FRESHER THE BETTER)

2 TABLESPOONS EACH: ORGANIC SUGAR, TAMARI (OR SHOYU OR SOY SAUCE), GRATED GINGER, TOASTED SESAME OIL, MELLOW WHITE MISO, AND RICE VINEGAR

Blend or whisk all of the ingredients together until *very* well combined. This will store in an airtight container, refrigerated, for up to two weeks.

MAKES A LITTLE OVER 1 CUP OF DRESSING; 30 MINUTES OR UNDER! GF/Blue

Cleansing Miso-Lime Dressing

Here is a dressing bursting with nutrients and superfoods, cleverly disguised as something yummy! Miso is renowned for its cleansing and detoxifying principles, while garlic and ginger are immune boosters. Nutritional yeast is a rich source of B-vitamins (including B-12), and lime juice is alkalinizing and cleansing. Use this elixir on salads, cold Asian noodles, or grains.

3 TABLESPOONS MELLOW WHITE MISO (DO NOT USE DARK MISO FOR THIS DRESSING)

2 LARGE CLOVES GARLIC, PRESSED OR CHOPPED

1 TABLESPOON GRATED OR CHOPPED FRESH GINGER

½ CUP EACH: CHOPPED ONION, OIL (SUNFLOWER, FLAX, OLIVE, OR HEMP), AND WATER

¼ CUP NUTRITIONAL YEAST POWDER

⅓ CUP FRESH LIME JUICE

Combine the miso, garlic, ginger, onion, and oil in a blender and mix until emulsified. If you need to add a little of the water to do this, go for it. Add the remaining water, nutritional yeast, and lime juice and blend again until very smooth. This will keep in an airtight container, refrigerated, for a week or more.

MAKES ABOUT 1 ½ CUPS DRESSING; 30 MINUTES OR UNDER! GF/BLUE

Tangy Basil Vinaigrette

This salad dressing is bold, beautiful, and a garlic lover's dream. It is absolute perfection on the "Italian Bread Salad with Tangy Basil Vinaigrette" (page 114), but it also works well on simple green salads or pasta salads.

4 LARGE CLOVES GARLIC, PEELED

⅓ CUP (TIGHTLY PACKED) FRESH BASIL LEAVES

¼ CUP EXTRA-VIRGIN OLIVE OIL

⅓ CUP EACH: REGULAR OLIVE OIL (OR ADDITIONAL EXTRA-VIRGIN) AND RED WINE VINEGAR

¾ TEASPOON SEA SALT

¼ TEASPOON GROUND BLACK PEPPER

1. Place the garlic, basil, and a little of the olive oil in a blender. Blend on low to emulsify the ingredients.
2. Add the remaining olive oil and all of the other ingredients. Blend on high for a minute, or until very smooth and fairly thick. This will keep refrigerated in an airtight container for a week or so.

MAKES ABOUT 1 CUP OF DRESSING; 30 MINUTES OR UNDER! GF/SF/BLUE

Light Ginger-Miso Dressing

This dressing is unique in the salad world, as it is both low in fat *and* high in flavor! It's also incredibly nourishing due to the fresh ginger and miso—both are perfect for building up the immune system and cleansing the body. Serve this over green salads or cold Asian noodles for a tasty yet light flavor boost.

2 TABLESPOONS MELLOW WHITE MISO (DO NOT USE DARK MISO)

½ CUP ORANGE JUICE (THE FRESHER THE BETTER)

1 TABLESPOON GRATED FRESH GINGER

2 TABLESPOONS TOASTED (DARK) SESAME OIL

¼ CUP <u>EACH</u>: *FRESH* LEMON JUICE *AND* ORGANIC "WHITE" SUGAR

2 TABLESPOONS TAMARI, SHOYU, OR SOY SAUCE

1. Whisk the miso with the orange juice until smooth.
2. Add the remaining ingredients and stir or whisk well to combine. This will store for 2 weeks or more in an airtight container in the fridge.

MAKES ABOUT 1 CUP OF DRESSING; 30 MINUTES OR UNDER! GF/GREEN

Light Balsamic Dressing

This is one of the few lowfat dressings that I can eat almost every day and never tire of. It goes well with any green salad and is the dressing for the "Spinach, Orange, and Toasted Almond Salad" (page 109). Balsamic vinegar is the ideal choice for lowfat dressings because its full, rich flavor makes extra oil superfluous. Plus, the three minute prep time doesn't hurt!

1 TABLESPOON <u>EACH</u>: ORANGE JUICE *AND* OIL (SUNFLOWER, OLIVE, HEMP, OR FLAX)

¼ CUP PLUS 2 TABLESPOONS BALSAMIC VINEGAR

2 TABLESPOONS PURE MAPLE SYRUP

½ TEASPOON POPPY SEEDS

¼ TEASPOON <u>EACH</u>: SEA SALT *AND* GROUND BLACK PEPPER

1 TEASPOON TAMARI, SHOYU, OR SOY SAUCE

Whisk or stir all of the ingredients together. This will keep in the fridge (stored in an airtight container) for several weeks or more. This is best served at room temperature.

MAKES ABOUT ½ CUP OF DRESSING; 30 MINUTES OR UNDER! GF/GREEN

Pomegranate Balsamic Molasses

This elixir of loveliness is the foundation for the "Moroccan Pomegranate Sauce" (below) and a crucial ingredient in the "French Lentil Salad with Sourdough Croutons and Pomegranate Balsamic Dressing" (page 112). This unique flavoring concentrate is also great to have on hand to liven up a variety of sauces, stir-fries, marinades, and dressings. It will keep in the fridge for at least a month, so it's well worth taking the time to make up a batch…or a double batch!

3 CUPS PURE POMEGRANATE JUICE

1 CUP BALSAMIC VINEGAR

¼ TEASPOON SEA SALT

1 TABLESPOON FRESH LEMON JUICE

¾ CUP ORGANIC "WHITE" SUGAR

1. Place all of the ingredients in a medium pot over medium-high heat. Do not cover. Bring to a boil, stirring often.
2. After the mixture has come to a boil, reduce the heat to low. Simmer uncovered, stirring or whisking occasionally.
3. After around 70 or 80 minutes, the mixture will be reduced to about 1¼ cups. Watch it carefully at this point, because it will change very quickly into a thicker, syrupy form and begin to bubble more rapidly. Once this happens, remove it from heat. Allow it to cool in the pan. Once cooled, it will thicken up to a molasses consistency. Store it in a glass jar in the refrigerator. It will keep for a month or more.

MAKES ABOUT 1¼ CUPS OF MOLASSES; GF/SF/BLUE

Moroccan Pomegranate Sauce

If you have some pomegranate balsamic molasses on hand in the fridge, this divine sauce will come together in about 15 minutes. It is unusual, rich, and crazy delicious! It can be served over crunchy tempeh (page 176), crusted tofu, "Moroccan Quinoa" (page 88), or sautéed veggies.

½ CUP EACH: POMEGRANATE BALSAMIC MOLASSES (PREVIOUS RECIPE) AND WATER

2 TABLESPOONS OIL (NON-VIRGIN OLIVE, SUNFLOWER, OR SAFFLOWER)

¼ CUP ORANGE JUICE (THE FRESHER THE BETTER)

2 TABLESPOONS FRESH LIME JUICE

4 TEASPOONS EACH: PURE MAPLE SYRUP AND TAMARI (OR SOY SAUCE OR SHOYU)

½ TEASPOON EACH: GROUND CINNAMON AND CUMIN POWDER

¼ TEASPOON EACH: SEA SALT, CORIANDER POWDER, AND RED PEPPER FLAKES

2 LARGE GARLIC CLOVES, MINCED OR PRESSED

2 TEASPOONS ARROWROOT POWDER (OR CORNSTARCH)

1. Combine all of the ingredients well (except for the arrowroot) in a medium saucepan. Cook over medium heat, stirring, for about 2-3 minutes. Next, add the arrowroot to the mixture by sprinkling it in very slowly. If you lightly dust the arrowroot evenly over the sauce and whisk it in immediately, it will dissolve and refrain from lumping.
2. Continue to cook, stirring, until the mixture is *just* thickened. Do not overcook, or it may become too thick and gooey. Remove from heat and serve hot or warm. This will keep in an airtight container in the fridge for one to two weeks. Unless you have taste buds.

MAKES ABOUT 1¾ CUPS OF SAUCE; 30 MINUTES OR UNDER! (WITH THE MOLASSES)/GF/BLUE

9½ Minute Green Chile Sauce

This is the perfect complement to tamales, burritos, tacos, tostadas, and beans. I especially love this sauce because of its nourishing qualities. For one thing, it's very high in vitamin C (from the green chilies). Plus, with the addition of fresh garlic and lime juice, this sauce is just the ticket if you want to kick out a cold! I was recently enlightened to the fact that roasted, chopped chilies are available in the frozen Mexican (or vegetable) section of most supermarkets. Knowing that makes it easy to keep this on hand—plus it's so much fresher and higher in nutrients than bottled salsa. Keep in mind that if you're using whole green chilies, they will need to be roasted and peeled before they are chopped and added to the sauce. For a flavor complement, serve this topped with some nondairy sour cream. Yum it up!

FIRSTLY:

1 TEASPOON OIL (NON-VIRGIN OLIVE, SUNFLOWER, OR SAFFLOWER)

1 TABLESPOON RICE FLOUR (OR WHOLE WHEAT PASTRY FLOUR)*

NEXTLY:

ONE 13 OZ. CONTAINER (ABOUT 1½ CUPS) ROASTED, PEELED, CHOPPED GREEN CHILIES (MILD, MEDIUM, OR HOT DEPENDING ON YOUR PREFERENCE), THAWED IF FROZEN

2 TEASPOONS ORGANIC SUGAR OR SUCANAT

OPTIONAL (FOR 11½ MINUTE SAUCE): ½ JALAPENO, MINCED (SEE PAGE 39 FOR TIPS)

FINAL FRESHNESS (LASTLY):

¼ CUP PLUS 1 TEASPOON *FRESH* LIME JUICE

1-1¼ TEASPOONS SEA SALT

5 MEDIUM CLOVES GARLIC, MINCED OR PRESSED

1. Place the oil and rice flour in a medium saucepan and stir until smooth. Add the green chilies, sugar, and jalapeno (if using) and cook over medium-high heat for about five minutes, stirring often, until a bit thicker in consistency.
2. Turn off the heat and stir in the lime juice, sea salt, and garlic. Combine well and serve. Incidentally, I like to serve this at room temperature (or cold) to maximize its nutritional impact (instead of reheating it). This will store, refrigerated in an airtight container, for about a week.

MAKES ABOUT 1¾ CUPS OF SAUCE; 30 MINUTES OR UNDER! GF/SF/GREEN

*If you prefer a very thick sauce, you may add a little more flour until the desired consistency is reached.

HOT PEPPERS AND GREEN CHILIES ARE JUST ABOUT MY FAVORITE FORM OF MEDICINE. NOT ONLY ARE THEY HIGH IN VITAMIN C, THEY'RE ALSO RICH IN ANTIOXIDANTS, FIBER, AND VITAMIN A. PLUS, THEY ARE KNOWN TO BOOST THE METABOLISM. BRING IT ON!

Alex's Pineapple Habanero Hot Sauce

This recipe is unlike the others in this book for two reasons. To begin with, it was given to me by Alex Barrows and contains no adjustments of my own. Secondly, this isn't the kind of sauce you want to drown your food in. It is to be used *very* sparingly, as it's extremely hot. However, it's also full of flavor and works as powerful, delicious medicine. The heat of the peppers along with the fresh garlic, ginger, and lime really rev up the immune system! This will make a fairly large batch, but it keeps well and makes great gifts. However, if you don't have any hot and spicy friends, simply cut the recipe in half.

I CUP FRESH HABANERO HOT PEPPERS

½ CUP EACH: DICED TOMATOES, CHOPPED CARROT, *AND* FRESH LIME JUICE

I PINEAPPLE, TRIMMED AND CUT INTO CHUNKS

6 SMALL-MEDIUM CLOVES GARLIC, PEELED

I TEASPOON SEA SALT (OR TO TASTE)

2 TABLESPOONS CHOPPED FRESH GINGER

1. Put on a pair of gloves to handle the hot peppers—seriously. *Please.* Since habaneros are considered the hottest of all peppers, you will most likely *not* want their oils lingering on your fingers, setting fire to everything you touch for days to come! Wash the habaneros well and place them under a broiler. Roast them until they are evenly browned. You may need to turn them over so that both sides are evenly roasted. Be sure to keep an eye on them so that they don't burn. Remove and allow them to cool down a bit.
2. Cut the habbies open. Remove the stem, seeds, and membranes. See page 39 for more tips if you like.
3. Place them in a blender along with the remaining ingredients. Blend very well until the mixture is smooth and no chunks remain. Pour into a large glass container with a tight fitting lid. This will keep for about a month in the refrigerator.

MAKES ONE QUART OF FLAVORFUL FIRE; 30 MINUTES OR UNDER! GF/SF/GREEN

You will notice a marked improvement in the flavor if you allow the ingredients to marry for several days in the fridge before using. Again, begin with only one or two drops of this, as it is hot, hot, hot!

Three Flavors Dressing

Three distinct flavors (lemon, sesame, and basil) come together to form one uniquely delectable taste!

6 TABLESPOONS TOASTED SESAME SEEDS (PLEASE SEE PAGE 42)

I CUP OIL (NON-VIRGIN OLIVE, LIGHT UNTOASTED SESAME, FLAX, OR SUNFLOWER)

½ CUP EACH: FRESH LEMON JUICE *AND* FRESH BASIL

2 SCALLIONS (GREEN ONIONS), TRIMMED (BOTH WHITE AND GREEN PARTS)

¾ TEASPOON SEA SALT

I TEASPOON DRIED ROSEMARY

Combine all of the items in a blender and go for it. Blend until as smooth as is humanly possible. Which is pretty smooth. This will store, refrigerated in an airtight container, for up to two weeks.

MAKES ABOUT 2 CUPS OF SALAD DRESSING; 30 MINUTES OR UNDER! GF/SF/BLUE

Vanilla Bean Caramel Sauce

This celestially delicious sauce is so easy to make, scrumptious, and addictive that it may be illegal in certain states. It is the sauce for the "Apple Puffs with Vanilla Bean Caramel Sauce" (page 231), and is also divine when drizzled over just about anything. If you've never used a whole vanilla bean before, don't be intimidated. They are *very* easy to use and really add an unbeatable element. Plus, this sauce still comes together in under ten minutes, start to finish.

4-INCH SEGMENT OF A VANILLA BEAN

4 TABLESPOONS <u>EACH</u>: NON-HYDROGENATED MARGARINE *AND* PURE MAPLE SYRUP

¼ TEASPOON SEA SALT

2 TABLESPOONS BROWN RICE SYRUP

2 TABLESPOONS PLUS 2 TEASPOONS ORGANIC "WHITE" SUGAR

1. Make a lengthwise cut all the way down the vanilla bean with a sharp knife. Then, open it like a pod and scrape out the gooey insides with a table knife. Place the sticky vanilla goodness in a small pot, making sure to add every last bit of vanilla from the bean. Sometimes, it's even helpful to scrape it out with the back of your fingernail. As least if no one's watching.
2. Add the remaining ingredients to the pot and set it to medium-low heat, stirring well to combine. When the sauce comes to a boil, turn the heat down to the lowest setting. Then, allow it to simmer gently for another 3-5 minutes, stirring often. Remove from heat and serve immediately. This will keep for…*I just don't know.* I have never served this and had even a drop left over!

MAKES ABOUT ¾ CUP OF SAUCE; 30 MINUTES OR UNDER! GF/PURPLE

Blueberry Citrus Sauce

This rich, fruity sauce is easy to make and delicious on pancakes, waffles, nondairy ice cream, and more.

¼ CUP ORANGE JUICE

¾ CUP WATER

1¼ CUPS FRESH OR FROZEN BLUEBERRIES

1½ TEASPOONS <u>EACH</u>: VANILLA EXTRACT *AND* NON-HYDROGENATED MARGARINE

½ CUP ORGANIC SUGAR OR SUCANAT

• 2 TABLESPOONS FRESH LEMON JUICE

• ¼ CUP PURE MAPLE SYRUP

• ⅛ TEASPOON SALT

ADD LAST: 1½ TABLESPOONS ARROWROOT (OR CORNSTARCH)

1. Combine all of the ingredients (except for the arrowroot) in a medium saucepan and stir. Cook over medium heat until the mixture begins to bubble.
2. Reduce the heat to low and simmer uncovered for about ten minutes, stirring often.
3. To add in the arrowroot, you can use one of two methods. You can place a little of the sauce in a small dish and stir in the arrowroot until very smooth. Then, add the mixture back into the sauce, whisking well. Alternatively, you can sprinkle the arrowroot lightly into the saucepan, whisking constantly to prevent lumping.
4. Once the arrowroot has been added, stir the sauce very often over medium heat just until it becomes thickened—don't overheat. This is best served warm. It will store in an airtight container in the refrigerator for several weeks. Unless you have a blueberry monster in your house.

MAKES ABOUT 2½ CUPS OF SAUCE; 30 MINUTES OR UNDER! GF/BLUE

Chapter Eleven: Everyday Entrées

These are the main dishes I make on a daily basis as they are generally easier to prepare, quicker, and lighter than the "extravagant entrées." Nonetheless, these "simple" entrées are still delicious and many are even impressive enough to serve guests. You may notice that there are a lot of beans wandering around in this section. This is because beans are just about the perfect choice for everyday eating—they are filling, nutritious, low in fat and calories, and high in fiber. Enjoy!

Fresh Greek Delight

I first tried this dish in an innovative, family owned Greek restaurant. They, of course, used their own freshly made pita bread as the base. I have recreated this delicious, fresh, and very addictive entrée using pre-made pita bread (or a tortilla) as it's much quicker. If you do use pita bread (instead of a tortilla), there are varieties on the market now that are so soft and delicious that they are almost mistakable for fresh. If you can find this kind, you will find that this dish quickly transcends above this "everyday" chapter into the *other* entrée section!

½ CUP OF THE "CREAMY HUMMUS" (RECIPE BELOW)

CREAMY HUMMUS:

15 OZ. CAN (1½ CUPS) GARBANZO BEANS (CHICKPEAS), RINSED & DRAINED*

2-3 MEDIUM GARLIC CLOVES, PEELED

¼ CUP TAHINI (SESAME PASTE)

¼ CUP PLUS 2 TABLESPOONS *FRESH* LEMON JUICE

1 TEASPOON SEA SALT (OR LESS TO TASTE)

¼ CUP PLUS 2 TABLESPOONS OLIVE OIL (REGULAR OR EXTRA-VIRGIN)*

FLAT BREAD:

ONE FRESH PITA BREAD ROUND (OR ONE 8-INCH SPROUTED OR WHOLE GRAIN FLOUR TORTILLA)**

TOPPINGS PER FLAT BREAD ROUND:

½ CUP (LIGHTLY PACKED) BABY SPINACH LEAVES

⅓ CUP CHOPPED TOMATOES (ROMA, CHERRY, OR GRAPE TOMATOES WORK WELL)

6 KALAMATA OLIVES, PITTED AND SLICED IN HALF

2 TABLESPOONS VERY THINLY SLICED RED ONION (SEVERAL THIN RINGS OF ONION)

1 TABLESPOON (*PACKED*) FRESH BASIL, SLICED INTO RIBBONS

GRAND FINALE: 2 TEASPOONS EXTRA-VIRGIN OLIVE OIL

1. Preheat the oven to 350° F. In a food processor, blend the chickpeas and garlic cloves very well. Add the tahini, lemon juice, salt, and oil and process until very smooth.
2. Place your pita bread (or tortilla) directly on a rack in the oven and allow it to become lightly browned. This should only take about 5-10 minutes.
3. Remove the flat bread from the oven and place it on your plate. Spread the ½ cup of hummus evenly over the top of it. Next, evenly distribute the spinach, tomatoes, olives, onion, and basil on top of the hummus. Drizzle with the additional olive oil and serve immediately.

SERVES 1; 30 MINUTES OR UNDER! GF (WITH SUBSTITUTION)/SF/BLUE

*For a lower fat hummus, reserve the bean liquid when you drain the beans. Use ¼ cup bean liquid (and 2 tablespoons olive oil) instead of the full amount of olive oil.

**If you are gluten intolerant, you may try a 100% sprouted grain tortilla or use a gluten-free tortilla.

Deluxe Almond-Veggie Burgers

Recently, I was informed by my friend Lizz Baldwin that every self-respecting vegetarian cookbook should have a proper veggie burger recipe. Therefore, we spent the next few hours developing this recipe. It's everything a good, standard veggie burger should be…it sticks together, it tastes great (yet neutral), and contains all manner of healthful, natural ingredients. Be sure to use *short* grain brown rice in this, however, as regular rice won't bind together properly. You do need to plan ahead for this as well, as it requires the rice to be cooked in advance. Good eats!

2 SLICES WHOLE GRAIN OR SPROUTED GRAIN BREAD, TORN INTO SMALL PIECES*

I CAN (15 OZ.) PINTO BEANS, RINSED AND DRAINED (OR 1 ½ CUPS COOKED BEANS)

3 LARGE CLOVES GARLIC, PEELED

2 TABLESPOONS CHOPPED CELERY

¼ CUP MINCED ONION (WHITE OR YELLOW)

½ CUP WHOLE ALMONDS

I TABLESPOON NUTRITIONAL YEAST POWDER

½ TEASPOON EACH: GROUND PAPRIKA *AND* GROUND BLACK PEPPER

1 ¼ TEASPOONS SEA SALT (OR LESS IF YOU PREFER)

¼ CUP PINE NUTS

2 TABLESPOONS EACH: SESAME SEEDS *AND* FRESH, MINCED PARSLEY

¼ CUP EACH: ROLLED OATS* (NOT INSTANT) *AND* GRATED CARROTS

I CUP COOKED *SHORT* GRAIN BROWN RICE

FOR FRYING OUT LOUD: 1-2 TABLESPOONS OIL (COCONUT, SUNFLOWER, OR OLIVE)

1. In a food processor, whirl the pieces of bread until they resemble fine crumbs. You should end up with about 1⅓ cups of breadcrumbs. Remove them from the food processor and set aside.
2. In the food processor, place the beans, garlic, celery, onion, almonds, yeast, paprika, pepper, and salt. Blend until relatively smooth. Smooth enough for your relatives, that is. Set aside (still in the processor).
3. In a dry skillet set to medium-low heat, place the pine nuts and sesame seeds. Toast, shaking the pan often, until the nuts and seeds are lightly browned and aromatic. This will take well under 5 minutes. Once toasted, add them to the mixture in the food processor (but don't blend yet).
4. Invite the breadcrumbs, parsley, oats, carrots, and rice to the food processor party. Next, your goal will be to blend these items in while still retaining most of their texture. To do this, pulse them in slowly a few times, *just* enough to combine everything together.
5. Form the mixture into small patties (or press flat and cut out fun shapes with a cookie cutter). Finally, pan-fry them in the oil over medium heat until browned on both sides. Serve plain or on a bun with your choice of fixings. For a special treat, serve these topped with some of the "Creamy Mayo to Play Dead For" (page 119) or "Creamy Fresh Herb Spread" (page 196).

SERVES 4-6; 30 MINUTES OR UNDER! (WITH COOKED RICE) GF (WITH SUBSTITUTIONS)/SF/GREEN

*If you cannot eat gluten, you may use gluten-free bread and substitute quinoa for the oats (see page 44).

Alethea's Caribbean Black Beans

One day, while playing in my young daughters "kitchen," I was served a bowl of imaginary black beans with plastic onions and cardboard pineapple. I looked at it for a moment, then realized it would make a delicious dish in the actual world of real food. I began to imagine caramelized pineapple and onions, complemented by orange juice and lemon zest. When I finally put everything together in my own kitchen, the result was delicious and nutritious! Do keep in mind, however, that this works best with soaked beans, so it's best to plan ahead when making this.

OVEN ROASTED GOODNESS:

2 CUPS EACH: FRESH PINEAPPLE CHUNKS *AND* CHOPPED ONION (YELLOW OR WHITE)

2 TABLESPOONS OIL (SUNFLOWER, COCONUT, OR NON-VIRGIN OLIVE)

1 TEASPOON ORGANIC SUGAR OR SUCANAT

BEAN THERE:

1 CUP DRY BLACK BEANS, PREFERABLY SOAKED IN WATER FOR 10-12 HOURS (SEE PAGE 39)

1¼ CUPS ORANGE JUICE, THE FRESHER THE BETTER

¾ CUP "VEGETARIAN 'CHICKEN' BROTH" (PAGE 194)—USE SLIGHTLY MORE FOR UNSOAKED BEANS

2 BAY LEAVES

3-INCH PIECE OF KOMBU (OPTIONAL BUT FABULOUS, SEE PAGE 252 FOR MORE INFORMATION)

1 TEASPOON DRIED THYME

⅛ TEASPOON GROUND CINNAMON

OPTIONAL: ¼ OF A HABANERO PEPPER (OR LESS—THEY'RE HOT!), SEEDS REMOVED & MINCED

LAST ORDER OF BUSINESS:

¾ TEASPOON SEA SALT (OR LESS IF YOU PREFER)

1 TABLESPOON ORANGE JUICE

ZEST OF ONE SMALL ORGANIC LEMON, MINCED OR CHOPPED

1. Preheat the oven to 350° F. Place the pineapple, onion, oil, and sugar in a baking pan or pie pan. Mix together to combine all of the ingredients well.
2. Bake for about 1½ hours, turning every 30 minutes or so with a spoon or spatula. When the pineapple and onions are very golden brown and lightly caramelized, remove from the oven.
3. While that mixture is still in the oven, you can start cooking the beans. First, drain the beans to remove the soaking water. Place them along with the 1¼ cups orange juice, broth, bay leaves, kombu, thyme, and cinnamon in a pressure cooker (or a pot with a tight fitting lid). If you are packing heat, add your minced habanero now as well (see page 39 for hot pepper tips). Cover and bring to a boil. Reduce heat to medium-low. In a pressure cooker, continue to simmer for about 20 minutes. In a conventional pot, continue to simmer for 40 minutes, or until the beans are tender. And loving. However, please note that if you are using unsoaked beans you will need to cook them for about twice as long.
4. Discard any excess liquid, along with the bay leaves and the kombu. Mix the beans with the pineapple-onion combo. Toss with the salt, one tablespoon of orange juice, and lemon zest. Serve it up, mon!

SERVES ABOUT 4; GF/SF/GREEN

> *Tip*: This goes great over couscous, quinoa, or coconut rice. Simply prepare your grain of choice while the beans are cooking.

Moong Dal

I was once lucky enough to watch an amazing Indian woman throw this together in her kitchen. Watching her cook, I can say that the most important ingredient she used was lots and lots of love! Although it may seem complicated at first glance, this recipe is actually very easy to prepare. It contains much less fat than the Indian dishes in the "Extravagant Entrée" section, making it a delicious choice for everyday eating. This is especially good served over basmati rice and topped with the "Cilantro Chutney Elixir" (p. 125).

2 CUPS DRY SPLIT MOONG (YELLOW MUNG) BEANS OR YELLOW SPLIT PEAS, SORTED AND RINSED

7½ CUPS WATER

I TEASPOON DRIED TURMERIC

2 TEASPOONS CUMIN POWDER

4 TEASPOONS EACH: CORIANDER POWDER *AND* FRESH LEMON JUICE

2 TABLESPOONS COCONUT OIL (OR NON-HYDROGENATED MARGARINE)

2 TEASPOONS SEA SALT (OR LESS IF YOU PREFER)

¾ CUP (LIGHTLY PACKED) CHOPPED CILANTRO

TOMATO DELICIOUSNESS:

2 TABLESPOONS OIL (COCONUT, NON-VIRGIN OLIVE, SUNFLOWER, OR SAFFLOWER)

I TABLESPOON BLACK (DARK BROWN) MUSTARD SEEDS

2 TEASPOONS CUMIN SEEDS

I CUP DICED ONION (WHITE OR YELLOW)

6 LARGE CLOVES GARLIC, MINCED OR PRESSED

I TEASPOON AMCHUR POWDER (SEE PAGE 251)

GREEN SERRANO CHILI, CHOPPED (SEE PAGE 39) OR ¼ TEASPOON CAYENNE POWDER

15 OZ. CAN DICED TOMATOES, JUICE INCLUDED

½ TEASPOON SEA SALT

GARNISH: CHOPPED FRESH CILANTRO TO TASTE

1. In a large pot, bring the moong beans, water, and turmeric to a boil over high heat. Turn the heat down to low and simmer for about 15 minutes. Add the cumin & coriander powders and stir well. Continue to simmer until the beans are soft and thickened, about another 30 minutes.

2. While the beans are cooking, we set our clocks to tomato time. First, heat the 2 tablespoons of oil in a large skillet over medium heat. Add the mustard and cumin seeds and cook, stirring, just until they begin to pop. Toss in the onion and cook, stirring, until soft and lightly browned, about 5 minutes. Add the garlic, amchur, chili, and tomatoes. Turn the heat down to low and simmer for about 20 minutes, or until almost all of the liquid is absorbed and the mixture is thick. As it is cooking, you may want to stir it occasionally. Stir in the ½ teaspoon of salt, remove from heat, and set aside.

3. Once the beans from step #1 are tender, place them in a food processor (or a really good blender) and puree them. Remove the pureed beans from the food processor and place them back into the pot. Stir in the lemon juice, coconut oil or margarine, 2 teaspoons of salt, and ¾ cup cilantro. Combine well.

4. *To serve*: Ladle the pureed bean mixture into bowls and swirl in the tomato mixture. Scatter the cilantro over the top. Serve plain or with basmati rice (or bread) and chutney.

SERVES 5-6; GF/SF/BLUE

Black-eyed Peas with Kale

This is one of those dishes I could practically live on. For one thing, it is very healthy and light, which makes it *perfect* for losing weight or staying trim. However, it's also extremely tasty and very easy to throw together. It is loosely based on the dish "Hoppin' John" which is meant to bring good luck in the New Year. This entrée does work best with soaked peas, so you may want to plan ahead just a bit for maximum goodness. If you like, you can serve this over a grain such as brown rice or amaranth. This also pairs nicely with the "Creamy Polenta" (page 94).

1 ½ CUPS DRY BLACK-EYED PEAS, PREFERABLY SOAKED (SEE PAGE 39 FOR BEAN TIPS)

½ CUP DICED ONION

3½ CUPS "VEGETARIAN 'CHICKEN' BROTH" (P. 194) OR OTHER LIQUID "CHICKEN" BROTH*

4 BAY LEAVES

4-INCH PIECE OF KOMBU (OPTIONAL BUT WONDERFUL—SEE PAGE 252 FOR MORE INFO)

2 CUPS (*PACKED*) KALE, PREFERABLY LACINATO (CUT INTO THIN RIBBONS)

6 MEDIUM CLOVES GARLIC, PRESSED OR MINCED

2 TEASPOONS EACH: SEA SALT, NUTRITIONAL YEAST POWDER, *AND* OLIVE OIL

¼ CUP (4 TABLESPOONS) *FRESH* LEMON JUICE

TO TASTE (OPTIONAL): HOT SAUCE OF YOUR CHOICE (HABANERO, TABASCO, ETC.)

1. If you're using soaked black-eyed peas, drain them to remove the soaking water and then rinse them. If you're using unsoaked beans, rinse them well, then drain them.
2. Place the beans in a pressure cooker (or a regular pot with a tight fitting lid). Add the onion, broth, bay leaves, and kombu and bring to a boil over high heat. Reduce the heat to low and simmer until the black-eyed peas are tender. For soaked peas, this will take about 15 minutes in the pressure cooker (after the top begins to spin) or 45 minutes in a regular pot. For unsoaked peas, this will usually take at least 10 minutes longer in the pressure cooker and 30 minutes longer in a regular pot.
3. Once them beans is finally done, drain off most of the excess liquid. Remove the bay leaves and kombu. Next, mix in the kale and garlic. Cook over medium-high heat for about 5 minutes, stirring often, until the kale is wilted.
4. Stir in the salt, nutritional yeast, olive oil, and lemon juice. Top with some of the hot sauce (if you are a spicy baby) and serve.

SERVES 4; GF/SF/GREEN

*You may need more liquid if you are using unsoaked peas. Please see page 39 for bean tips.

Easy Indian Mung Beans

As the name implies, this recipe makes for a very easy and simple main dish. However, it's also yummy, satisfying, and one of those rare Indian dishes that's still delicious despite being so low in fat! In case you are unfamiliar with these little gems, mung beans are khaki green in color, small, and cook more quickly than many other types of legumes. They're also easy to digest and very high in fiber.

I CUP DRY MUNG BEANS
I TABLESPOON GRATED FRESH GINGER
I TABLESPOON COCONUT OIL
I ½ TEASPOONS EACH: CUMIN SEEDS AND GROUND (DRIED) CORIANDER
½ JALAPENO, STEM REMOVED AND DICED (SEE PAGE 39)

• 3 CUPS WATER
• I ¼ TEASPOONS SEA SALT
• 2 TABLESPOONS LEMON JUICE
TO TASTE: FRESH CILANTRO, CHOPPED

1. Sort through the beans to remove any bad beans, stones, debris, cat hair, or paper clips. Next, rinse the beans and drain them.
2. Place the drained beans, ginger, oil, cumin seeds, coriander, jalapeno, and water in a large pot with a tight fitting lid (or a pressure cooker). Bring to a boil (covered) over high heat. Reduce the heat to low and simmer for about 45 minutes to an hour, or until the beans are tender. If you are using a pressure cooker, this will instead take about 20 minutes. When the beans are tender, stir in the sea salt and fresh lemon juice. Garnish with fresh cilantro and serve.

SERVES ABOUT 4; 30 MINUTES OR UNDER! (IF USING A PRESSURE COOKER) GF/SF/GREEN

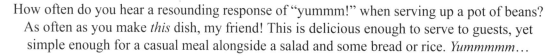

Creamy Adzuki Beans

How often do you hear a resounding response of "yummm!" when serving up a pot of beans? As often as you make *this* dish, my friend! This is delicious enough to serve to guests, yet simple enough for a casual meal alongside a salad and some bread or rice. *Yummmmm…*

I ½ CUPS DRY ADZUKI BEANS
3-INCH PIECE OF KOMBU (SEE PAGE 252)
2 CUPS WATER
½ CUP DICED ONION
2 ½ TEASPOONS CUMIN POWDER
14.5 OZ. CAN DICED TOMATOES
14 OZ. CAN COCONUT MILK

• ¼ CUP PLUS I TEASPOON *FRESH* LEMON JUICE
• 2 TABLESPOONS CREAMY PEANUT BUTTER
• 4 MEDIUM-LARGE CLOVES GARLIC, PRESSED
• 2 ½ TEASPOONS SEA SALT (OR LESS)
OPTIONAL GARNISH:
• ¼ -½ CUP CHOPPED FRESH CILANTRO

1. In a pressure cooker (or a large pot with a tight fitting lid), bring the beans, kombu, water, onion, cumin, tomatoes, and coconut milk to a boil over medium-high heat.
2. Reduce the heat to low and simmer, covered, until the beans are tender. In a pressure cooker, this will take about 25-35 minutes. In a regular pot, this will usually take about two hours. Am I selling anyone on the idea of a pressure cooker here? Any pressure cooker executives want to give me some money? Once the beans are tender, remove the kombu and stir in the remaining items (all but the cilantro). Serve plain or garnished with cilantro. *Yummmm……*

SERVES 4-6; GF/SF/BLUE

Artichoke, Kalamata, & Sun Dried Tomato Mini-Pizzas
with Garlic and Rosemary (p. 71)

Raspberry Lemon Zest Pancakes (p. 59)

Creamy Hummus with Variations (p. 79)

Righteously Rich Hot Cocoa (p. 207)

Dolmadas,
pictured right
(p. 85)

Rosemary Mushroom Strudel (p. 70)

Virtuous Vanilla Shake (p. 48)

Earth's Healthiest Waffles (p. 60)

Easy and Addictive Eggplant "Chips" (p. 98)

Indian Spiced Supergrain Cereal (p. 52)

Rosemary White Beans with Artichokes
and Sun Dried Tomatoes (p. 142)

Blueberry Waffles (p. 59) with Blueberry Citrus Sauce (p. 133)

Yellow Tofu (p. 64)

Cucumber-Dill Toss (p. 90)

Mexican Fiesta Rice (p. 96)

Moroccan Quinoa (p. 88)

Anna's Zucchini (p. 91)

Quick and Healthy Herbed Garlic Bread (p. 102)

Magical Multigrain Pancakes (p. 57)

Clockwise
from left:

Kid's Choice
Guacamole
(p. 101)

Perfect Pinto
Beans (p. 95)

Cilantro-
Lime Rice
(p. 89)

Yummy Fat
Free Refried
Beans (p. 96)

Fatoush Salad (p. 109)

Princess Salad (p. 106)

Light Balsamic Dressing (p. 129)

Spinach, Orange, and Toasted Almond Salad (p. 109)

Thai Sweet Chili Sauce (p. 118)

Dark Chocolate Shake (p. 49)

Lowfat
Basil-Garlic
Linguine
(p. 150)

Creamy Adzuki Beans
(p. 140)

Bailey's Tofish with Tartar Sauce (p. 144)

Spiced Lime Tortilla Chips (p. 206)

Lemon Asparagus Linguine (p. 168)

Love Bug Parfaits (p. 53)

Grandma's Favorite French Toast (p. 62)

Tomato, Basil, and
Roasted Pine Nut
Penne (p. 167)

Spinach-Strawberry Salad (p. 104)

Olive Oil w/ Crispy Garlic & Rosemary (w/ Sourdough) (p. 80)

Deluxe Almond-Veggie Burgers (p. 136) w/ Creamy Fresh Herb Spread (p. 196)

Luscious Lemon Bars with Ginger Shortbread Crust (p. 224)

Lemon-Poppy Seed Muffins w/ Zesty Lemon Glaze (p. 202)

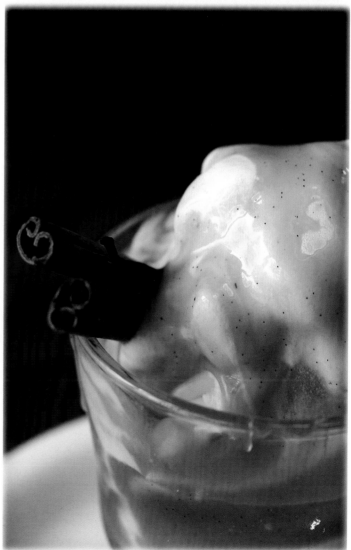

Vanilla Bean Caramel Sauce (p. 133)

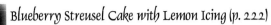

Blueberry Streusel Cake with Lemon Icing (p. 222)

Oven Roasted Cauliflower with
Rosemary and Garlic (p. 100)

Delectable Lowfat
"Egg Rolls" (p. 67)

Creamy Potato-Dill Soup with Pan-
Toasted Croutons (p. 214)

Red Lentil, Spinach, and Lemon Soup (p. 212)

Hearty Vegetarian Chili
(p. 215)

Mulligatawny (p. 209)

Grandma's Apple Crisp (p. 223)

Oatmeal Raisin Cookies with Vanilla Icing (p. 228)

Chocolate Decadence Cake (p. 218)

Apple Puffs
with Vanilla
Bean Caramel
Sauce (p. 231)

Blackberry Peach Goodness (p. 226)

Googy Granola (p. 63)

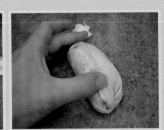

Twisting the Green Chili
& Tomatillo Tamales
(p. 174)

Thai Drunken Noodles (p. 155)
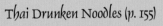

Apple
Cinnamon
Flapjacks,
left
(p. 58)

Sesame Tofu with Fresh Basil and Thai Sweet Chili Sauce (p. 164)

A visual aid on the process of making nori rolls

Pan Grilled Burrito or "Big Taco"

I pretty much live on these. Since I almost always keep cooked beans on hand, I find this method of making burritos (or tacos) to be *very* user-friendly. Because it saves me the trouble of heating everything up separately, cleanup becomes incredibly quick. Plus, this cooking method turns the tortilla into a crisp, golden brown "crust." These also happen to be filling, nutritious, low in fat and calories, and very high in fiber! I've given you a loose recipe so that you can firm up the details in the way that best suits your taste.

ONE 8-INCH SPROUTED OR WHOLE GRAIN FLOUR TORTILLA (OR GLUTEN-FREE TORTILLA)

BEANS, YOUR CHOICE: ½ CUP "PERFECT PINTO BEANS" (PAGE 95), "YUMMY FAT-FREE REFRIED BEANS" (PAGE 96), OR CANNED VEGETARIAN REFRIED BEANS

OPTIONAL: "CILANTRO-LIME RICE" (PAGE 89) OR "MEXICAN FIESTA RICE" (PAGE 96)

VEGGIE GOODNESS:

DICED ONIONS TO TASTE (ABOUT 2 TABLESPOONS)

CHOPPED RED TOMATO (OR GREEN TOMATILLO) TO TASTE (ABOUT ¼ CUP)

FINELY CHOPPED RED AND/OR GREEN CABBAGE TO TASTE (ABOUT ¼ CUP)

½ CARROT, GRATED

OPTIONAL YUMMINESS: I TABLESPOON NONDAIRY SOUR CREAM, ¼ AVOCADO (PEELED AND CHOPPED), OR GUACAMOLE OF YOUR CHOICE (PAGE 101)

OPTIONAL SAUCE (CHOOSE ONE OR MORE):

"9½ MINUTE GREEN CHILE SAUCE" (PAGE 131)

"ALEX'S PINEAPPLE HABANERO HOT SAUCE" (PAGE 132)

GREEN TOMATILLO SAUCE OR PACKAGED SALSA/HOT SAUCE OF CHOICE

FINAL MATTER OF BUSINESS: ¼ OF A FRESH LIME (OR LESS IF YOU PREFER)

1. Prepare all of the ingredients you will be using and set them aside.
2. Preheat a dry skillet (that has a lid) over medium-low heat.

3. TO MAKE A BURRITO: Place the beans, rice (if using), and onion along the middle of the tortilla. Fold the sides around the filling (as if you were making, say, a burrito). Spray the preheated skillet lightly with oil and place the burrito, seam side down, on the pan. Cover the pan and cook until the underside is golden brown. Gently flip it over to cook the other side. If a few fillings try to escape, just tuck them back in the burrito. When the other side is golden brown as well, remove from the pan. Open the "seam" gently and fill the burrito with your remaining toppings of choice. Squeeze the fresh lime over the top of the fillings. Close the seam back up to the best of your ability and dig on in.

4. TO MAKE A BIG TACO: Spread the beans over the bottom half of the tortilla and then add the rice (if using) and onions. Next, fold the top half of your tortilla over the bottom to make, yes, a big taco. Spray the preheated skillet lightly with oil and place your taco on the skillet. Cover and cook for a few minutes, or until nicely browned on the underside. Next, flip the taco over and brown the other side. Remove the taco from the pan and fill it with your remaining toppings of choice. Squeeze the fresh lime over the top of the fillings and re-fold the taco. Serve immediately and enjoy your taco in a big way.

SERVES 1

30 MINUTES OR UNDER! GF (WITH GLUTEN-FREE TORTILLA) /SF (WITHOUT NONDAIRY SOUR CREAM)/GREEN

Rosemary White Beans with Artichokes and Sun-Dried Tomatoes

Here's an example of how a simple bean dish can become elevated to a delicious, impressive entrée just by using a few gourmet ingredients that pack lots of flavor! This dish pairs nicely with "Green Bread" (page 69) and a tossed salad.

WHERE HAVE YOU BEAN ALL MY LIFE?:

1 CUP DRY GREAT WHITE NORTHERN BEANS, PREFERABLY SOAKED (SEE PAGE 39 FOR TIPS)

2 TEASPOONS DRIED ROSEMARY LEAF

2-INCH PIECE OF KOMBU (OPTIONAL BUT WORTH IT!); SEE PAGE 252 FOR MORE INFO

2 BAY LEAVES

1 ½ CUPS WATER*

1 CUP "VEGETARIAN 'CHICKEN' BROTH" (PAGE 194) OR OTHER VEGAN "CHICKEN" BROTH

STIR IT UP:

½ TEASPOON SEA SALT

1 TABLESPOON EXTRA-VIRGIN OLIVE OIL

2 TEASPOONS *FRESH* LEMON JUICE

3 MEDIUM-LARGE CLOVES GARLIC, MINCED OR PRESSED (OR LESS IF YOU PREFER)

¾ CUP MARINATED ARTICHOKE HEARTS, DRAINED

FRESH FINALE:

1 TABLESPOON (*PACKED*) FRESH BASIL, SLICED THINLY INTO RIBBONS

2 TABLESPOONS JULIENNE SLICED, MARINATED SUN-DRIED TOMATOES

1. If you are using soaked beans, drain and rinse them. If you are using unsoaked beans, rinse them well, then drain them. Place the beans in a large, covered pot (or pressure cooker) with the dried rosemary, kombu, bay leaves, water, and broth. Bring to a boil, then reduce the heat to low and simmer until the beans are tender. In a pressure cooker, this will take about 25-35 minutes for soaked beans (or about an hour for unsoaked beans). In a regular pot, this will usually take 1-2 hours for soaked beans (or 2-3 hours for unsoaked beans).

2. When the beans are tender, drain off any excess liquid and remove the kombu and bay leaves. Stir in the salt, oil, lemon juice, garlic, and artichokes.

3. Serve topped with the basil and tomatoes.

SERVES 4; GF/SF/GREEN

*You may need more water if you are using unsoaked beans. Please see page 39 for bean cooking tips.

Spinach Quesadilla

This easy dish is perfect for a busy day. It's quick, filling, healthy, and delicious. It's even popular with kids (with a lighter dose of spinach and sans the onions). Keep in mind that this recipe is based on one individual quesadilla. To feed a larger group, simply double or triple the amounts given.

TWO 8-INCH SPROUTED OR WHOLE GRAIN TORTILLAS (OR GLUTEN-FREE TORTILLAS)

½ CUP OF THE "YUMMY FAT-FREE REFRIED BEANS" (PAGE 96)*

½ CUP GRATED SOY CHEESE

FINELY CHOPPED ONION TO TASTE (ABOUT 3 TABLESPOONS)

BABY SPINACH TO TASTE (ABOUT I CUP PACKED)

OPTIONAL:

I-2 TABLESPOONS NONDAIRY SOUR CREAM

"KID'S CHOICE GUACAMOLE" (PAGE IOI) OR "JOE'S GUACAMOLE" (PAGE IOI)

SALSA OR HOT SAUCE OF YOUR CHOICE

FINAL TOUCH: ½ FRESH LIME, CUT INTO WEDGES (OR LESS IF YOU PREFER)

1. Prepare all of the ingredients that you will be using and set them aside.
2. Preheat a large skillet over medium-low heat.
3. Spread one tortilla with the beans. Top evenly with the soy cheese, onion, and spinach. Place the other tortilla on top.
4. Lightly oil the skillet and place the quesadilla in it. Cover and cook for 5 minutes, or until the bottom is nicely browned. Spray the top tortilla lightly with oil (or not), then gently flip the whole flippin' thing over.
5. Place the cover on the pan again and cook until the underside is golden brown.
6. Carefully remove the quesadilla from the pan. Cut it into eight wedges (as if it were a pizza). Top with the optional items, if using, and squeeze the fresh lime on top. Finally, get your feed on!

SERVES I-2

30 MINUTES OR UNDER! GF (WITH GLUTEN-FREE TORTILLAS)/GREEN

*You may substitute canned vegetarian refried beans if you are short on time...and homemade beans.

Bailey's Tofish with Tartar Sauce

I don't know anyone named Bailey, but if I did, she'd have a big plate of this coming to her. This fishy monkey makes a quick and satisfying meal, especially paired with the "Oven Fries" (page 92) and a light salad. Or serve it on a bun for a mighty fine Tofish sandwich. Anything for you, Bailey.

ONE 12.3 OZ. PACKAGE SILKEN TOFU, FROZEN AND THAWED*

MARINADE:

4 TABLESPOONS *FRESH* LEMON JUICE

2 TABLESPOONS TAMARI, SHOYU, OR SOY SAUCE

¾ TEASPOON EACH: DRIED GARLIC GRANULES *AND* GRANULATED (OR POWDERED) KELP

½ TEASPOON EACH: GROUND PAPRIKA *AND* DRIED ONION GRANULES

CORNMEAL BREADING:

¼ CUP EACH: DRY CORNMEAL *AND* DRY POLENTA

¼ CUP WHOLE WHEAT PASTRY FLOUR (OR GLUTEN-FREE ALL-PURPOSE FLOUR)

½ TEASPOON EACH: DRIED GARLIC GRANULES *AND* DRIED ONION GRANULES

1 TEASPOON SEASONED SALT

TARTAR SAUCE:

• ½ CUP "VEGENAISE" VEGAN MAYONNAISE

• ¼ CUP FINELY GRATED DILL PICKLE

• 2 TABLESPOONS FINELY MINCED WHITE OR YELLOW ONION

• ⅛ TEASPOON EACH: DRIED GARLIC GRANULES *AND* GROUND BLACK PEPPER

OIL: COCONUT, OLIVE, OR SUNFLOWER OIL (ENOUGH TO MAKE A LIGHT LAYER OF OIL IN YOUR PAN)

1. Carefully slice the container of thawed tofu through the middle. Gently extract the tofu from its container, doing your level best to keep it in tact. Next, *lightly* squeeze the tofu to remove some of the excess water. Slice the tofu into 12-14 thin slabs and place in between paper towels on your counter top. Press according to the instructions on page 43. Allow to press for 10 minutes or longer, or until most of the water has been extracted.

2. Stir the marinade items together in a bowl until well mixed. Place the pressed tofu slices on a plate (in a single layer) and pour the marinade evenly over the top of them. Turn the tofu so as to coat both sides with the mixture. Allow to sit for 10 minutes or more, or until the marinade has been mostly absorbed.

3. While the tofu is marinating, mix together the items for the tartar sauce. Pop it into the fridge until you are ready to use it so that it retains its thick consistency.

4. Measure the breading ingredients into a wide bowl or dish and stir well to combine.

5. When the tofu is done marinating, set a large skillet over medium-high heat. Pour enough oil into the skillet to make a thin layer in the bottom of the pan. Dredge the tofu slices in the breading (using a gentle touch) until all sides are very well coated. Place on the oiled skillet in a *single* layer. Cook for about 5 minutes, or until crisp and golden brown on the underside.

6. Turn over and pan-fry for another 3-5 minutes, or until both sides are gloriously golden browned. If necessary, repeat steps 5 and 6 until all of the tofu is used up. Remove to a plate and serve with the sauce.

SERVES 2-3; GF (WITH SUBSTITUTIONS)/PURPLE

*Freezing the tofu will give it a more complex, fish-like texture. Simply place the whole package of tofu in the freezer for at least 12 hours and then allow it to thaw in the fridge overnight (or longer).

NOTE: Instead of pan-frying, this dish may also be baked at 400° F. until golden brown on both sides. The trick to crispy *baked* tofu is to use enough oil, coating the baking pan well before adding the tofu and also spraying the top of the tofu with oil. Baked tofu will take about 10-20 minutes per side.

Lemon Tempeh Burgers

I once served this to a devoted meat eater who not only gobbled it down and asked for more, but actually requested the recipe! Tempeh is a wonderfully healthy food that is delicious when prepared properly. If you associate tempeh with blandness, it's probably because you've eaten tempeh that wasn't marinated properly (or at all). Plenty of marinade (and using very flavorful ingredients) makes all the difference. I prefer five-grain tempeh, but you can use whatever type strikes your fancy.

8 oz. package tempeh, thawed if frozen

Marinade:

4 tablespoons (¼ cup) fresh lemon juice

2½ tablespoons tamari, shoyu, or soy sauce

4 large cloves fresh garlic, minced or pressed

1 teaspoon dried onion granules

Oil for Pan-frying: 1 tablespoon olive, coconut, sunflower, or safflower oil

Are we Having Bun Yet?: 2 sprouted or whole grain buns (or gluten-free)

Fixin's: sliced dill pickles, "Creamy Mayo to Play Dead For" (page 119) or Vegenaise vegan mayo, mustard, thinly sliced onions, and lettuce

1. Carefully open the package of tempeh. Slice in half, then cut each slice through the middle. What you are aiming for are four slabs that are 2¼ x 4-inches long (and ½-inch thick).
2. Place the patties in a skillet and add about ¼-inch of water. Cover and cook on medium heat until the water has evaporated. This steams the tempeh so that it will absorb the marinade better.
3. Place the tempeh cutlets in a container (or on a pan) in a single layer. Stir the marinade items together and pour over the tempeh. Turn the cutlets over so as to coat both sides with the marinade. Allow the tempeh to marinate as long as you can—overnight is ideal, but try to allow at least an hour if possible.
4. Heat a medium-large skillet over medium heat. Add the oil and make sure it's evenly distributed over the bottom of the pan.
5. Add your tempeh cutlets, making sure you get all of the garlic from the marinade on them. Cook until the undersides are golden brown.
6. Flip the cutlets over. Don't be discouraged if they stick a little. Just pry them up with a good spatula. Cook until golden brown on both sides.
7. Warm your buns. No, I'm not suggesting a tropical getaway. I'm suggesting a very easy way to make your whole grain buns nice and toasty. Place them in the pan with the tempeh (with the inside portions of the buns facing down) and then cover the pan with a lid.
8. When the buns are warm, top them with whatever you like. I personally like to have a decent amount of mayo, pickles, mustard, and onions for maximum flavor.
9. For smaller burgers, place one patty on each bun. For heartier burgers, place two patties on each bun (hence the 2-4 serving size range). Serve immediately.

Makes 2-4 tempeh burgers; GF (with substitution)/Blue

Mommo's DLT Sandwich

My mom got me hooked on these babies last summer while I was vacationing at her home. She says she could practically live on these. It's no wonder! The mineral kick of the dulse paired with the creaminess of the mayo is good taste and nutrition all rolled into one. The other thing that makes these sandwiches a staple, of course, is their utter simplicity. They come together in under five minutes and contain only whole, natural ingredients. No soy-isolated fake bacon to be found here! In case you're unfamiliar with dulse, it's a mineral-rich sea veggie and can be found in flake form in any health food store.

2 SLICES SPROUTED OR WHOLE GRAIN BREAD (OR GLUTEN-FREE BREAD)
"CREAMY MAYO TO PLAY DEAD FOR" (PAGE 119) OR VEGENAISE
1-3 TEASPOONS DRY DULSE FLAKES (SEE PAGE 251)
THINLY SLICED FRESH TOMATO
BABY GREENS OR ROMAINE LETTUCE LEAVES

OPTIONAL FIXIN'S:
• ALFALFA SPROUTS
• SLICED RED ONION
• AVOCADO SLICES

1. If you like, toast your bread. If you have a toaster, this will expedite the process greatly.
2. Spread with your mayo of choice.
3. Sprinkle the dulse flakes evenly on the mayo. Add the tomato and lettuce. If desired, add any or all of the optional remaining ingredients. Enjoy the mineral boost!

SERVES 1; 30 MINUTES OR UNDER! GF (WITH SUBSTITUTION)/SF/BLUE

Pan Fried Polenta with Rich Tomato Sauce

If you have chilled polenta in the fridge and the tomato sauce on hand, this dish will come together in under ten minutes!

POLENTA:
1 CUP DRY POLENTA MEAL
3¼ CUPS WATER
3 TABLESPOONS NUTRITIONAL YEAST POWDER
¾ TEASPOON SEA SALT
2 TABLESPOONS NON-HYDROGENATED MARGARINE

IT'S YOUR PARTY AND YOU'LL FRY IF YOU WANT TO:
• 1 TABLESPOON MARGARINE (OR OLIVE OIL)

• ONE RECIPE "RICH TOMATO SAUCE"
(PLEASE SEE RECIPE ON PAGE 118)

1. Follow the directions for making polenta on page 94. You can then choose to press it into a pan or roll it log-style. Allow the polenta to set for several hours or overnight.
2. Make the sauce according to the recipe on page 118. When the sauce is almost done cooking, you can pan-fry the polenta. First, slice it (or use cookie cutters to make fun shapes). Next, heat the margarine or olive oil in a large skillet and fry the polenta over medium-low heat for a few minutes, or until the underside is golden brown. Carefully flip over and cook on the other side. Remove when both sides are golden brown and look totally delicious!
3. Top the polenta with some of the sauce, and party like there *is* a tomorrow.

SERVES ABOUT 4-6; GF/BLUE

Tasty Lowfat Tostadas

This is one of those dishes that I rely on constantly for light, yet filling sustenance. I never seem to tire of the flavors and I love the freshness of the toppings. I've also found a way to serve tostadas to picky children. I simply cut the tortillas into smaller shapes (before baking them), then top them off with some beans, carrots, lime juice, and nondairy sour cream. Yum!

"Yummy Fat-Free Refried Beans" (page 96)

OR:

15.4 oz. can refried beans

1 teaspoon EACH: dried onion granules AND cumin powder

2 medium cloves fresh garlic, minced or pressed

½ teaspoon EACH: seasoned salt AND ground paprika

2-3 teaspoons fresh lime juice

4 corn tortillas (regular or sprouted corn)

MANDATORY TOPPINGS:

¼ cup EACH: chopped tomato, chopped fresh cilantro, shredded carrots, AND finely chopped (or grated) red cabbage

3 tablespoons minced red onion

OPTIONAL TOPPINGS:

Fresh salsa or hot sauce

Nondairy sour cream or guacamole of your choice (page 101)

Lime wedges (or an additional 1-2 teaspoons fresh lime juice)

1. If you'll be using the recipe for "Yummy Fat-Free Refried Beans," you will need to start them first. Please see the directions on page 96. If using canned beans, skip to step two.

2. Preheat the oven to 400° F. Place the corn tortillas on a lightly oiled cookie sheet in a single layer. Spray (or brush) the tops of the tortillas lightly with oil and bake for about 10 minutes, or until crisp and lightly browned. Remove from the oven and set aside.

3. If using canned beans, place them in a medium sized pot over low heat. Stir in the onion granules, cumin, garlic, seasoned salt, paprika, and lime juice. Cook, stirring often, until they are hot to trot.

4. Prepare the toppings. If varying from the mandatory items, please make sure to get a permission slip.

5. *To serve*: Place some of the beans on each tortilla and cover with them there good toppings. Serve immediately. Crunch out.

Serves 2-4; 30 minutes or under! (with cooked or canned beans)
GF/SF (without nondairy sour cream)/Green

Lo Fat Lo Mein

Here is an ideal dish for everyday eating. It's yummy, quick, and chock full of life-enhancing veggies.

8.8 OZ. UDON NOODLES (SOBA, LINGUINE, OR RICE NOODLES CAN STAND IN IF UDON IS TEMPORARILY OUT OF TOWN)

2 TEASPOONS TOASTED (DARK) SESAME OIL

2 TABLESPOONS LIQUID VEGETABLE BROTH OR "VEGETARIAN 'CHICKEN' BROTH" (PAGE 194)

SMALL ONION, SLICED VERY THINLY

I CUP DICED (OR JULIENNE CUT) ZUCCHINI

2 CUPS THINLY SLICED SHIITAKE MUSHROOM CAPS

MEDIUM CARROT, JULIENNE CUT OR DICED

2 CUPS CHOPPED NAPA CABBAGE

I TABLESPOON GRATED FRESH GINGER

5 MEDIUM CLOVES GARLIC, MINCED OR PRESSED

4 TABLESPOONS TAMARI, SHOYU, OR SOY SAUCE (OR LESS IF YOU PREFER)

I TABLESPOON ORGANIC SUGAR OR SUCANAT

½ TEASPOON (OR MORE TO TASTE) DRIED RED CHILI FLAKES

I TEASPOON ARROWROOT (OR CORNSTARCH)

GARNISH:

I TABLESPOON TOASTED SESAME SEEDS (SEE PAGE 42)

1. Prepare all of the vegetables (onion, zucchini, shiitakes, carrot, and cabbage) and set them aside individually (do not mix all of the veggies together as they will cook at different rates). If you like, get the ginger and garlic ready for the big show as well.

2. Boil the noodles according to the directions on their package. While the noodles are cooking, skip to step three. When the noodles are al dente, drain them and gently toss with one teaspoon of the toasted sesame oil. Set aside until step six.

3. While the noodles are cooking, you should be able to prepare the rest of the dish. Place the other one teaspoon of the toasted sesame oil in a wok (or very large skillet) along with the broth. Sauté the onion for about 5-6 minutes over medium-high heat, until soft and lightly browned.

4. Add the zucchini and shiitakes to the onion mixture and cook until the zucchini becomes softened as well. This should take about 3-5 minutes.

5. Add the carrot, cabbage, ginger, garlic, tamari, sugar, and chili flakes to the wok. Lightly sprinkle the arrowroot evenly over the mixture and stir it in immediately to prevent lumping. Continue to sauté over medium heat until the cabbage is wilted and all of the ingredients are well combined, about 2-3 minutes.

6. Add the noodles to the wok and gently toss with the veggies until well combined. If you prefer a saucier situation, you can add just a little more liquid broth to the mixture and stir it in well.

7. Serve topped with the toasted sesame seeds. This will keep for up to one week in the fridge.

SERVES 4; 30 MINUTES OR UNDER! GF (WITH RICE NOODLES)/GREEN

Skinny Dinny

If you have the teriyaki sauce on hand, this dish will be very easy to prepare. As the name implies, this is perfectly filling, yet extremely light. If you like heat, try adding some chili-garlic sauce at the end—those yummy little devils (chilies) are notorious for boosting the metabolism!

"Toasted Sesame-Orange Teriyaki Sauce" (page 124)

That's Rice:
⅓ cup dry long grain brown rice (or brown basmati rice)

⅔ cup water

Skinny Tofu:
¼ lb. firm or extra-firm tofu (not silken)

1 teaspoon tamari, shoyu, or soy sauce

½ teaspoon toasted (dark) sesame oil

1 teaspoon nutritional yeast powder

Vitalizing Veggies:
2 tablespoons liquid broth, vegetable or "Vegetarian 'Chicken' Broth" (page 194)

1 teaspoon tamari, shoyu, or soy sauce

½ cup sliced shiitake mushroom caps

1 cup chopped broccoli

½ cup EACH: chopped red cabbage AND chopped (or julienne cut) carrots

Optional Boom-Boom:
2 teaspoons toasted sesame seeds (see page 42)

Hot chili-garlic sauce (available in the Asian section of most supermarkets)

1. If you have not yet made the sauce, you'd better get on that. Please see page 124.
2. Next, we cook the rice. Place the rice and water in a small covered pot and bring to a boil over medium-high heat. Reduce the heat to low and simmer (covered the entire time) until all of the water is absorbed. Do not stir the rice until it is done. Obviously, if you have a rice cooker, you can simply place the rice and water into that instead and hit the "on" button.
3. Cut the tofu into slabs that are about ½-inch thick. Press the tofu between paper towels according to the instructions on page 42. Preheat the oven to 400° F.
4. Cut the tofu into ¾-inch cubes and place them in a small bowl. Pour the 1 teaspoon of tamari and the sesame oil over the tofu cubes and toss gently to coat. Spread the tofu out in a single layer on a lightly oiled baking sheet. Place in the oven and cook for about 10 minutes. Turn the tofu over and bake for another 10 minutes or so, until nicely browned. Toss the tofu cubes with the nutritional yeast and set aside.
5. In a medium skillet, heat the broth and 1 teaspoon of tamari over medium-high heat. Add the shiitakes and broccoli and sauté, stirring often, for about 5 minutes (or until the broccoli is crisp-tender). Toss in the red cabbage and carrots and cook for another minute, stirring often.
6. *To serve*: Top the cooked rice with the tofu and veggies. Drizzle with the desired amount of teriyaki sauce. If you like, sprinkle some sesame seeds over the top and serve with a little (or a lot, sister) of the hot chili-garlic sauce.

Serves 2; GF/Green

Illegal Pizza

Although you may not end up on "Cops," this pizza would be borderline legal in the eyes of many Italians. Why did I buck the system and include this, then? Well, it's one of those recipes that is insanely easy, very low in fat and calories, and still quite tasty. I also like the feeling of eating pizza, but without all of pizza's usual calories and fat. I regularly look to this recipe when I need something quick and light.

ONE 8-INCH SPROUTED OR WHOLE GRAIN FLOUR TORTILLA (OR A GLUTEN-FREE TORTILLA)

½ CUP (OR MORE, TO TASTE) "RICH TOMATO SAUCE" (PAGE 118) OR BOTTLED VEGAN PIZZA SAUCE

TO TASTE: GRATED SOY CHEESE

VEG OUT: THINLY SLICED ONION, THINLY SLICED GARLIC, SLICED SHIITAKE MUSHROOM CAPS, FRESH BASIL, BABY SPINACH, AND KALAMATA OLIVES)

1. Preheat the oven to 400° F. Top the tortilla evenly with the sauce, then add the soy cheese. Distribute the vegetables over the top. Place the so-called pizza directly on the middle baking rack in the oven.
2. Bake until the soy cheese is lightly browned (and the tortilla is lightly browned and crisp), about 5-10 minutes. Cut into wedges and serve immediately. Lay low for a while.

SERVES 1; 30 MINUTES OR UNDER! GF (WITH SUBSTITUTION)/GREEN

Lowfat Basil-Garlic Linguine

This is a dish I used to make almost every week for my weight loss clients. They said it perfectly fulfilled their pasta craving, yet without the extra calories. As the sauce is not cooked, this dish is also extremely quick, fresh, and nourishing!

8 OZ. LINGUINE (OR GLUTEN-FREE PASTA IF YOU ARE GLUTEN INTOLERANT)

SAUCE:

1 TABLESPOON EACH: REGULAR OR EXTRA-VIRGIN OLIVE OIL AND BALSAMIC VINEGAR

15 OZ. CAN CRUSHED TOMATOES, LIGHTLY DRAINED

4-5 MEDIUM CLOVES GARLIC, PRESSED OR MINCED

2 TEASPOONS DRIED OREGANO

¼ CUP (PACKED) FRESH BASIL, CUT INTO THIN RIBBONS

1 TEASPOON SEA SALT

FRESHLY GROUND PEPPER TO TASTE (I USE ABOUT ½ TEASPOON)

1. Begin cooking the linguine according to the directions on the package.
2. While the noodles are cooking, you can place the ingredients for the sauce in a large bowl. You can… and you will.
3. When the linguine is al dente, drain it and toss it with the sauce. Serve immediately. All right!

SERVES 4; 30 MINUTES OR UNDER! GF (WITH SUBSTITUTION)/SF/BLUE

Light Night Asparagus-Bean Curry

As the name implies, this dish is perfect for when you want something filling, quick, and low in fat.
It's very unusual, rather spicy, and quite tasty. I use black-eyed peas as the beans in this dish,
but I have left it open because just about any legume will work here.
If you pay them enough and offer them benefits, that is.

2 TEASPOONS FRESH LEMON JUICE

¾ - 1 TEASPOON THAI RED CURRY PASTE (THAI KITCHEN MAKES A GOOD VERSION)

1 TEASPOON OIL (COCONUT, NON-VIRGIN OLIVE, SESAME, SUNFLOWER, OR SAFFLOWER)

½ TEASPOON EACH: BLACK (DARK BROWN) MUSTARD SEEDS *AND* CUMIN SEEDS

½ TEASPOON EACH: CUMIN POWDER *AND* CORIANDER POWDER

½ CUP (ROUNDED) CHOPPED ASPARAGUS

2 LARGE CLOVES GARLIC, MINCED OR PRESSED

1 CUP (ABOUT HALF OF A 15 OZ. CAN) CHOPPED TOMATOES (WITH JUICE)

1½ CUPS COOKED BEANS (OR ONE 15 OZ. CAN), DRAINED AND RINSED

½ TEASPOON SEA SALT (OR LESS IF YOU PREFER)

1. In a small bowl, mix the lemon juice and curry paste until the consistency is smooth and no lumps
remain. If necessary, you can stir in some juice from the tomatoes if you need a little more liquid. Set
aside.

2. In a medium skillet, heat the oil over medium-high heat. Add the mustard and cumin seeds and cook
them, stirring, *just* until they begin to pop. This should take about a minute or less. Stir in the cumin and
coriander powders and sauté for another minute (or less).

3. Add the asparagus, garlic, tomatoes, and beans. Cook, stirring often, until the asparagus is bright green
and crisp-tender. Stir in the lemon-curry paste mixture and combine well.

4. Sprinkle in the salt. Stir well to combine and serve immediately.

SERVES 2; 30 MINUTES OR UNDER! GF/SF/GREEN

Vitality Noodles

As the name implies, you may feel like running a marathon after eating this dish! The abundance of fresh ginger and garlic are part of the magic, as they are renowned immune boosters and detoxifying agents. The fresh lime juice and veggies also add to the vitamin party. Because this is so low in fat, it also feels very "clean."

2 "NESTS" BEAN THREAD NOODLES (ABOUT 3½ OZ. TOTAL); SEE PAGE 251

VITAMIN PARTY:

3 TABLESPOONS *FRESH* LIME JUICE

1 TEASPOON TOASTED (DARK) SESAME OIL

2½ TABLESPOONS TAMARI, SHOYU, OR SOY SAUCE

3 MEDIUM-LARGE CLOVES GARLIC, MINCED OR PRESSED

1½ TABLESPOONS GRATED FRESH GINGER

¼ CUP MINCED CILANTRO

ONE SCALLION (GREEN ONION), TRIMMED AND DICED (ABOUT 2 TABLESPOONS)

ONE SMALL CARROT, JULIENNE CUT OR DICED (ABOUT 2 TABLESPOONS)

¼ CUP DICED CUCUMBER (PEELED IF NON-ORGANIC)

GARNISH:

2 TABLESPOONS TOASTED SESAME SEEDS (SEE PAGE 42)

1. Cover the bean thread noodles with boiling water and let them sit for about 15 minutes (or until they've learned their lesson).
2. While the noodles are soaking, place all of the other ingredients (except for the sesame seeds) in a medium sized bowl.
3. When the noodles are soft, drain them well. Cut the noodles a few times with a sharp knife (or kitchen scissors), as this will help them to mix into the toppings more evenly.
4. Place the noodles into the party that's happening in the medium sized bowl. Combine thoroughly with a large spoon. Serve this dish cold or at room temperature, topped with the toasted sesame seeds. Do not heat this dish at any point, however, as it may ruin the freshness mojo.

SERVES 2-4; 30 MINUTES OR UNDER! GF/GREEN

This dish is a favorite food of herbalist Jennie Blechman. I have traded many a batch of this for some of her wonderful tinctures and products. Thanks, Jennie, for letting me know how much you love this. Otherwise I might not have included this recipe!

Vegetable Pancakes with Lemon-Lime Soy Sauce

If you are in the habit of keeping the "Magical Multigrain Mix" on hand, this dish will come together in no time. It's easy to prepare, quite light, and very nourishing! These Asian pancakes pair very nicely with a salad for a quick, healthy meal.

LEMON-LIME SOY SAUCE:

1 TEASPOON EACH: FRESH LIME JUICE *AND* FRESH LEMON JUICE

1 TABLESPOON TAMARI, SHOYU, OR SOY SAUCE

VEGGIE PANCAKES:

½ CUP OF THE "MAGICAL MULTIGRAIN MIX" (PLEASE SEE RECIPE ON PAGE 57)

⅛ TEASPOON EACH: DRIED TURMERIC *AND* SEA SALT

1 TEASPOON DRIED ONION GRANULES

½ CUP PLUS 1 TABLESPOON NONDAIRY MILK, PLAIN AND UNSWEETENED

1 LARGE CLOVE GARLIC, MINCED OR PRESSED

1 ½ TEASPOONS TOASTED (DARK) SESAME OIL

2 TABLESPOONS EACH: MINCED SCALLION *AND* GRATED CARROT

3 TABLESPOONS FINELY CHOPPED SHIITAKE MUSHROOM CAPS

OIL FOR FRYING: NON-VIRGIN OLIVE, SESAME, SUNFLOWER, OR COCONUT

1. Mix the lime juice, lemon juice, and tamari together. Set aside.
2. Combine the multigrain mix, turmeric, salt, and onion granules together well. Stir in the milk, garlic, and sesame oil until thoroughly combined. Make sure to stir well enough so that there are no stray bits of dry batter. Give the stray bits a home.
3. Finally, stir in the scallion, carrot, and shiitakes until well mixed.
4. Set a large skillet over medium-high heat and spray or lightly coat with oil. Make sure the pan is very hot before adding the mixture. Next, pour the mixture onto the hot pan in small amounts to form several pancakes that are around 3-inches or so in diameter. Making these relatively small will make it easier to keep them in one piece.
5. When the undersides are golden brown, flip them over and cook the other side. When both sides are browned, remove to a plate. Continue to cook in this manner, spraying or coating the pan lightly with oil in between batches until all of the batter is used up.
6. *To serve*: Drizzle a bit of the sauce on top of the pancakes or use it as a dip. However, start with a *small* amount as a little of the sauce goes a long way! You will likely have some of the sauce left over, but it will store for several weeks or so in the fridge.

SERVES 1-2; 30 MINUTES OR UNDER! GF (WITH SUBSTITUTIONS)/GREEN

Fat-Free Red Lentils & Spinach with Tamarind

The essence of simplicity, good health, and great flavor come together in this light dish. Keep in mind, though, that this was not invented as a show-stopper—it's humble in appearance and subtle in taste. However, I do tend to make a staple of this dish, as it satisfies my tummy and taste buds like few other dishes that are so low in fat and high in nutrients. The high fiber and iron content of the lentils, paired with the nutrient dense spinach and tamarind make this one feel good affair! Plus, this is incredibly easy to toss together if you make a habit of keeping the tamarind chutney in your fridge.

⅓ CUP OF THE "TAMARIND-DATE CHUTNEY" (PLEASE SEE RECIPE ON PAGE 126)

½ CUP DRY RED LENTILS
1 ½ CUPS WATER
1 TEASPOON CUMIN SEEDS

½ CUP (PACKED) FRESH BABY SPINACH LEAVES
¼ TEASPOON SEA SALT (OR TO TASTE)
⅛ TEASPOON GROUND CORIANDER (OPTIONAL)

1. If you don't have any of the chutney on hand, you will need to begin this now. No dilly-dallying. Please see page 126 for instructions.
2. Place the lentils, water, and cumin seeds in a covered pot (or pressure cooker) and bring to a boil over medium-high heat. Reduce the heat to very low and simmer gently until the lentils are soft. In a regular pot, this will take about 25-35 minutes. In a pressure cooker, this will take about 15 minutes.
3. When the lentils are softened, turn off the burner and stir in the spinach leaves. No need to "cook" the spinach, though. Simply put the lid back on and allow the spinach to wilt. If necessary, stir a few more times until the leaves are wilted to your satisfaction.
4. Stir in the chutney, salt, and coriander (if using) and serve immediately.

SERVES 2
GF/SF/GREEN

This dish, humble as it may seem, has *versatility*! Wrap it in phyllo and bake it for an elegant presentation (especially if served drizzled with additional chutney). This can also be served over basmati rice along with a green salad, some warm bread, and the Indian Phyllo "Samosas" (page 86) for a casually elegant, nourishing meal. Can you feel the love?

Thai Drunken Noodles

This very saucy noodle dish was named (long ago and not by me) for its ability to be a hangover helper. I've tasted many different takes on this, but my favorite was in a small Thai restaurant in Virginia. I have tried to recreate the same fresh flavor here. With the heat of the chili peppers, the tang of the lime, and the nourishment of the garlic, ginger, turmeric, and shiitake mushrooms, this dish will pick you up anytime of day!

GOOD SHIIT SAUCE:

½ OZ. DRIED SHIITAKE MUSHROOMS (ABOUT ¾ CUP)

3 TABLESPOONS TAMARI, SHOYU, OR SOY SAUCE

1 ¼ CUPS WATER (PLUS AN ADDITIONAL ½ CUP)

½ CUP EACH: CHOPPED ONION AND THINLY SLICED SHIITAKE MUSHROOM CAPS

5 LARGE CLOVES GARLIC, PEELED

1 TABLESPOON CHOPPED FRESH GINGER

2 TABLESPOONS EACH: TOASTED (DARK) SESAME OIL AND ALL-PURPOSE OIL (SUNFLOWER, NON-VIRGIN OLIVE, OR COCONUT)

¼ CUP PLUS 1 TABLESPOON FRESH LIME JUICE

1 TABLESPOON EACH: PACKED BROWN SUGAR AND PURE MAPLE SYRUP

1 TEASPOON DRIED ONION GRANULES

⅛ -¼ TEASPOON GROUND CAYENNE POWDER (TO TASTE)

⅛ TEASPOON SEA SALT

NOODLES-N-MORE:

½ LB. FLAT, STRAIGHT RICE NOODLES (LIKE THE KIND TYPICALLY USED FOR PAD THAI)

1 LB. EXTRA-FIRM TOFU (NOT SILKEN)

2 TABLESPOONS EACH: OIL (SUNFLOWER, NON-VIRGIN OLIVE, OR COCONUT) AND TAMARI OR SHOYU

1 TEASPOON GROUND DRIED TURMERIC

4 SCALLIONS (GREEN ONIONS), TRIMMED AND CHOPPED (USE BOTH WHITE AND GREEN PARTS)

1-3 FRESH OR DRIED WHOLE THAI CHILIES (OPTIONAL)

1 TABLESPOON ARROWROOT (OR CORNSTARCH)

½ CUP (PACKED) EACH: CHOPPED FRESH CILANTRO AND FRESH BASIL (DO NOT USE DRIED)

1 FRESH LIME, CUT INTO QUARTERS

1. First, we make the sauce. Place the dried shiitake mushrooms in a small pan along with the 3 tablespoons tamari and 1 cup of the water. Bring to a boil over medium-high heat and then reduce the heat to low. Allow the mixture to simmer, stirring occasionally. Make sure to scrape the mushrooms off the sides of the pan if necessary so that they all cook evenly in the liquid. After about 15 minutes, turn off the heat and set aside.

2. Meanwhile, place the chopped onion and sliced shiitake mushroom caps in a medium skillet along with ¼ cup of the water. Set to medium-high heat and sauté, stirring often, for about 10 minutes, or until the onions are very soft. Set aside.

3. Place the garlic and ginger in a blender. Add the dried shiitake mixture (from step one), the onion-mushroom mixture (from step two) and the 2 tablespoons each of toasted sesame oil and all-purpose oil. Blend very well until smooth.

4. Add the remaining sauce items (lime juice, brown sugar, maple syrup, onion granules, remaining ½ cup water, cayenne, and sea salt) to the blender and puree. Set aside.

5. Place the rice noodles in a large bowl and cover with boiling water. Be sure to use plenty of water so that they don't come up for air while they are still "cooking." When they are al dente (usually in about 15-20 minutes), drain them and set them aside.

6. Slice the tofu into eight slabs. Press the tofu slabs gently yet firmly with paper towels to remove any excess moisture (or see page 43 for tofu pressing tips). Cut the slabs into ¾-inch cubes. In a large skillet or wok, heat the oil, tamari, and turmeric over medium heat. Add the tofu cubes and stir-fry them until they are golden browned. Remove to a plate and set aside.

7. Into the same wok or pan, add the scallions, whole chilies (if using), sauce, and drained noodles. Stir gently yet thoroughly to combine. Increase the heat to high, evenly sprinkle in the arrowroot, and stir until thickened. This shouldn't take too long, as arrowroot thickens quickly once it becomes hot.

8. When the sauce has thickened, toss in the tofu, cilantro, and basil. Stir well and immediately remove from heat. Serve garnished with lime wedges and prepare to be delayed at the intersection of delicious and nutritious.

SERVES 4-6; GF/BLUE

This was once a dish that I thought was only *truly* loved by me. However, when I was in the process of standardizing this recipe, I got brave and tried it out at a local event. Everyone who tasted it said they absolutely adored it, plus it was the first item to sell out! Needless to say, it ended up in the book. For the perfect accompaniment to these noodles, you may wish to try the "Delectable Lowfat 'Egg Rolls'" (page 67) or "Fresh Thai Spring Rolls" (page 72).

Chapter Twelve: Extravagant Entrées

Want to impress your guests with a knockout main dish? Here are just the recipes to do so.
In general, these dishes are a bit more time consuming and/or rich than the "Everyday Entrées,"
but they are well worth it! Each one is tried and true, totally scrumptious,
and sure to make you quite popular if you decide to share.

Soba Noodles *with* Tempura Vegetables *and* Ginger-Daikon Sauce

As with many of my recipes, this dish is much easier to make than it sounds. Plus, it's definitely worth the effort, as it is *insanely* delicious! I have taught several classes on tempura and people are always surprised at how easy it is to make. Even so, I do recommend reading through the directions first, so that you're familiar with all of the steps before you begin. *One final tip*: Although tempura is best served fresh, it also reheats nicely in a 400° F. oven.

GINGER-DAIKON SAUCE:

3 TABLESPOONS <u>EACH</u>: FINELY GRATED FRESH GINGER *AND* PEELED, FINELY GRATED DAIKON

⅓ CUP TAMARI, SHOYU, OR SOY SAUCE

3 TABLESPOONS *FRESH* LIME JUICE

TEMPURA VEGETABLES:

4 CUPS ASSORTED VEGETABLE SPEARS (SUCH AS ZUCCHINI, CARROTS, ASPARAGUS, DAIKON, SCALLIONS, AND SHIITAKE MUSHROOM CAPS)*

SOBA NOODLES:

1 2.8 OZ. PACKAGE BUCKWHEAT SOBA NOODLES (OR GLUTEN-FREE NOODLES)

1 TABLESPOON <u>EACH</u>: TOASTED (DARK) SESAME OIL, TAMARI (OR SHOYU OR SOY SAUCE), *AND* FRESH LIME JUICE

TEMPURA BATTER:

1 CUP FLOUR (WHOLE WHEAT PASTRY, WHITE, OR GLUTEN-FREE ALL-PURPOSE**)

2 TABLESPOONS ARROWROOT (OR CORNSTARCH)

¼ TEASPOON BAKING SODA

½ TEASPOON SEA SALT

1 CUP ICE WATER

FOR FRYING: PEANUT OR COCONUT OIL (ENOUGH TO MAKE A ½-INCH WELL IN THE SKILLET)

GLORIOUS GARNISHES:

3 TABLESPOONS FRESH CHIVES OR SCALLION TOPS, MINCED

WASABI PEAS, OPTIONAL (TO TASTE)

TOASTED SESAME SEEDS (SEE PAGE 42)

1. To prepare the sauce, place the finely grated ginger and daikon in a bowl along with the ⅓ cup of tamari and 3 tablespoons of lime juice. Stir to mix. If it looks *way* too thick, you've done quite well for yourself. Set aside.

2. *Prepare the vegetables by cutting them into spears or julienne strips (see page 41 for julienne tips). If you are using shiitake mushrooms, remove the stems and slice the caps thinly. Basically, you want uniformly sized and shaped veggies that are relatively thin, so that they will cook quickly and evenly. An ideal size would be about ¼-inch thick and 2½ inches long. You should end up with about 4 cups of prepared vegetables.

3. Next, we rock the noodles: Boil according to the package instructions, being careful not to overcook. Al dente is perfect, *especially* with soba noodles. Toss very gently with the one tablespoon each of sesame oil, tamari, and lime juice. Cover and set aside.

4. To mix the tempura batter, combine the flour, arrowroot, baking soda, and salt. Stir well to combine, using a wire whisk or sifter if necessary. Next, add the ice water into the dry mix and stir *just* enough to mix the items together. It is better to have a few lumps than to over-mix.

5. Preheat the oil in a large heavy skillet over medium-high heat. Now, pay extra attention to this next part, as it's very important to have your oil at just the right temperature. When you think the oil is getting hot, test it by dropping a pinch of batter into the oil. If it sizzles immediately, it is too hot. If it sinks and rises rather slowly, it isn't quite hot enough. When it sinks and rises fairly quickly, it is perfect.

6. Are you ready to bust a move? Is your test batter sinking and rising fairly quickly? Then it's show time! Coat your vegetables in the tempura batter and place them one by one into the oil, being careful not to burn your fingers. Be sure to leave enough space so that no more than half of the pan is filled with tempura at any given time. If you place too much tempura in the pan, it can cause the oil to cool down too much and you will end up with the oily goop you often find in restaurants.

7. When the tempura is golden brown on the underside, turn it over with a metal slotted spoon or spatula. When it is golden brown all over, remove and drain on paper towels. Continue to cook in batches until all of your veggies are used up.

8. *To assemble*: Put some of the soba noodles on each plate and top with tempura. Drizzle evenly with the ginger-daikon sauce (clumps and all), and sprinkle with the chives or scallion tops. Scatter the wasabi peas and sesame seeds on top of that, if using. Serve *immediately*! We're not messing around anymore.

Serves 4-6; GF (with substitutions)/Purple

**If using an all-purpose gluten-free flour, please note that you may need to use an *extra* ¼ cup of flour to achieve the proper consistency. Also, don't be tempted to substitute rice flour—trust me.

> ### *Note of Happiness*:
> The ginger and daikon are not just in the sauce to complement the flavor. They are also the perfect nutritional accompaniment. Ginger stimulates digestion, boosts immunity, and is very cleansing. Daikon is traditionally served alongside Japanese foods that are higher in fat as it is so high in digestive enzymes!

Crusted Tempeh with Avocado-Mango Salsa

This is one of my favorite ways to introduce people to tempeh. The crunch of the tempeh's crust paired with the creamy salsa create a dish that is absolutely *divine*! This recipe makes quite a bit of salsa— if you don't wish to serve it all on the tempeh, it also makes a gorgeous dip for blue corn chips. Tempeh is a wonderfully nutritious and immune-boosting food, and is also high in protein, Omega-3 fatty acids, and B-vitamins. The perfect excuse!

SHOCKINGLY SERIOUS SALSA:

1 LARGE RIPE MANGO, PEELED AND DICED

1 RIPE AVOCADO, PEELED AND DICED

2 TABLESPOONS *FRESH* LIME JUICE

1 TABLESPOON MINCED FRESH MINT

½ TEASPOON PLUS ⅛ TEASPOON EACH: DRIED RED CHILI FLAKES *AND* SEA SALT

1 ½ TEASPOONS PURE MAPLE SYRUP

1 ¼ TEASPOONS FRESH LEMON JUICE

3 TABLESPOONS EACH: MINCED WHITE ONION *AND* MINCED FRESH CILANTRO (LIGHTLY PACKED)

GO FOR A DIP:

⅓ CUP NONDAIRY MILK (PLAIN AND UNSWEETENED)

¼ CUP OIL (NON-VIRGIN OLIVE, COCONUT, OR PEANUT)

TEMPEH CUTLETS:

- 8 OZ. PACKAGE OF TEMPEH
- ½ CUP WATER
- 2 TABLESPOONS TAMARI OR SHOYU
- 1 TABLESPOON FRESH LIME JUICE

COATING:

- ¾ CUP WHOLE WHEAT PASTRY FLOUR (OR GLUTEN-FREE FLOUR)
- 2 TABLESPOONS EACH: DRY POLENTA *AND* DRY CORNMEAL
- 1 TEASPOON DRIED OREGANO
- ½ TEASPOON EACH: GROUND BLACK PEPPER *AND* PAPRIKA

¼ TEASPOON SEA SALT

1. Gently toss the salsa ingredients together and set aside—out of immediate danger.
2. Slice the package of tempeh in half (width-wise) and then gently remove the tempeh from its package. Next, slice each half through its center in order to form a total of four rectangular cutlets that are approximately 2½ x 4-inches in size (and ½ inch thick, or half of their original thickness).
3. Place the tempeh cutlets in a single layer in a large skillet. Evenly pour the water, tamari, and the 1 tablespoon of lime juice over the tempeh cutlets. Turn the cutlets over to coat both sides in the liquid. Cook, covered, over medium heat for 5 minutes. Flip the cutlets over and cook for another 5 minutes, or until all of the liquid has been absorbed. Remove from heat and set aside. You have now steamed and marinated your tempeh in one step!
4. Prepare the coating by combining the flour, polenta, cornmeal, oregano, pepper, paprika, and salt in a medium sized bowl. Stir very well and set aside. Place the milk in a small bowl and set it aside as well.
5. Heat the ¼ cup of oil in a large skillet over medium-high heat.
6. Dip your tempeh cutlets in the soymilk, then dip them in the coating. Next, be a double dipper. Place the tempeh back in the milk again, then into the coating a second time. Make sure there is an even, thick layer of coating on all sides of the cutlets.
7. When the oil is hot, place the cutlets in a single layer in the pan. When the undersides are browned, turn the cutlets over and brown the other side. Remove with a heat proof spatula and drain on paper towels. If necessary, repeat with the remaining tempeh until you are finished.
8. Remove the tempeh to plates and top each cutlet evenly with the salsa. Serve immediately. If you do have some salsa left over, it will keep in an airtight container, refrigerated, for a day or two. As *if*.

SERVES 2; GF (WITH SUBSTITUTION)/BLUE

Saag "Paneer"

This popular Indian entrée is delicious, easy to make, and loaded with iron, calcium, and antioxidants. Since tofu stands in for the traditional paneer (cheese), it is also cholesterol-free!

OPTIONAL:

1 CUP DRY BROWN BASMATI RICE

2 CUPS WATER

TOFOOLED YOU PANEER:

4 OZ. EXTRA-FIRM TOFU, CUT INTO ½-INCH CUBES (YOU SHOULD HAVE ¾ CUP OF TOFU CUBES)

2 TEASPOONS FRESH LEMON JUICE

1 TEASPOON OIL (COCONUT, NON-VIRGIN OLIVE, SUNFLOWER, OR SAFFLOWER)

SAAGNESS:

2 TEASPOONS OIL (COCONUT, NON-VIRGIN OLIVE, SUNFLOWER, OR SAFFLOWER)

1 TEASPOON EACH: CUMIN SEEDS AND BLACK MUSTARD SEEDS

⅛ TEASPOON DRIED TURMERIC

½ TEASPOON ASAFETIDA (SEE PAGE 251 FOR INFORMATION)

¾ TEASPOON DRIED DILL

2 TEASPOONS EACH: CORIANDER POWDER AND CUMIN POWDER

⅛ -¼ TEASPOON CAYENNE POWDER (OPTIONAL)

1 CUP FINELY DICED ONION, YELLOW OR WHITE

4 TABLESPOONS NON-HYDROGENATED MARGARINE

1 CUP NONDAIRY MILK (PLAIN AND UNSWEETENED)

5 LARGE CLOVES GARLIC, MINCED OR PRESSED

1 TEASPOON GRATED FRESH GINGER

ONE 10 OZ. PACKAGE OF FROZEN SPINACH

FINAL ADDITIONS:

• 1 ¼ TEASPOONS SEA SALT (OR LESS)

• 2 TABLESPOONS FRESH LEMON JUICE

• ½ CUP CILANTRO, MINCED

1. Are you going to be making rice on this fine day? If so, you'll want to start that first. Simply bring the rice and water to a boil in a covered pot and simmer on low until all of the liquid has been absorbed.

2. Next, take the spinach out of the freezer so that it can start to thaw. In a small bowl, gently toss the tofu cubes with the lemon juice and allow to sit for a few minutes. While the tofu is marinating, get all of the spices and remaining ingredients together. Once you begin cooking this dish, you'll need to move quickly.

3. Place the 1 teaspoon of oil in a large skillet set to medium-high heat. Add the tofu and cook, turning often, for about 5 minutes or until it is golden on all sides. Remove the tofu and set it aside.

4. In the same skillet, heat the 2 teaspoons of oil over medium heat and add the cumin and mustard seeds. They will begin to pop in under a minute, so be ready to add your spices as soon as they do.

5. Next, the spices (turmeric, asafetida, dill, coriander, cumin powder, and cayenne) join the party. Stir them in well and allow them to cook for a minute or so, until very aromatic.

6. Add the onion to the skillet and stir well to combine with the seasonings. Cook over medium-low heat, stirring often, for about 5-10 minutes (or until the onion becomes soft). During this time, you may add in a little of the margarine if the pan gets too dry. Add the remaining margarine to the skillet along with the milk, garlic, ginger, and spinach. Cook over medium-low heat for about 10 minutes, stirring occasionally. It should remain at a gentle simmer.

7. Next, it's baby time. Place the spinach mixture along with the salt, lemon juice, and cilantro in a blender or food processor. Blend until relatively smooth and then place back in the pan.

8. Add the tofu cubes back into the pan and combine with the spinach mixture. Stir well and allow to cook for 2-3 minutes, or until warmed through. Serve plain, with the basmati rice, or with some good bread.

SERVES 2-4; 30 MINUTES OR UNDER! GF/Blue

Mexican Polenta Bake

This dish is a serious crowd pleaser! It's also *very* easy to make—I promise. Simply prepare the polenta the night before (or morning of) and you can throw this together in no time. Invariably, people will request the recipe for this very flavorful and satisfying dish.

POLENTA:

1 CUP DRY POLENTA MEAL

3 CUPS WATER

3 TABLESPOONS NUTRITIONAL YEAST POWDER

¾ TEASPOON SEA SALT

2 TABLESPOONS NON-HYDROGENATED MARGARINE

LAYERS OF LOVE:

2 CANS (15 OZ. EACH) OF BLACK OR PINTO BEANS, DRAINED AND RINSED (3 CUPS COOKED BEANS)

1¾ CUPS FINELY CHOPPED YELLOW OR WHITE ONION

2 CUPS (LIGHTLY PACKED) BABY SPINACH

12 OZ. JAR OF GREEN TOMATILLO SAUCE

12 CORN TORTILLAS

2 CANS (14 OZ. EACH) OF VEGAN ENCHILADA SAUCE (MSG-FREE)

JUICE OF 1 LIME

2 CUPS GRATED SOY CHEESE (6 OZ.)

3 SMALL-MEDIUM TOMATILLOS, THINLY SLICED (PAPER-LIKE SKINS REMOVED)

¾ CUP CHOPPED KALAMATA OLIVES (PITTED OF COURSE!)

GARNISH:

3 SCALLIONS (GREEN ONIONS), CHOPPED <u>AND</u> ½ CUP CHOPPED CILANTRO

1. Place the polenta and water in a medium pot set to medium-high heat. Allow it to cook, whisking it continually, until it begins to thicken. Once it begins to thicken a bit, turn it down to the lowest heat possible and continue to cook, whisking constantly, until it is very thick (usually about 5-10 more minutes). Stir in the nutritional yeast, salt, and margarine until well combined. Press into a large, lightly oiled oven proof pan (the kind you would use for lasagna, one that is *at least* 9.5 x 13.5-inches in size). Make the layer of polenta as compressed and flat as possible, using the palms of your hands. Cover and allow to chill in the fridge for several hours or overnight (until very firm).
2. Now the fun starts. Preheat your oven to 400° F. Remove the polenta from the fridge and evenly scatter half of the beans and onions over the top of it. Place all of the spinach on top of the beans and onions. Pour all of the tomatillo sauce on top of the spinach.
3. Next, place six of the tortillas in a (relatively) single layer on top of the spinach and sauce. Cover the tortillas evenly with the remaining beans and onions. Pour one can of enchilada sauce evenly on top of that. Sprinkle the sauce with the juice of ½ lime.
4. For the next layer, do that tortilla thang again with the remaining six tortillas. Get yo funky bad self to pour the other can of sauce onto the tortillas and place the soy cheese evenly on top of that. Can you dig it? Place the tomatillos evenly on top of the cheese and scatter the kalamata olives on top of that. Sprinkle with the juice of ½ lime.
5. Lightly cover the pan and place it in the oven. Bake for about 30 minutes, then uncover and bake until it is golden browned and bubbly. Serve immediately. This will keep for about a week in the refrigerator and it also freezes well. Enjoy your funky, fabulous, freaky feast!

SERVES ABOUT 12 (ONE LARGE PAN); GF/BLUE

Aloo Gobi Chole

I *had* to create this dish. Indian food was my favorite cuisine and I'd moved to an area with no Indian restaurant within 300 miles! I used to tell myself I could cook any cuisine properly except Indian. I found out what I had previously been doing wrong (aside from having a defeatist attitude). I'd been making Indian food too low in fat, sodium, and calories! As such, it is not something I eat every day, but it's fully delectable as an occasional dinner. This recipe is an example of a basic Indian curry formula: First, the seeds are popped in the oil. Next come the spices, which get sautéed to bring out their flavors. The reason I add the lemon juice and garlic last is because they retain more of their nutritional value in their uncooked state. One final note: I've found that people really vary on their preferences for the thickness of this curry. If you prefer a very thick curry, increase the amount of chopped potatoes. If you prefer a thinner curry, you may add in a little more coconut milk or water.

OPTIONAL:

"TAMARIND-DATE CHUTNEY" (PAGE 126)

"SEASONED INDIAN BASMATI RICE" (PAGE 102)

OIL AND SEEDS:

2 TABLESPOONS OIL (SUNFLOWER, COCONUT, NON-VIRGIN OLIVE, OR SAFFLOWER)

1 TABLESPOON EACH: BLACK MUSTARD SEEDS, CUMIN SEEDS, *AND* SESAME SEEDS (OR 3 TABLESPOONS OF THE INDIAN SEED BLEND FROM PAGE 195)

SECRET SPICES:

(YOU CAN SUBSTITUTE 3 TABLESPOONS PLUS ½ TEASPOON OF THE INDIAN SPICE BLEND FROM PAGE 195 FOR THE FOLLOWING SPICES)

¾ TEASPOON EACH: ASAFETIDA POWDER, RED CHILI FLAKES, *AND* DRIED TURMERIC

1 TABLESPOON EACH: CUMIN POWDER *AND* CORIANDER POWDER

¼ TEASPOON FENUGREEK, OPTIONAL

1 TEASPOON AMCHUR POWDER (SEE PAGE 251 FOR INFORMATION)

NEXT:

1 ¼ CUPS DICED ONION

1 ½ CUPS (OR ONE 15 OZ. CAN) COOKED GARBANZO BEANS, DRAINED AND RINSED

14 OZ. CAN COCONUT MILK

14.5 OZ. CAN DICED TOMATOES (WITH LIQUID)

1 ¼ CUPS DICED POTATO (CUT INTO ½-INCH CUBES)

LAST ADDITIONS:

1 CUP CAULIFLOWER FLORETS

3 TABLESPOONS FRESH LEMON JUICE

5 LARGE CLOVES GARLIC, PRESSED OR MINCED

2 TEASPOONS SEA SALT

½ - 1 CUP CHOPPED CILANTRO (OPTIONAL FOR GARNISH)

1. If you will be using the chutney or rice with this dish, you may wish to start them first. Also, if you like, you can pre-measure the spices into a small dry bowl and set them aside. Next, place a large pot or wok over medium heat and add the oil. Add the seeds and cook, stirring, *just* until they begin to pop. Add the spices and cook, stirring, for another minute.

2. Toss in the diced onion and cook, stirring, until it becomes soft and translucent. At this point, it helps to add a little of the coconut milk so that the mixture does not become too dry.

3. Add the beans, remaining coconut milk, tomatoes, and potatoes. Stir well and bring to a boil, then reduce the heat to medium-low so that the mixture simmers. While this is cooking, you will want to stir it every 4-5 minutes. When you do so, be sure to scrape up any mixture that has started sticking to the bottom of the pan. Otherwise, it can burn and cook unevenly.

4. Allow the mixture to cook until the potatoes are almost tender, then add in the cauliflower. Continue to cook until all of the veggies are tender and the sauce has thickened. If you prefer a thicker sauce, you can turn the heat up and cook (stirring often) for several minutes, until the liquids cook off a bit. If you prefer a thinner sauce, you can add a touch more coconut milk (or some water). Stir the lemon juice, garlic, and sea salt into the curry until well combined. Serve the rice alongside (or underneath) the curry and top each plate with the cilantro. Oooh baby!

SERVES 6-8; GF/SF/PURPLE

Sesame Tofu with Fresh Basil and Thai Sweet Chili Sauce

Here is a dish that is very easy to make, yet completely delicious and impressive! If you use both black and brown sesame seeds, it will look beautiful as well. You can serve this plain or alongside some rice or Asian noodles. This is also a hit with kids. The last time I served this to a group of children, I was asked: "How do you spell *good dinner?*"

I LB. TOFU, EXTRA-FIRM (NOT SILKEN)

½ CUP OF THE "THAI SWEET CHILI SAUCE" (PAGE 118)

FLAVOR THAT TOFU:

I TEASPOON DRIED GARLIC GRANULES

2 TABLESPOONS GRATED FRESH GINGER

2 TABLESPOONS PLUS 2 TEASPOONS TAMARI, SHOYU, OR SOY SAUCE

2 TABLESPOONS "VEGETARIAN 'CHICKEN' BROTH" (PAGE 194) OR OTHER LIQUID VEGAN BROTH

CRISPY COATING:

¾ CUP SESAME SEEDS (PREFERABLY A MIXTURE OF BLACK AND BROWN SESAME SEEDS)

I TABLESPOON DRY CORNMEAL

2 TABLESPOONS RICE FLOUR (OR WHOLE WHEAT PASTRY FLOUR)

PAN-FRYING: 3-4 TABLESPOONS OIL (SUNFLOWER, NON-VIRGIN OLIVE, OR COCONUT)

GARNISH: 4 TEASPOONS FRESH BASIL, MINCED OR CUT INTO THIN RIBBONS

1. Cut the tofu into eight slabs. Press the tofu between paper towels to remove excess moisture for at least 30 minutes (see page 43 for tips).

2. While the tofu is pressing, make the chili sauce. Set it aside.

3. Flavor that tofu! Remove the tofu from the paper towels and cut it into triangles that are about two inches in size. Place the pieces in a single layer on a plate. Combine the garlic, ginger, and tamari. Pour this mixture over the tofu, turning the pieces to coat all sides with the marinade. When most of the liquid has been absorbed, pour the broth over the tofu to moisten it. This will help bind the coating to the tofu.

4. Place the seeds, cornmeal, and flour in a large plastic bag and shake well to combine.

5. In a large skillet or wok, heat the oil over medium-high heat.

6. Place several of the tofu triangles in the bag and gently shake to thoroughly coat the tofu with the breading. When the oil in the pan becomes hot, add the tofu in a single layer.

7. When the tofu pieces are golden brown and crisp on the bottom, turn them over. When both sides are

golden and crisped, remove and allow them to drain on paper towels.

8. Repeat steps 6 and 7 until all of the tofu has been used up.

9. Distribute the tofu onto four plates. Shake or stir the chili sauce and drizzle it evenly over the tofu. Top each portion with one teaspoon of the fresh basil and serve immediately. One final note: Once you begin eating this dish, you may inadvertently begin cursing loudly to yourself due to the excessive yumminess present on your plate. Don't be alarmed—this is a standard reaction and will subside when you're done.

SERVES 4; GF/PURPLE

Thai Emerald Noodles

This dish is visually beautiful, bursting with flavor, and very easy to prepare. If you prefer a thinner, more traditional sauce, you can omit the arrowroot. I like to use it, however, because it ensures that every last morsel is coated with the deliciousness!

ONE FULL RECIPE OF THE "THAI GREEN CURRY SAUCE" (PAGE 127)

6.75 OZ. PACKAGE RICE NOODLES

1 CUP FROZEN BROCCOLI FLORETS

½ CUP FROZEN EDAMAME OR CORN KERNELS

2 CUPS (LIGHTLY PACKED) BABY SPINACH

OPTIONAL: 2 TABLESPOONS BLACK SESAME SEEDS, PREFERABLY TOASTED (PAGE 42)

GARNISHES:

¼ CUP CHOPPED FRESH CILANTRO

¼ CUP CHOPPED DRY-ROASTED, UNSALTED PEANUTS (SEE PAGE 41)

2 SCALLIONS (GREEN ONIONS), THINLY SLICED

OPTIONAL GARNISH: ADDITIONAL FRESH BASIL OR THAI BASIL, CUT INTO THIN RIBBONS

1. Prepare the sauce and set it aside.

2. Bring a large pot of water to a rolling boil. Turn off the heat and add the rice noodles, broccoli, and edamame or corn. Cover tightly and allow it to sit for about 10 minutes, or until the noodles are tender. Drain the mixture well in a strainer and set it aside. When fully drained, add it back to the pot.

3. Stir the spinach, sesame seeds, and green curry sauce into the noodle pot. Cook (uncovered) over medium-high heat, stirring gently, *just* until the spinach wilts and the sauce becomes thickened. This should only take about 2-3 minutes.

4. Serve sprinkled with the garnishes. If desired, turn your phone off and pull down the blinds. You may want to be alone with this bad boy.

SERVES 5-6; 30 MINUTES OR UNDER! GF (WITH RICE NOODLES)/SF/PURPLE

> I've used one of my favorite shortcuts here by tossing frozen veggies into the hot water. I used to resist using frozen vegetables before I learned that in some ways they rival fresh. They are usually picked at the peak of their freshness and immediately frozen, while fresh vegetables are often not in season and shipped for long distances. Of course, fresh is *usually* ideal. However, frozen is a very close second, especially because the convenience factor can make it easier to eat more veggies, period!

Simple & Spicy Thai Red Curry Vegetables over Jasmine Rice

This dish is truly delicious, fairly spicy, and quite simple to prepare. For a totally elegant yet easy dinner to serve guests, try this paired with the "Thai Spinach Nests" (page 81) and the "Apple Puffs with Vanilla Bean Caramel Sauce" (page 231).

JASMINE RICE:

1 CUP DRY JASMINE RICE

2 CUPS WATER

RED CURRY VEGETABLES:

ONE MEDIUM ONION, THINLY SLICED

2 TEASPOONS TOASTED (DARK) SESAME OIL

1 TEASPOON THAI RED CURRY PASTE (THAI KITCHEN IS A GOOD BRAND)

1 CUP COCONUT MILK

2 CUPS CHOPPED BROCCOLI (CUT INTO BITE SIZED PIECES)

1 CUP THINLY SLICED SHIITAKE MUSHROOM CAPS

ONE MEDIUM CARROT, JULIENNE SLICED OR FINELY CHOPPED

1 TABLESPOON ORGANIC SUGAR OR SUCANAT

2 TEASPOONS FRESH LEMON JUICE

2 LARGE CLOVES GARLIC, MINCED OR PRESSED

½ TEASPOON SEA SALT

OPTIONAL: 1 TEASPOON ARROWROOT (OR CORNSTARCH)

GARNISHES:

2 TEASPOONS TOASTED SESAME SEEDS (SEE PAGE 42)

2 TABLESPOONS EACH: CHOPPED FRESH CILANTRO AND CRUSHED, DRY-ROASTED PEANUTS (SEE PAGE 41)

1. Place the rice and water in a covered pot and bring to a boil over high heat. Reduce the heat to low and simmer until all of the water is absorbed. While the rice is cooking, you can skip to step two.

2. In a wok or large skillet, sauté the onion in the sesame oil over medium-high heat for about 5 minutes, or until the onion becomes soft and begins to brown.

3. Add the red curry paste to the wok along with a tablespoon or two of the coconut milk. Whisk or stir the curry paste and coconut milk together until smooth and no lumps remain. Add the remaining coconut milk and stir very well to combine.

4. Add the broccoli and shiitakes and cook, stirring often, for about 5 minutes.

5. Add the carrot, sugar, lemon juice, garlic, and sea salt. Cook, stirring often, until the broccoli and carrots are crisp-tender. If the sauce needs thickening, sprinkle the arrowroot on top of the curry and *immediately* mix it in to prevent lumping. Continue to stir over medium heat until the sauce is just thickened, about 2 minutes or so.

6. Serve on top of the jasmine rice, topped with the garnishes. Get curried away.

SERVES 2-3; 30 MINUTES OR UNDER! GF/SF/PURPLE

Tomato, Basil, and Roasted Pine Nut Penne

Know any people with bad attitudes about vegan food? This dish will *totally* mess with their heads. Put some "Green Bread" (page 69), "Spinach Strawberry Salad" (page 104), and "Chocolate Bliss Pie" (page 232) on the table as well and you may even score yourself some stalkers. Also, because this sauce isn't cooked, you can throw this entrée together in about twenty minutes!

16 OZ. PENNE PASTA (OR GLUTEN-FREE PASTA IF YOU ARE GLUTEN INTOLERANT)

2½ CUPS GRAPE OR CHERRY TOMATOES

½ CUP KALAMATA OLIVES, PITTED AND CHOPPED (OR OTHER HIGH QUALITY GREEK OLIVES)

5 LARGE CLOVES GARLIC, PRESSED OR MINCED

¼ CUP OLIVE OIL (REGULAR OR EXTRA-VIRGIN)

2 TABLESPOONS *FRESH* LEMON JUICE

1 TABLESPOON BALSAMIC VINEGAR

2 TEASPOONS SEA SALT (OR LESS IF YOU PREFER)

LOTS OF FRESHLY GROUND BLACK PEPPER (TO TASTE)

¼ CUP PINE NUTS

½ CUP (PACKED) *FRESH* BASIL, CUT INTO THIN RIBBONS OR CHOPPED

1. Cook the pasta according to the directions on its former home.
2. While the penne is cooking, you can toss the sauce together. First, wash the tomatoes and cut them in half. Place them in the largest bowl you have. No bowl is too big.
3. Add the chopped kalamatas, garlic, oil, lemon juice, balsamic vinegar, salt, and pepper to the giant bowl. Gently toss well to combine.
4. Toast the pine nuts in a dry pan over medium-low heat until they are aromatic and lightly browned, shaking the pan often so that they cook evenly. Watch them closely, as this process will take well under 5 minutes. As soon as they are done, remove them from heat and set aside.
5. When the pasta is al dente, drain it well in a colander or strainer. Add it to the big bowl and toss it with the sauce. Mix well to combine. Add the pine nuts and basil. Toss lightly and serve immediately. Gloat.

SERVES 6-8

30 MINUTES OR UNDER! GF (WITH SUBSTITUTION)/SF/PURPLE

Lemon Asparagus Linguine

I once served this to a friend who said he hated asparagus. I'm not sure why he tried this dish, but he couldn't stop saying: "This is so good! I can't believe this is asparagus!" over and over. I still laugh, remembering the astounded look on his face. Needless to say, this dish has it all. It's delectable, nutritious, quick, and impressive! If that's the kind of situation you like to get yourself into.

1 LB. LINGUINE*

2 SLICES BREAD (I USE EZEKIEL 4:9 BREAD)*

1 TABLESPOON EXTRA-VIRGIN OLIVE OIL

½ TABLESPOON DRIED ONION GRANULES

3 CUPS CHOPPED ASPARAGUS (TRIMMED AND CHOPPED INTO 1½-INCH PIECES)

¼ CUP "VEGETARIAN 'CHICKEN' BROTH" (PAGE 194) OR OTHER LIQUID VEGAN BROTH

¼ CUP PLUS 2 TABLESPOONS *FRESH* LEMON JUICE

¼ CUP <u>EACH</u>: EXTRA-VIRGIN OLIVE OIL, NON-VIRGIN OLIVE OIL, *AND* ADDITIONAL VEGAN BROTH

8 MEDIUM-LARGE CLOVES GARLIC, MINCED OR PRESSED

2 TEASPOONS SEA SALT (OR LESS IF YOU PREFER)

LOTS OF FRESHLY GROUND BLACK PEPPER

2 TABLESPOONS (PACKED) FINELY CHOPPED FRESH CURLY PARSLEY

ZEST OF 2 ORGANIC LEMONS, CHOPPED (ABOUT 1 TABLESPOON OF CHOPPED ZEST)

1. Begin cooking the linguine according to the instructions on the package.
2. While the noodles cook, you can get the rest of the dish ready. Start by crumbling the bread into a medium skillet. Rub your hands together (with the bread in between them) to create coarse crumbs. Add the 1 tablespoon of oil and onion granules to the pan and stir well to combine. Cook the seasoned crumbs for about 5 minutes, stirring often, until they are golden browned. Remove from heat immediately and set aside in a small bowl.
3. Place the asparagus and the ¼ cup of broth in the skillet and cook over medium-high heat until the asparagus is bright green and crisp tender, about 5 minutes.
4. Place the asparagus in the biggest bowl you can muster up. Add the lemon juice, oils, the other ¼ cup of broth, garlic, salt, pepper, parsley, and zest to the big bowl. Stir well to combine with the asparagus.
5. When noodles are al dente, drain them well in a colander or strainer. Add them to the big bowl and combine them well with the asparagus mixture.
6. Just before serving, add the breadcrumbs to the bowl. Stir well and serve immediately. If this is simply too delicious to deal with, you have my permission to pack it in some dry ice and send it my way.
SERVES 6-8; 30 MINUTES OR UNDER! GF (WITH SUBSTITUTIONS)/SF/PURPLE

*If you are gluten intolerant, you may substitute gluten-free noodles and a gluten-free bread.

Kung Pao Tofu with Broccoli & Shiitake Mushrooms

The crisp of the tofu, paired with the fullness of the yummy sauce, makes this almost too tasty to tolerate!

1 LB. TOFU (EXTRA-FIRM)

3 TABLESPOONS TAMARI, SHOYU, OR SOY SAUCE

OH SO RICE:

1½ CUPS DRY BROWN BASMATI RICE

3 CUPS WATER

SAUCE OPTIONS: "TOASTED SESAME-ORANGE TERIYAKI SAUCE" (PAGE 124) OR "DELICIOUS AND QUICK ASIAN BROWN SAUCE" (PAGE 123)

VEGETABLES:

3 CUPS CHOPPED BROCCOLI (CUT INTO BITE SIZED PIECES)

2 CUPS THINLY SLICED SHIITAKE MUSHROOM CAPS

2 TEASPOONS TOASTED (DARK) SESAME OIL

1 TABLESPOON TAMARI, SHOYU, OR SOY SAUCE

MEDIUM SIZED CARROT, PEELED AND JULIENNE SLICED (SEE PAGE 41 FOR JULIENNE TIPS)

2 SCALLIONS, TRIMMED AND CHOPPED

BREADING:

½ CUP WHOLE WHEAT PASTRY FLOUR (OR RICE FLOUR)

½ TEASPOON GROUND BLACK PEPPER

¼ CUP DRY POLENTA OR CORNMEAL

¼ TEASPOON GROUND PAPRIKA

OIL: ½ CUP OIL (PEANUT, NON-VIRGIN OLIVE, OR COCONUT)

GARNISH: ½ CUP DRY-ROASTED UNSALTED PEANUTS, CRUSHED (SEE PAGE 41)

1. Cut the tofu into eight slabs and press between paper towels according to instructions on page 43. Allow the tofu to continue to press until step five.

2. Begin cooking your rice. Bring the rice and water to a boil over high heat in a covered pot. Reduce the heat to low and simmer (covered) until all of the water is absorbed.

3. While the rice is cooking, make your sauce of choice. Set it aside.

4. Chop or slice all of the vegetables so that they are ready to go. Set them aside.

5. Cut the tofu into ¾-inch cubes. Sprinkle with the 3 tablespoons of tamari and toss to coat.

6. Pour the breading ingredients (flour, pepper, polenta or cornmeal, and paprika) into a plastic bag and shake to combine. Next, add the tofu cubes to the bag. Shake the bag gently until the tofu is well coated with the breading mixture.

7. Heat the ½ cup of oil in a large, heavy skillet over medium-high heat. When the oil is hot, place the coated tofu cubes in the pan in a single layer. Allow the tofu pieces to brown on one side, then turn them over. When the tofu is golden brown on both sides, remove and drain on paper towels. If there is any uncooked tofu remaining, repeat this step until all of the tofu has been browned. Allow the tofu to continue to drain on paper towels until it is summoned.

8. Place the broccoli, shiitakes, sesame oil, and 1 tablespoon tamari in a large skillet or wok. Stir-fry for about 5 minutes (stirring often), or until the broccoli becomes bright green. Add the carrot and scallions and cook for another minute. Turn the heat off. *To serve*: Place the rice on plates and top with the veggies. Place the tofu on the veggies and cover everything with sauce. Sprinkle with some peanuts and serve.

SERVES 4; GF (WITH RICE FLOUR)/PURPLE

Shiitake & Tempeh Puffs with Rosemary

I once made this for a Thanksgiving catering event that included both vegetarians and omnivores. To my surprise and relief, even those who were originally quite concerned about missing turkey were raving about this dish! I rounded out the meal with the "Apple Pie Acorn Squash" (page 93), "Spinach-Strawberry Salad" (page 104), "Garlic Mashers" (page 99), "Scrumptious Shiitake Gravy" (page 122), "Asian Asparagus Wraps" (page 78), and "Chocolate Bliss Pie" (page 232). I think even the most devoted meat eaters survived without emotional scars after that meal.

⅓ LB. PUFF PASTRY DOUGH, THAWED FOR 45 MINUTES (OR AS DIRECTED ON PACKAGE)

2 TABLESPOONS NON-HYDROGENATED MARGARINE

½ OF AN 8 OZ. PACKAGE FIVE-GRAIN TEMPEH (A TOTAL OF FOUR OUNCES)

ONE SMALL ONION, THINLY SLICED

1 TABLESPOON TAMARI, SHOYU, OR SOY SAUCE

1 TEASPOON DRIED ROSEMARY LEAF

2 TEASPOONS FRESH LEMON JUICE

1 TABLESPOON BALSAMIC VINEGAR

5 CLOVES GARLIC, PRESSED OR MINCED

½ CUP SLICED SHIITAKE MUSHROOM CAPS

6 KALAMATA OLIVES, PITTED AND CHOPPED

¼ TEASPOON SEA SALT

GARNISH:

2 TABLESPOONS JULIENNE SLICED MARINATED SUN-DRIED TOMATOES, DRAINED

½ TEASPOON DRIED ROSEMARY LEAF

1. Preheat the oven to 400° F.
2. In a large pan, melt the margarine over medium-low heat. Crumble the tempeh into the pan (using your fingers to break it into small crumbly bits) and add the onion and tamari. Cook, stirring often, for about 15-20 minutes, or until the onion begins to caramelize and turn brown.
3. Add the 1 teaspoon rosemary, lemon juice, balsamic vinegar, garlic, shiitakes, olives, and salt to the pan. Sauté for another 5 minutes or so, stirring often. Remove from heat.
4. Cut the pastry dough into three or four pieces. Place them on a lightly oiled cookie sheet. Top each piece evenly with the tempeh-shiitake mixture. Place some of the sun-dried tomatoes in the center of each puff and sprinkle them evenly with the ½ teaspoon of rosemary.
5. Bake for about 10 minutes, or until the pastry becomes puffed and golden brown. Serve to the lucky recipients!

SERVES 3-4; PURPLE

Cornmeal Tofu & Asian Vegetables w/ Sweet and Sour Sauce

This entrée comes together much more quickly than you might think. It is a very brightly flavored dish and makes for a truly satisfying meal with the rice.

I LB. FIRM OR EXTRA-FIRM TOFU

¼ CUP TAMARI, SHOYU, OR SOY SAUCE

A RICE TOUCH:

I CUP LONG GRAIN BROWN RICE (OR BROWN BASMATI RICE)

2 CUPS WATER

SAUCE: ONE FULL RECIPE "CHUNKY GINGER-PINEAPPLE SWEET AND SOUR SAUCE" (PAGE 123)

VEGETABLES AND FRIENDS:

I TABLESPOON TOASTED (DARK) SESAME OIL

SMALL ONION, THINLY SLICED OR CHOPPED

I CUP SLICED SHIITAKE MUSHROOM CAPS

3 CUPS CHOPPED BROCCOLI

I ½ TABLESPOONS TAMARI, SHOYU, OR SOY SAUCE

ONE MEDIUM CARROT, JULIENNE CUT OR DICED

OPTIONAL CUTIFICATION:
• TOASTED BLACK SESAME SEEDS TO TASTE (SEE PAGE 42)

COATING:

½ CUP RICE FLOUR (OR WHOLE WHEAT PASTRY FLOUR)

½ TEASPOON EACH: GROUND PAPRIKA AND GROUND BLACK PEPPER

¼ CUP DRY POLENTA OR CORNMEAL (OR A MIXTURE OF BOTH)

OIL: ¼ CUP COCONUT, NON-VIRGIN OLIVE, OR PEANUT OIL

1. Cut the tofu into eight slabs. Press the tofu according to the directions on page 43. Allow the tofu to press until step five.
2. This is the big opportunity you've been waiting for to start the rice. Place the rice and water in a covered pot and bring to a boil over high heat. Reduce the heat to low and simmer for about 45 minutes, or until the rice is tender and all of the water has been absorbed.
3. If you haven't made the sauce yet, now is your chance. Please see page 123 for directions. When the sauce is done, remove it from heat and set it aside.
4. Wash and cut up all of your vegetables. Set them aside.
5. Cut the tofu into bite sized cubes and sprinkle with the ¼ cup of tamari. Gently toss to coat.
6. Place the flour, paprika, pepper, and polenta (and/or cornmeal) in a gallon size plastic bag. Shake the bag well to evenly mix the coating ingredients together. Toss the tofu cubes into the bag and gently shake to coat the tofu evenly with the flour mixture (you may need to do this in two batches).
7. Heat the ¼ cup oil in a large skillet or wok over medium-high heat. When the oil is hot, add the tofu and cook, stirring occasionally with a heat proof spatula, until the tofu is golden brown on all sides (about 5-10 minutes). Remove to a plate.
8. Heat the toasted sesame oil in the same pan over medium heat. Toss in the onion and shiitake mushrooms and cook, stirring often, for about 5 minutes (until the onion begins to soften).
9. Add the broccoli and the 1½ tablespoons tamari and cook, stirring often, until the broccoli is crisp-tender and bright green (about 5 minutes). Add the carrot and tofu, stirring very gently, and cook another minute, or until heated through. Fluff the rice, reheat the sauce briefly if necessary, and do it up! Serve the rice alongside the tofu-veggie mixture, pour the sauce over everything, and top with sesame seeds.

SERVES 4; GF/BLUE

Chili-Lime Noodles

These noodles are tangy, spicy, yummy, and addictive! Perfect for whenever your taste buds need a treat, this dish will also give your immune system a boost. Most of the ingredients in this dish remain uncooked to retain their maximum nutritional impact. So, you can dig on in and feel totally good about it! You are *so* worth it.

½ LB. RICE NOODLES OR LINGUINE

SAUCY SAUCE:

3 TABLESPOONS OIL (LIGHT UNTOASTED SESAME, NON-VIRGIN OLIVE, OR SUNFLOWER)

I TABLESPOON <u>EACH</u>: GRATED FRESH GINGER *AND* SRIRACHA THAI CHILI SAUCE

¼ CUP PLUS I TABLESPOON *FRESH* LIME JUICE

I TEASPOON KETCHUP

5 LARGE CLOVES GARLIC, MINCED OR PRESSED

2 TABLESPOONS PLUS I TEASPOON TAMARI, SHOYU, OR SOY SAUCE

½ TEASPOON SEA SALT (OR LESS IF YOU PREFER)

I ½ TEASPOONS ORGANIC SUGAR OR SUCANAT

VEGGIES:

I MEDIUM CARROT, PEELED AND JULIENNE SLICED (SEE PAGE 41 FOR TIPS)

4 SCALLIONS (GREEN ONIONS), THINLY SLICED (GREEN AND WHITE PARTS)

¼ CUP (LIGHTLY PACKED) CHOPPED FRESH CILANTRO

GARNISH:

¼ CUP (4 TABLESPOONS) DRY-ROASTED UNSALTED PEANUTS, CRUSHED (SEE PAGE 41)

1. Cook the noodles until al dente according to the package's instructions. Drain in a strainer or colander.
2. While the noodles are cooking, place all of the sauce ingredients in a large bowl. Stir very well to combine.
3. Prepare the veggies and add them to the sauce bowl. Toss them thoroughly with the sauce.
4. Pour the drained, hot noodles into the bowl and toss well with the sauce and veggies until well combined. Garnish with the peanuts and serve. This dish is good hot, cold, or at room temperature. It is good in a chair, it is good *every*where. It is good for a bribe, it will give you a good vibe. However, it isn't so good *re*-heated. If there are any leftovers, they are best served cold or at room temperature.

SERVES 4; 30 MINUTES OR UNDER! GF (WITH RICE NOODLES)/BLUE

John from Colorado says: "These are the perfect food for guests! You can make them anytime and serve them cold or at room temperature. Plus, they're *incredibly* delicious!"

Luscious Lasagna

Although there are all kinds of recipes for lasagna floating around these days, this version is so delicious and fresh tasting that I had to share. Plus, this dish never fails to be a big hit—the flavor is so delectable and complex that no one ever seems to notice it's also healthy and vegan!

12 LASAGNA NOODLES (ONE 10 OZ. PACKAGE), REGULAR OR GLUTEN-FREE

TOFU-SHIITAKE FILLING:

2 TABLESPOONS EXTRA-VIRGIN OLIVE OIL (OR ROSEMARY-INFUSED OLIVE OIL)

1 CUP EACH: FINELY CHOPPED ONION AND THINLY SLICED SHIITAKE MUSHROOM CAPS

1 ½ CUPS CRUMBLED FIRM TOFU (SEE PAGE 42 FOR TOFU TIPS)

ONE 8 OZ. CONTAINER NONDAIRY CREAM CHEESE, PLAIN

¼ CUP "VEGETARIAN 'CHICKEN' BROTH" (PAGE 194) OR OTHER LIQUID VEGETARIAN BROTH

1 ¼ CUPS GRATED CARROTS (ABOUT 2 LARGE CARROTS)

5 LARGE CLOVES GARLIC, MINCED OR PRESSED

2 TABLESPOONS FRESH LEMON JUICE

⅓ CUP NUTRITIONAL YEAST POWDER

⅛ TEASPOON GROUND NUTMEG

2 TEASPOONS EACH: DRIED PARSLEY AND DRIED OREGANO

1 TEASPOON EACH: DRIED BASIL AND DRIED THYME

½ TEASPOON GROUND BLACK PEPPER

1 ½ TEASPOONS SEA SALT

ADDITIONAL GOODNESS:

5 OZ. BABY SPINACH (ABOUT 6 CUPS LIGHTLY PACKED)

25 OZ. BOTTLED VEGAN SPAGHETTI SAUCE OF CHOICE (ABOUT 3 CUPS OF SAUCE)

1 ¾ CUPS GRATED MOZZARELLA SOY CHEESE (6 OZ.)

1. Cook the noodles according to the package directions. When they are still fairly firm (*very* al dente), drain them and set them aside until step four.

2. In a large skillet or wok, heat the olive oil over medium-high heat. When the oil is hot, add the onion and sauté for 5 minutes, stirring often.

3. Add the remaining tofu-shiitake filling items to the pan and mix very thoroughly with the onion until well combined. You don't need to cook this mixture any further, so remove it from heat. Don't be alarmed if this looks like a big goopy mess—I promise it won't taste like one!

4. Lightly oil a 9.5 x 13.5-inch baking pan. Preheat the oven to 400° F. Place four cooked lasagna noodles in a single layer on the bottom of the pan.

5. Top with half of the spinach. Place half of the tofu-shiitake mixture on top of the spinach, distributing it as evenly as possible over the pan.

6. Next, bring on another single layer of noodles and top them with half of the spaghetti sauce.

7. Evenly distribute the remaining spinach over the sauce and top with the remaining tofu-shiitake mixture. Next, place the last of the noodles in a single layer over the top. Pour the remaining sauce evenly over the noodles.

8. Sprinkle the cheese on top of the sauce and cover the pan with foil. Bake for 40 minutes.

9. Remove the foil and allow the lasagna to bake, uncovered, for another 10 minutes, or until golden brown and bubbly. Remove from the oven and allow it to sit for 3-5 minutes. Cut, serve, and enjoy the good life.

SERVES 8-12; GF (IF USING GLUTEN-FREE LASAGNA NOODLES)/PURPLE

Green Chili & Tomatillo Tamales

Well, I just got the report. I recently gave a few of these to some friends to double check the yum factor of this recipe, and everyone loved them. One person (a meat eater, mind you) said that they were the best tamales he'd ever eaten! Quite a compliment, considering that these have about one fourth the fat of traditional tamales. I have used several shortcuts here to make these easier to assemble. Instead of making a separate filling, I have mixed it right into the batter. I have also shown a way to wrap them that is much quicker than the traditional method of tying the ends off. For a visual aid on the process of wrapping the tamales, please see the pictures on the last color insert page. I highly recommend serving these tamales with the "9½ Minute Green Chili Sauce" (page 131) and a bit of nondairy sour cream. Oh yeah!

LOVE THOSE VEGGIES:

1 TEASPOON OIL (COCONUT, SUNFLOWER, OR NON-VIRGIN OLIVE)

1 MEDIUM ZUCCHINI, DICED (UNPEELED)

1 ½ CUPS DICED TOMATILLOS (HUSKS REMOVED AND WASHED)

4 TABLESPOONS (¼ CUP) NON-HYDROGENATED MARGARINE (OR COCONUT OIL IF YOU'RE SOY-FREE)

8 OZ. PEELED, ROASTED, AND CHOPPED GREEN CHILIES (FRESH, FROZEN, OR CANNED)

½ CUP CORN KERNELS, FRESH OR FROZEN

4 SCALLIONS (GREEN ONIONS), TRIMMED AND CHOPPED (USE BOTH GREEN AND WHITE PARTS)

3 TABLESPOONS FRESH LIME JUICE

2 TEASPOONS DRIED MEXICAN OREGANO (OR REGULAR OREGANO)

1 TABLESPOON NUTRITIONAL YEAST POWDER

½ CUP (PACKED) CHOPPED FRESH CILANTRO

CORN FLUFF STUFF:

2¾ CUPS DRY CORN MASECA (INSTANT CORN MASA MIX)

1 TEASPOON BAKING SODA

2 TEASPOONS SEA SALT

2 CUPS PLUS 2 TABLESPOONS WATER

WRAP PARTY: 26 CORN HUSKS

TOPPINGS:

NONDAIRY SOUR CREAM

"9½ MINUTE GREEN CHILE SAUCE" (PAGE 131) OR TOMATILLO SALSA

OPTIONAL GARNISHES:

CILANTRO AND GREEN ONIONS (SCALLIONS) TO TASTE, CHOPPED

HOT SAUCE OF CHOICE

1. In a medium-large skillet set to medium-high heat, cook the oil, zucchini, and tomatillos. Sauté, stirring often, for about 5 minutes, or until the zucchini is lightly browned.

2. Stir in the margarine, green chilies, corn, and scallions. Cook for another minute, stirring well, until the margarine is melted.

3. Add the lime juice, oregano, nutritional yeast, and cilantro to the pan. Stir well and remove from heat.

4. In a large bowl, mix the corn maseca, baking soda, and salt very well with a wire whisk until thoroughly combined. Stir in the water until evenly mixed.

5. Add the vegetable combination to the corn mixture. Be sure to scrape all of the goodness out of the pan and into the corn mixture using a rubber spatula. Stir everything together very well. Very well, my dear.

6. Place the corn husks in a large bowl and cover them with warm or hot water. Allow them to soak for several minutes, or until they become soft. When they're ready to use, drain the excess water off.

7. Place a vegetable steamer insert inside a four quart pot with a lid. Pour enough water into the pot so that it comes up to the bottom of the steamer.

8. To roll the tamales: Place a corn husk on a clean counter top in such a way that the longest sides are horizontal in front of you (rather than placing the husk in a way that it is vertically tall). Place about ¼ cup of the filling in the center of the husk. Bring the top and bottom of the corn husk up and around the filling, pressing them firmly against the filling. It's important to compact the filling so that it becomes dense and firm when steamed. Fold the husks around the filling so that it's enclosed.

9. Keeping the husks wrapped around the filling in this way, take the right end of the husk and twist it to close, tucking it underneath the tamale. Repeat with the left side of the husk. Place the tamale, tucked ends down, in the steamer insert.

10. Repeat this step with the other corn husks until all of the filling is gone.

11. Cover the pot and bring it to a boil over high heat. Turn the heat down to low and allow the tamales to steam for an hour. *This next tip is very important*: Please be sure that there is some water in the pot the entire time the tamales are steaming. There is nothing sadder than a pot of tamales that taste like a burned, dry pan!

12. When the tamales are done, the filling should be firm (although the filling will firm up even more after about an hour). Remove the husks from the tamales and serve them with your choice of toppings. They will store for about a week in an airtight container, refrigerated. They also freeze well. Enjoy!

MAKES 26 TAMALES; GF/SF (WITH SUBSTITUTION)/BLUE

To reheat tamales:

If the tamales are frozen, they should be thawed first. Next, place the whole tamales (still in husks) in a skillet with a little water. Cover the skillet with a lid and steam them over medium-high heat for about 5 minutes, or until hot. Halfway through, check to make sure the water hasn't evaporated and add more water if necessary. Peel and eat. Yep—still yummy!

Crunchy Tempeh with Moroccan Pomegranate Sauce

This elegant entrée is luscious, impressive, and still manages to be chock full of antioxidants and nutrients! I have given a fairly modest ratio of sauce to tempeh here for a delicate result. If you prefer a richer taste, you may wish to double the amount of sauce you make (or halve the amount of tempeh). If you really want to go all out, serve the tempeh cutlets atop some of the "Moroccan Quinoa" (page 88) and garnish with pomegranate seeds, cilantro, and almonds.

ONE FULL RECIPE OF THE "MOROCCAN POMEGRANATE SAUCE" (PAGE 130)

OPTIONAL: "MOROCCAN QUINOA" (PAGE 88)

TEMPEH CUTLETS:

16 OZ. TEMPEH, PREFERABLY FIVE-GRAIN (TWO 8 OZ. PACKAGES OF TEMPEH)

1 CUP WATER

¼ CUP TAMARI, SHOYU, OR SOY SAUCE

1 CUP NONDAIRY MILK (PLAIN AND UNSWEETENED)

½ CUP OIL (COCONUT, NON-VIRGIN OLIVE, OR PEANUT) FOR PAN-FRYING

CRAZY GOOD COATING:

1½ CUPS WHOLE WHEAT PASTRY FLOUR (OR GLUTEN-FREE ALL-PURPOSE FLOUR)

¼ CUP EACH: DRY POLENTA, CORNMEAL, AND BLACK (OR BROWN) SESAME SEEDS

1 TEASPOON EACH: SEA SALT, GROUND BLACK PEPPER, AND GROUND PAPRIKA

OPTIONAL GARNISHES (USE NONE, ANY, OR ALL OF THE FOLLOWING):

1 TABLESPOON EACH: POMEGRANATE SEEDS, MINCED CILANTRO, AND TOASTED ALMONDS

A FEW STRIPS OF ORGANIC LEMON, LIME, AND/OR ORANGE ZEST

1. Make the Moroccan Pomegranate Sauce (please) and set it aside.
2. If you'll be using the Moroccan Quinoa, go ahead and make that happen. Set it aside.
3. Slice each package of tempeh in half (width-wise) and then gently remove each piece of tempeh from its package. Next, slice each half of tempeh through its center in order to form a total of eight rectangular cutlets that are approximately 2½ x 4-inches in size (and ½ inch thick, or half of their original thickness).
4. Place the tempeh cutlets in a single layer in a very large skillet. Evenly pour the water and tamari over the tempeh cutlets. Turn the cutlets over to coat both sides in the liquid. Cook, covered, over medium heat for 5 minutes. Flip the cutlets over and cook for another 5 minutes, or until all of the liquid has been absorbed. Your tempeh is now steamed, marinated, and ready for action!
5. Prepare the coating by combining the flour, polenta, cornmeal, sesame seeds, salt, pepper, and paprika in a medium sized bowl. Stir or whisk very well and set aside. Place the milk in a shallow bowl and set it aside as well.
6. Heat the ½ cup of oil in a large skillet over medium-high heat.
7. Dip your tempeh cutlets in the soymilk, then dip them in the coating. Next, it's time for déjà vu. Dip the tempeh back into the milk again, then into the coating a second time. Make sure there is an even, thick layer of coating on all sides of each tempeh cutlet.
8. When the oil is hot, place the cutlets in a single layer in the pan. When the undersides are browned, turn the cutlets over and brown the other side. Remove and drain on paper towels. Repeat with the remaining tempeh until you are finished.
9. If you are using the quinoa, place a scoop of it on each plate. Arrange the tempeh on top of the quinoa and drizzle the sauce over the top.
10. Garnish each plate with whatever inspires you. Serve immediately and get ready for the yum.

SERVES 4; GF (WITH SUBSTITUTION)/BLUE

Spinach Artichoke Pizza with Rosemary

What goes together better than spinach and artichokes? Well, maybe a few things—but we won't go there now. With the addition of fresh rosemary and chunky garlic, this pizza is bursting with flavor. *Bursting.*

½ BATCH OF THE "ROSEMARY HERB PIZZA CRUST" (PAGE 204), THAWED IF FROZEN
1 ½ CUPS PIZZA SAUCE OR "RICH TOMATO SAUCE" (PAGE 118)

1 ½ CUPS GRATED NONDAIRY MOZZARELLA CHEESE

6-8 MEDIUM CLOVES GARLIC, PEELED AND SLICED
¾ CUP ARTICHOKE HEARTS, DRAINED (MARINATED OR WATER-PACKED)
1 CUP (PACKED) BABY SPINACH
⅔ CUP THINLY SLICED SHIITAKE MUSHROOM CAPS (LIFE WITHOUT SHIITAKES? I THINK NOT.)
1 ½ TEASPOONS CHOPPED FRESH ROSEMARY LEAF

1. If you need to make your pizza crust and sauce, there's no time like the present. Please see the recipes on pages 204 and 118. Set the dough and sauce aside when they are finished.
2. Preheat the oven to 425° F. To shape your pizza crust, place the dough in the center of a round, lightly oiled pizza pan and evenly push it toward the outer edges of the pan. Form the outer rim by pinching up about ½-inch of dough around the edge of the pan. Make sure there are no gaps in the crust anywhere. If there are, simply pinch the dough together to "patch" the crust. Prick it with a fork a few times (evenly over the top of the crust) to ensure that it won't poof up too much while it's baking.
3. Bake the crust for about 10 minutes, or until very lightly browned.
4. Remove the crust from the oven and evenly distribute the sauce over it, using the back of a large spoon. Sprinkle the cheese on top of the sauce. Top evenly with the garlic, artichokes, spinach, shiitakes, and rosemary. Bake for another 10-15 minutes, or until the cheese and toppings are lightly browned. Allow to cool for just a few minutes, then slice and serve. You can take it from here. You don't need me anymore.

SERVES 4 (MAKES ONE PIZZA PIE)
BLUE

Beer Battered Tofish with Tartar Sauce

This dish is the *definition* of extravagant! This is the only recipe in this cookbook that uses beer, but I have found it makes an irreplaceable component in a good, crunchy batter. Of course, all of the alcohol will cook off upon frying, for teetotalers like me who care. Although this dish is very decadent, it's still a healthier option for those who crave fried fish. This version has no mercury risks, trans-fats, refined flours, or cholesterol. I have purposely included a bit of extra batter here, so that you can make a few beer battered onion rings while you're at it. However, if you will only be cooking the Tofish, you can simply cut the batter amount in half. For those who prefer a lighter and quicker version of this whole experience, I would recommend the "Bailey's Tofish with Tartar Sauce" (page 144).

ONE 12.3 OZ. PACKAGE SILKEN TOFU (EXTRA-FIRM), FROZEN AND THAWED (PLEASE SEE NOTE AT THE BOTTOM OF PAGE 179)

MARINE-ADE:

4 TABLESPOONS *FRESH* LEMON JUICE

2 TABLESPOONS TAMARI, SHOYU, OR SOY SAUCE

1 TEASPOON EACH: GROUND PAPRIKA, DRIED GARLIC GRANULES, *AND* POWDERED KELP

TASTY TARTAR SAUCE:

½ CUP "VEGENAISE" VEGAN MAYONNAISE

¼ CUP FINELY GRATED DILL PICKLE

2 TABLESPOONS FINELY MINCED WHITE OR YELLOW ONION

⅛ TEASPOON EACH: DRIED GARLIC GRANULES *AND* GROUND BLACK PEPPER

OIL: PEANUT, COCONUT, OR NON-VIRGIN OLIVE (ENOUGH TO MAKE A ½-INCH WELL IN YOUR SKILLET)

BEER BATTER:

1½ CUPS WHOLE WHEAT PASTRY FLOUR (OR ALL-PURPOSE GLUTEN-FREE FLOUR)

1 TEASPOON EACH: DRIED GARLIC GRANULES *AND* DRIED ONION GRANULES

2 TEASPOONS SEASONED SALT

⅛ TEASPOON BAKING SODA

1½ CUPS (OR SLIGHTLY MORE IF NEEDED TO THIN) VERY COLD BEER

FISH-ISH: 1 SHEET NORI, TORN INTO PIECES THE SAME SIZE AS YOUR TOFU SLICES

OPTIONAL DECADENCE:

2 CUPS THICKLY SLICED ONION (WHITE OR YELLOW)

FOR SERVING: LEMON WEDGES

1. Gently slice the container of thawed tofu through the middle to open it. Carefully extract the tofu from its package, doing your darndest to keep it in tact. Next, gently squeeze the tofu to remove some of the excess water. Slice the tofu into fourteen thin slabs and place them on paper towels in a single layer. Cover with more paper towels and press according to the instructions on page 43. Allow the tofu to sit and press for 10 minutes or longer, or until most of the water has been extracted.
2. Stir the marinade (yes, marine-ade) items together in a small bowl until well combined.
3. Place the pressed tofu slices in a pan or on a plate (in a single layer) and pour the marinade evenly over the top. Turn the tofu so as to coat both sides evenly with the mixture. Allow to sit for 10 minutes or more, or until the marinade has been absorbed.
4. While the tofu is marinating, check the time. Yes, you guessed it—it's tartar time. Place the ingredients

for the tartar sauce in a bowl and stir well with a spoon to combine. Cover and pop the sauce into the fridge until you're ready to use it.

5. When the tofu is done pressing, you can preheat the oil. Pour enough oil into a large, heavy skillet to make a ½-inch deep well. Set to medium-high heat.

6. While the oil is preheating, combine the flour, garlic and onion granules, salt, and baking soda together until they are well mixed, using a whisk if necessary. Stir in the beer and combine well.

7. To test the oil to see if it is the right temperature, drop a smidge of batter into it. If it sizzles quickly, it should be good to go. Do not put your Tofish into the oil before it is hot enough or it will become overly greasy.

8. Set some paper towels close to the pan (away from the burner, though!) so you will be ready to drain the tofu.

9. When the oil is sufficiently hot, you can begin to fry the Tofish. Wrap a piece of nori around a slice of tofu, then dip the whole thing into the batter. You will have to hold the nori in place during this process (yes, awkwardly) so that it doesn't slip off. Carefully place it in the oil, being careful not to burn your fingers. Repeat this process with the remaining tofu. Flip each piece over when their underside becomes golden browned. When both sides are browned, remove the Tofish with a slotted metal spoon or spatula and allow to drain on paper towels.

10. If desired, use up the remaining batter with onions, frying them in the same manner as the tofu. Allow to drain on paper towels.

11. Serve the Tofish immediately with a squeeze of lemon and some tartar sauce.

SERVES 4
GF (WITH SUBSTITUTION)/PURPLE

*Freezing the tofu will give it a more complex, fish-like texture. Simply place the whole aseptic package of tofu in the freezer for at least 12 hours and then allow it to thaw in the fridge overnight (or longer).

Chapter Thirteen: The Raw Dimension

Incorporating raw foods into your diet can open up a whole new dimension of possibilities! They are easy to prepare, fresh, and extremely nutritious. In my experience, however, it is not necessary to adopt an *entirely* raw foods diet in order to achieve maximum health. Even so, as we eat more fresh and raw foods, our bodies easily get the nourishment they seek and repay us with glowing health! The most important thing to remember is that eating more fresh, raw foods does not have to be intimidating. For example, the daily act of eating plenty of fresh fruits and veggies can translate into something as simple as a smoothie for breakfast, some carrots and celery during the day, and a nice, big salad with dinner.

Additional Recipes that Contain a Majority of Fresh, Raw Ingredients:

Triple Omega Dip

This yummy dip is absolutely chock full of essential Omega-3 fatty acids. Not only that, it contains *three* excellent sources of them! Olive oil, flax oil, and walnuts give this delicious dip its name and make triple sure you are getting all the Omega-3s your body could ever want. Plus, with the addition of sprouted chickpeas, lemon, garlic, and tahini, this dip is nutritionally out of control! To keep it strictly raw, you can serve this in the "Triple Omega Wrap with Basil and Tomatoes" (page 183) or on its own with some crudités (raw veggies) for dipping. *Ah, life is good.*

¼ CUP DRY CHICKPEAS (GARBANZO BEANS), SPROUTED (PLEASE SEE PAGE 191)

¼ CUP PLUS 2 TABLESPOONS RAW WALNUTS

2 TABLESPOONS MARINATED SUN-DRIED TOMATOES, DRAINED

3 LARGE CLOVES OF GARLIC, PEELED

2 TABLESPOONS EXTRA-VIRGIN OLIVE OIL (COLD PRESSED)

3 TABLESPOONS EACH: FLAX OR HEMP OIL (OR ADDITIONAL OLIVE OIL) *AND* RAW TAHINI

4 TABLESPOONS (¼ CUP) *FRESH* LEMON JUICE

1 ⅛ TEASPOONS SEA SALT (OR LESS IF YOU PREFER)

⅛ TEASPOON PAPRIKA (OPTIONAL FOR COLOR)

¼ CUP (LIGHTLY PACKED) FRESH BASIL, SLICED INTO THIN RIBBONS.

1. If you have not yet sprouted the chickpeas, please see the directions on page 191. It will take a few days before the sprouts are ready, so you may want to get out a good book or something while you wait.

2. In a food processor, blend the sprouted chickpeas, walnuts, tomatoes, and garlic until as smooth as possible. If necessary, add a little of the oil.

3. Add the remaining oil and other ingredients (except for the basil) and blend well. Puree until everything is as smooth as possible. Ideally, this should be refrigerated overnight (or for several hours) to allow the flavors to marry. However, if you don't have the time to allow the flavors to marry, simply allow them to have a long engagement.

4. Serve with the basil scattered on top. This will keep for up to a week or more refrigerated in an airtight container.

MAKES ABOUT 1 ½ CUPS OF DIP
GF/SF/BLUE

Triple Omega Wrap with Basil & Tomatoes

This is an easy, elegant, and nourishing way to use the "Triple Omega Dip."
Plus, it goes a long way in proving that raw foods can be absolutely *scrumptious*!

ONE RECIPE "TRIPLE OMEGA DIP" (PLEASE SEE PAGE 182—IT'S NOT FAR)

8 LARGE ROMAINE OR RED LETTUCE LEAVES

1 CUP CHOPPED FRESH TOMATOES AND/OR SUN-DRIED TOMATOES

½ CUP EACH: FRESH BASIL, CUT INTO RIBBONS *AND* MINCED OR THINLY SLICED RED ONION

OPTIONAL: ALFALFA SPROUTS, CHOPPED CUCUMBER, KALAMATA OLIVES, AND/OR PINE NUTS

FOR A FLAVOR SPLASH: FRESH LEMON WEDGES

1. Make the dip if you haven't yet done so. Allow the flavors to marry for as long as possible.
2. Wash and dry the lettuce leaves and carefully remove the tough portion of their stem bases.
3. Spread the dip over the middle portion of each leaf and top with all of the goodies. If desired, you can also add some sprouts, cucumber, olives, and/or pine nuts. Next, squeeze a little fresh lemon on top.
4. Roll the bottom of the leaf up and over the fillings. Fold the sides in, then roll up like a burrito. Serve.

SERVES 8; 30 MINUTES OR UNDER! GF/SF/Blue

Divine Mango Pie

This pie is so nourishing that I consider it a serious form of love to feed this to anyone, including myself!
It is, in fact, so delightfully healthy that I even use it as a breakfast item. Many thanks to Jennifer
Cornbleet, as her recipe for mango pudding (from her book *Raw Foods Made Easy for 1 or 2 People*)
inspired this creation. Score another hit for the beloved mango!

CRUST OF LOVE:

1 CUP EACH: RAW ALMONDS *AND* SHREDDED COCONUT

½ CUP (TIGHTLY PACKED) CHOPPED, PITTED DATES

¼ TEASPOON SEA SALT

FILLING WAY TOO GOOD:

1 ¼ CUPS DRIED MANGO, CHOPPED (WITH SHARP SCISSORS) AND SOAKED FOR 15 MINUTES

3 CUPS CHOPPED FRESH MANGO (PEELED)

OVER THE TOP:

• 2 CUPS SLICED FRESH STRAWBERRIES
(SEE PAGE 221 FOR CUTE TIPS)

1. If you haven't yet soaked the dried mango, place in a bowl and cover completely with water. Set aside.
2. Blend the almonds in a food processor until crumbly. Add the coconut, dates and salt and process until very well combined. However, don't over-blend as you will want to retain some of the original texture of the ingredients. Evenly distribute the mixture into an ungreased 9-inch pie pan. Press firmly to make a crust on the bottom and 1½ inches up around the sides. Place it in the freezer until the filling is ready.
3. Drain the dried mango and blend for about a minute in a clean food processor. Add the fresh mango and blend very well, using a rubber spatula to scrape down the insides of the food processor as needed. Keep on a-blendin' until totally smooth. It may take a while!
4. Remove the crust from the arctic circle. Spoon the filling into it. Cover and refrigerate for several hours.
5. Before serving, decorate the top of the pie evenly with the sliced strawberries. This will store, tightly covered and refrigerated, for about 3 days.

MAKES ONE 9-INCH PIE; GF/SF/Green

Moroccan Barley-Spinach Toss

I could live on this stuff! It's fat-free, raw, nourishing, easy to make, *and* tasty! Sprouting newbies, please don't be scared to try this. It may look intimidating, but it couldn't be easier. The actual time involved in making this is well under 30 minutes, it's just that the steps are spread out. If you haven't guessed yet by now, I'm a big fan of Moroccan seasonings—sweet, tart, and savory all at once. Yum!

1 CUP DRY BARLEY, SPROUTED (PLEASE SEE PAGE 191 FOR TIPS)

SWEET-SAVORY SAUCE:

1 TEASPOON EACH: GROUND CUMIN *AND* MINCED ORGANIC ORANGE ZEST

¾ CUP FRESH SQUEEZED ORANGE JUICE

4 TEASPOONS EACH: FRESH LEMON JUICE *AND* VERY FINELY MINCED ONION

2 TEASPOONS GROUND CINNAMON

2 TABLESPOONS RAW AGAVE NECTAR

SIMPLE SALAD:

½ CUP RAISINS

1 CUP (PACKED) BABY SPINACH, CUT INTO VERY THIN RIBBONS OR MINCED

OPTIONAL:

FRESH MINT, MINCED (ABOUT 1½ TABLESPOONS)

SEA SALT TO TASTE (EVEN I DON'T SALT THIS ONE, THOUGH!)

1. If you haven't yet sprouted the barley, please see the sprouting "recipe" on page 191. It will take a few days before the barley will be ready to use in this recipe.
2. Stir the sauce ingredients together in a medium sized bowl until well combined.
3. Add the sprouted barley, raisins, and spinach to the sauce and toss to thoroughly combine.
4. Allow the mixture to marinate for at least 20 minutes, stirring occasionally to saturate the sauce into everything. If you do have the time to marinate this for an hour, that's even better.
5. After the dish has finished marinating, you can add the mint and/or some salt if you like. If you have leftovers, this will keep for a few days in an airtight container, refrigerated.

SERVES ABOUT 4-6

GF/SF/GREEN, SO GREEN

Raw Pesto Dip

This yummy dip is perfect with crudités (fresh vegetables) or raw crackers. It's also very
nice rolled up in a lettuce or Swiss chard leaf, topped with veggies, and eaten like a raw burrito.

½ CUP RAW ALMONDS	• ½ CUP WATER
I CUP RAW SUNFLOWER SEEDS	• ½ CUP (PACKED) *FRESH* BASIL LEAVES
½ CUP (PACKED) FRESH PARSLEY	• I TEASPOON SEA SALT
I SCALLION, TRIMMED AND CHOPPED	• I TABLESPOON *FRESH* DILL
2-3 CLOVES GARLIC, PEELED	• JUICE OF I LEMON AND I LIME

1. In a food processor, blend the almonds, sunflower seeds, parsley, scallion, and garlic until as smooth as
possible. If necessary, add a little of the water. As you are blending, you may need to use a rubber spatula
(or your tongue) to scrape down the insides of the food processor.
2. Add the remaining water and other ingredients and blend well. Puree until everything is as smooth as
possible. If possible, refrigerate overnight (or for several hours) before using to allow the flavors to blend.
MAKES ABOUT 2½ CUPS OF DIP; 30 MINUTES OR UNDER! GF/SF/Blue

Nori Rawls with Sprouted Barley

These wraps are a delicious meal all by themselves! They're also sky-high in minerals, nutrients, and
beneficial enzymes. You can vary this any way you like, according to your preferences. You can also
substitute raw pumpkin seeds for the flax (or sunflower) seeds for similar results. Enjoy!

SPROUTED BARLEY:
¼ CUP DRY BARLEY, SPROUTED (PLEASE SEE PAGE 191)

FLAX-ALMOND SPREAD:
¼ CUP EACH: RAW FLAXSEEDS, RAW WHOLE ALMONDS, *AND* RAW SUNFLOWER SEEDS
¼ TEASPOON EACH: SEA SALT *AND* GROUND (POWDERED) KELP
2 TABLESPOONS EACH: FRESH LEMON JUICE *AND* WATER
I TABLESPOON EACH: CHOPPED CELERY, CHOPPED ONION, *AND* (PACKED) CHOPPED CILANTRO

ASSORTED VEGGIES—YOUR CHOICE: AVOCADO, CARROTS, GREEN ONIONS, CUCUMBERS,
AND/OR SPROUTS

ADDITIONAL GOODNESS:
2 SHEETS OF RAW NORI
"CREAMY GINGER WASABI SAUCE" (PLEASE SEE PAGE 124), OPTIONAL (NOT 100% RAW)

1. Sprout the barley according to the directions on page 191. This will take a few days, so you may want
to find something else to do for a while.
2. In a food processor, blend the flaxseeds, almonds, and sunflower seeds until they become coarse
crumbs. During this process, you may need to occasionally scrape the inside of the food processor with a

rubber spatula to ensure even blending.

3. Add in the sea salt, kelp, lemon juice, and water. Blend until well combined. Lightly pulse in the celery, onion, and cilantro (just enough to mix them in). Be careful not to over-blend, as you want to retain some of their texture.

4. To prepare your veggies of choice, cut them into thin, 3-inch long spears. The carrots may be julienne cut or grated if you prefer. Once your veggies are prepared, set them aside.

5. Before you begin the next step, you may wish to refer to the pictures on the last color insert page for a visual aid (keeping in mind that the pictures are of non-raw nori rolls). Place one sheet of nori (shiny side down) on a bamboo sushi mat. Gently press half of the flax-almond spread evenly onto the lower half of the nori. Next, lightly push half of the sprouted barley onto the spread.

6. Place your veggies in the middle of the spread-barley goodness in a straight horizontal line. Roll up the wrap, using both of your hands. Bring the bottom of the mat/nori roll up and over, using your fingers to secure the fillings. Gently squeeze this portion with your hands (and the mat) in order to make sure that all of the fillings are stabilized.

7. Roll the rest of the way up. With your finger, spread a little water along the border of the nori to seal the edge. Now, place the nori, seam side down, on a cutting board. Dip a sharp knife into a bowl of water and cut the nori roll into slices. Continue to dip the knife into the water bowl as often as necessary. If your knife remains wet and free of debris, your nori roll pieces will be much neater and less likely to tear.

8. Now, repeat with the remaining sheet of nori and fillings. Serve with the Creamy Ginger-Wasabi Sauce if you feel like taking the deliciousness volume up to eleven.

MAKES 2 NORI ROLLS; GF/SF/GREEN

Main Dish Salad with Tahini-Lemon Dressing

Here is an example of a relatively "normal" (I use that term lightly) dish that also happens to be raw. The colors in this salad are lovely and the heartiness of the walnuts and tahini make this a one dish meal. This is exceptionally nice when you want something that is all at once quick, light, and satisfying.

¼ -½ CUP "TAHINI-LEMON DRESSING" (PLEASE SEE THE RECIPE ON PAGE 120)

4 CUPS (PACKED) BABY GREENS, ARUGULA, AND/OR SPINACH
1 LARGE CARROT, GRATED OR VERY THINLY SLICED (OR JULIENNE CUT)
½ CUP EACH: GRATED RED CABBAGE AND CHERRY (OR GRAPE) TOMATOES

TO TASTE: VERY THINLY SLICED RED ONION

OPTIONAL: ½ CUP SPROUTS (ALFALFA, BARLEY, OR GARBANZO), PLEASE SEE PAGE 191

TOP IT: ¼ CUP RAW WALNUTS

1. Make the dressing according to the directions on page 120. Set aside.
2. Place the greens, carrot, cabbage, and tomatoes in two nice, big bowls. Top with the onions and sprouts (if using) and add the desired amount of dressing.
3. Sprinkle the walnuts on top and serve.

SERVES 2; 30 MINUTES OR UNDER! GF/SF/GREEN

Almond Milk

This is the perfect base for morning shakes and cereals. It is unsweetened, which makes it totally versatile. It's also surprisingly easy to make and extremely nourishing.

1 CUP RAW SLIVERED ALMONDS (WITHOUT SKINS)
3 CUPS FILTERED WATER (OR, YOU MAY USE 4-5 CUPS IF YOU PREFER A LOWER-FAT MILK)
1/8 TEASPOON SEA SALT
MINIMAL MATERIALS:
BLENDER
VERY FINE MESHED STRAINER
GLASS QUART JAR (OR OTHER STORAGE CONTAINER WITH A TIGHT FITTING LID)

1. Place the almonds in a blender. Blend on low speed, adding *just* enough of the water to make your blender happy (or at least content), until the almonds are ground as finely as possible.
2. Add the remaining water and salt. Blend on high speed until the milk is as smooth as possible.
3. Little by little, pour the milk through the strainer into your glass quart jar (or into another container with a wider mouth if necessary). Use the back of a spoon to press all of the milk through, so that all you have left in the strainer is pulp. During this process, you will want to occasionally discard the pulp and rinse the strainer to ensure that you get the maximum amount of milk into the container. This will store, covered tightly, in the refrigerator for about one week.
MAKES ABOUT 3½ CUPS ALMOND MILK; 30 MINUTES OR UNDER! GF/SF/GREEN

Almond-Banana Power Morning Shake

What a feel-good breakfast drink! This is alkalinizing, filling, and nutrient dense. However, it does take a little planning as the dates need to be soaked beforehand. Although this makes them easier to blend, there may still be a few small bits of date remaining. Don't be tempted to omit them, though—they make this shake extra nutritious and *perfectly* sweet.

4 DRIED DATES, PITTED
1½ CUPS ALMOND MILK (RECIPE ABOVE)

2 FROZEN BANANAS (PAGE 47)
1 TEASPOON VANILLA EXTRACT

1. Soak the dates for at least an hour in *just* enough of the almond milk to fully cover them.
2. Place the dates in a blender along with the milk they were soaking in. Blend on low, until the dates are as blended as they're gonna get. Ever.
3. Add the bananas, vanilla, and remaining milk and blend until smooth. Serve immediately.
SERVES 2; GF/SF/GREEN

Blackberry Peach Cobbler

Many thanks to Jennifer Cornbleet, as her recipe for crumble topping inspired this dessert. Her recipe (from the book *Raw Foods Made Easy for 1 or 2 People*) is good enough to eat by the spoonful! Be sure to use sweet, ripe blackberries and peaches here, as they provide the natural sweetness for this dessert. As this dish is so light and fruity, it even makes a great breakfast item. Good morning, sunshine!

OVERLY DELICIOUS TOPPING:

I CUP RAW WALNUTS

¼ CUP DRIED, SHREDDED COCONUT

¼ TEASPOON GROUND CINNAMON

½ CUP RAISINS

2 TABLESPOONS ORGANIC RAW SUGAR

¼ TEASPOON SEA SALT

FRUIT FRESHNESS:

• 6 OZ. (I CUP) FRESH BLACKBERRIES

• 2 RIPE PEACHES, CHOPPED OR SLICED

• ½ TEASPOON ORGANIC RAW SUGAR

• PINCH OF GROUND NUTMEG

1. Place all of the topping ingredients in a food processor and process just until crumbly and well mixed. Be **very** careful not to over-blend or it will lack "crumbliness." Set aside.
2. In a medium bowl, mash half of the blackberries. You can use a fork or your fingers to do this.
3. *Gently* stir in the remaining whole blackberries and peaches. Sprinkle in the sugar and nutmeg. Toss gently to combine.
4. Place the fruit mixture in bowls and sprinkle with the desired amount of topping. Serve immediately. If you don't wish to use all of the topping on the fruit, you can store it in the fridge. It will keep for a month or more in an airtight container. From there, you can also form it into "cookies" for a raw treat.

SERVES 2; 30 MINUTES OR UNDER! GF/SF/BLUE

Zucchini Chips to Dry For

Although this is the only recipe in this book to require a food dehydrator, I *had* to include it. These chips are easy to make, healthy, and completely delicious! For once, decadent snacking means guilt-free eats!

3 CUPS SLICED ZUCCHINI (2 MEDIUM ZUCCHINIS), SLICED VERY THINLY

2 TEASPOONS OLIVE OIL

½ TEASPOON <u>EACH</u>: GARLIC GRANULES *AND* SEASONED SALT

¼ TEASPOON SALT-FREE LEMON-PEPPER

1. Place the zucchini slices in a medium bowl and toss very well with all of the remaining ingredients.
2. Spread out in a single layer in your food dehydrator (I use a *ParaFlexx* sheet as it makes for much easier clean-up) and dry at 105° F. for about 10 hours, or until you can no longer stand the delicious smell.
3. Store in an airtight container at room temperature. These don't last long in our house!

SERVES 2; GF/SF/GREEN

Tip: An Excalibur food dehydrator is an excellent investment. Drying at 105° F. still makes for "living" foods, and is a great way to provide on-the-go snacks that are totally healthy!

Funky Chunky Guacamole Wrap

This is a very simple and delicious way to enjoy raw food. It's satisfying, nourishing, and leaves you feeling light and healthy. If you are serving this to children (or other peeps who prefer milder foods), substitute a double batch of "Kid's Choice Guacamole" (page 101) for this fairly spicy version.

GUACAMOLE:

2 RIPE AVOCADOS

½ CUP CHOPPED TOMATOES (FLAVORFUL TOMATOES SUCH AS CHERRY OR GRAPE ARE IDEAL)

⅓ CUP FINELY MINCED WHITE, YELLOW, OR RED ONION

2 LARGE CLOVES GARLIC, MINCED OR PRESSED

3 TABLESPOONS MINCED JALAPENO (SEE PAGE 39 FOR TIPS)

2 TABLESPOONS EACH: FRESH LIME JUICE *AND* CHOPPED FRESH CILANTRO

½ TEASPOON SEA SALT

FILLINGS (USE ANY COMBINATION OF THE FOLLOWING):

ALFALFA SPROUTS (PAGE 191), GRATED CARROTS, CHOPPED TOMATO, MINCED CILANTRO, THINLY SLICED RED ONION, GRATED CABBAGE, AND/OR SUNFLOWER SEEDS.

LETTUCE WRAP THINGS UP: 6 LARGE LETTUCE LEAVES (ROMAINE OR RED LEAF)

TANG IT ALL: 6 FRESH LIME WEDGES

1. Begin by making the guacamole. Place the flesh of one avocado in a medium bowl. Mash it well with a fork. Chop the flesh of the other avocado into small or medium sized chunks. Add it to the bowl and gently mix it into the mashed avocado. This will lend you a creamy base, but with lots of funky, chunky avocado pieces remaining. Stir in the additional guacamole items and stir well to combine. Set aside.
2. Prepare the fillings you wish to use and set them aside.
3. Wash and dry your lettuce leaves and remove the tough portion of their stem bases.
4. Spread the guacamole evenly over the middle portion of a lettuce leaf and top it with your desired fillings. If you live life on the tangy side, squeeze a little lime juice over the top.
5. Roll the bottom of the leaf up and over the fillings and then fold the sides in. Roll up like a burrito. Repeat. Repeat. Repeat…and serve.

SERVES 4; 30 MINUTES OR UNDER! GF/SF/BLUE

Raw Radiance Superballs

While hiking through an aspen forest, the idea for these little nuggets came to me. Although there are a million and one energy bars on the market, a picky monkey like me was yet to be totally satisfied with any of them. Sure, some taste great and others are relatively healthy. However, I wanted a truly fresh and *supremely* nourishing snack that was also simple, easy to make, and free from added sweeteners. The ingredients I have used here are specially selected because they are all superfoods. Amaranth is ridiculously nutrient rich and strengthening, whereas almonds are alkalinizing and very nourishing to the body and mind. Figs are energizing and extremely high in calcium and fiber. Although nettles are not as well known, they are available in most herb shops and health food stores. They're extraordinarily nourishing and an excellent energy builder. Knowing all of this, you can count on this super-snack to really keep you going!

¼ CUP <u>EACH</u>: DRY AMARANTH GRAIN *AND* WHOLE RAW ALMONDS

¾ CUP DRIED FIGS (STEMS REMOVED)

2 TABLESPOONS DRIED NETTLES (OPTIONAL BUT AWESOME)

⅛ TEASPOON <u>EACH</u>: SEA SALT *AND* GROUND CINNAMON

OPTIONAL COATING: FINELY SHREDDED COCONUT

1. Soak and sprout the amaranth according to the instructions on page 191. This will take about 2-3 days.
2. Once the amaranth is relatively tender, place it in a food processor along with all of the remaining ingredients. Blend until the ingredients are very well mixed and the figs are emulsified.
3. Pinch off small bits of the mix and roll them into 1-inch balls. If desired, roll in coconut until evenly coated. Place on a plate or in a covered container. They will store, refrigerated in an airtight container, for up to a week.

MAKES 14 1-INCH SUPERBALLS

GF/SF/GREEN

For a more savory snack, use only ¼ cup of the dried figs. From there you can add more of them into the mix as desired.

Sprouting

I have always been intimidated by those endlessly long charts of what to sprout and how long to sprout. Therefore, I've simplified things here by giving you just the basics, plus a few tips to help you avoid some common obstacles. Why sprout at home, you ask? Mainly, sprouting at home will ensure that you have truly fresh sprouts, rather than the half-gone ones you often see at the market. Plus, sprouting provides you with an incredibly inexpensive and nourishing food source. It is also surprisingly easy to incorporate into just about any daily routine. Notably, sprouts are one of the most nutritious foods available, as sprouting a seed or legume makes it exponentially higher in nutrients.

EASY, FOOLPROOF "SPROUTABLES:"

ALFALFA SEEDS (ONE TABLESPOON SEEDS=ABOUT ONE QUART OF SPROUTS)

DRY BARLEY AND DRY AMARANTH (THESE WILL ONLY DOUBLE IN SIZE AT THE MOST)

DRY GARBANZO BEANS/CHICKPEAS (¾ CUP DRY BEANS=ABOUT ONE QUART OF SPROUTS)

DRY LENTILS (¾ CUP DRY LENTILS=ABOUT ONE QUART OF SPROUTS)

THINGS THAT MAKE SPROUTING EASY:

WIDE MOUTH BALL GLASS JARS

SMALL DISHES OR BOWLS (ABOUT 4 INCHES WIDE) TO SET THE JARS IN (FOR DRAINAGE)

SPROUTING LIDS (THESE SCREW ONTO WIDE MOUTH JARS AND COME WITH VARIOUS SIZED HOLES TO

ACCOMMODATE DIFFERENT SIZED SPROUTS), PLEASE SEE NOTE ON PAGE 192

ALSO GOOD TO HAVE ON HAND:

POWDERED KELP (SEE PAGE 252)

HOW TO SPROUT:

1. Place the appropriate amount of sproutables (alfalfa seeds, barley, amaranth, or legumes) in a wide mouth glass jar. Cover with plenty of water, keeping in mind that the sproutables will expand in size as they soak. If desired, you can add a pinch of kelp to the soaking water to increase the mineral content. Alfalfa seeds seem to do better when soaked for around 6 hours or less, while the other items can be soaked overnight (8-10 hours).

2. After your sproutables have soaked sufficiently, you will want to screw on one of the sprouting lids (or secure some cheesecloth around the top with a rubber band). Choose a lid with appropriately sized holes. For example, for alfalfa sprouts or amaranth, use the lid with the smallest sized holes. Pour all of the soaking water out, through the lid and into the sink (please see note on the bottom of page 192). Next, fill the jar with water, allowing it to overflow until the water runs clear. Pour the water out.

3. *Gently* shake the sproutables around the jar to spread them out as much as you can. Give them a little elbow room. Place the jar upside-down to drain at a 45° angle in the small dish or bowl. Leave them until that evening (or the next morning if you are doing this at night).

4. From that point, you will be spending about 30 seconds on them every morning and every night until they're done. Each morning and night, rinse them well until the water overflows and runs clear. Then pour the water out, shake the sprouts around the glass jar *gently*, and store them at a 45° angle in the small dish until the next session.

5. As the sprouts get bigger, you may wish to change the type of lid you are using. This especially applies to alfalfa sprouts. As they get bigger, using a lid with larger holes will help wash away the hulls during the rinsing times.

6. Continue to rinse and repeat until your sprouts are done. For alfalfa sprouts, this usually takes about four days, or until the end splits into two parts (kind of like a "T"). For barley or amaranth, this usually

takes two or three days, or until they are tender enough to chew. For garbanzos, this usually takes about four days, or until they are just under one inch long. For lentils, this also takes about four days, or until they are roughly half an inch long.

7. For the barley, amaranth, garbanzos, and lentils, you can now refrigerate your sprouts for a few days in an airtight container. For the alfalfa sprouts, you will want to "green" them in order to increase their nutritional content (chlorophyll = goodness). To do this, place them in sunlight for a few hours (in their clear glass jar), turning them toward the sun as needed, until the tops have turned a happy shade of green. Then place them immediately in the fridge in an airtight container where they will usually last for a few days.

Troubleshooting Tips:

♥There is a fine line between perfectly pleasant and spoiled rotten—don't let your sprouty babies sprout too long, as they can spoil *very* quickly. Even just an extra half day in the jar can make a good sprout turn bad.

♥If you are using the recommended lids, be careful not to screw them on *too* tightly. I have often screwed them on so securely that I almost had to get a hammer! I am not sure how they mystically expand, but it's something to be aware of.

♥If your sprouts are spoiling or not coming out as you had hoped, you can try varying the soaking time. The perfect amount of time for one person may not work for another, due to climate differences and amount of exposed light, etc. You may also try keeping your sprouts out of the light (aside from greening the alfalfa sprouts) and see if this helps. Another thing you can try is adding an extra rinse session daily. It is important to remember that *sprouts generally prefer to be kept moist*. Sometimes learning to sprout can take a few tries, but I know that if I can do it, you definitely can too!

GF/SF/Green (as green as it gets, baby!)

Sprouting lids are available in many health food stores and online. However, you can instead use cheesecloth (fastened with a rubber band to keep it on the jar). I much prefer the lids, though, because they are so user-friendly, easy to clean, and work wonderfully to eliminate hulls.

INSTEAD OF POURING THE KELP-LADEN SOAKING WATER OUT INTO THE SINK, YOU CAN INSTEAD WATER YOUR PLANTS WITH IT. THEY'LL LOVE YOU FOR IT!

Chapter Fourteen: This, That, and Bread!

Need some croutons or crazy flavored popcorn?
You've come to the right place.

Chicky Baby Seasoning

This seasoning works great for gravies and as an all-purpose "chicken" flavoring—plus it only takes five minutes to toss together! I stopped buying expensive, clumpy, pre-made vegetarian chicken seasonings when I realized how easy it was to make my own. I also love how healthy this version is, as it's totally free from suspicious ingredients and chock full of B-vitamins from the nutritional yeast. Incidentally, this was a favorite item of my recipe testers. They loved it so much they inspired *me* to use it more!

I CUP NUTRITIONAL YEAST POWDER

3 TABLESPOONS EACH: DRIED ONION GRANULES *AND* SEASONED SALT

2 TEASPOONS EACH: CELERY SEED *AND* DRIED GARLIC GRANULES

2 TABLESPOONS DRIED PARSLEY FLAKES

½ TEASPOON EACH: GROUND BLACK PEPPER *AND* WHITE PEPPER

I TEASPOON EACH: LEMON-PEPPER, ORGANIC SUGAR, DRIED DILL, *AND* DRIED ROSEMARY

Simply combine all of the ingredients with a whisk or spoon until well mixed. Store in an airtight container out of direct sunlight. This will keep for several months.

MAKES ABOUT I ½ CUPS OF SEASONING MIX; 30 MINUTES OR UNDER! GF/SF/GREEN

Vegetarian "Chicken" Broth

This is a wonderful replacement for processed liquid "chicken" broth. Or so the chickies tell me.

I CUP WATER

I TABLESPOON "CHICKY BABY SEASONING" (RECIPE ABOVE)

Stir well and use as you would any liquid broth. This will keep (refrigerated) for about 10 days.

MAKES ABOUT I CUP OF BROTH; 30 MINUTES OR UNDER! GF/SF/GREEN

Seaweed Gomasio

This is a tasty, nourishing condiment to put on just about anything. *Almost*. You may notice that this version is less salty than many store bought gomasio mixtures—if you prefer, you may double the salt.

I CUP BROWN (UNHULLED) SESAME SEEDS

½ TEASPOON EACH: DRIED GARLIC GRANULES *AND* DULSE FLAKES

I TEASPOON SEA SALT

¼ TEASPOON KELP POWDER

¼ SHEET NORI, TORN INTO SMALL PIECES

Place all of the ingredients in a food processor and blend just until the sesame seeds are broken down and all of the seaweed is in small speckles. Don't over-blend, or you'll end up with seaweed tahini!

MAKES ABOUT I CUP OF GOMASIO; 30 MINUTES OR UNDER! GF/SF/GREEN

194

Indian Seed and Spice Blends

This is actually two recipes, as these mixtures are to be combined and stored separately. However, as they are generally used in conjunction with each other, they're under one recipe heading. These mixes make it very easy to throw an authentic Indian curry together in no time. To use these blends in a curry, start by sautéing some of the seeds blend in hot oil until the seeds begin to pop. Then, add some of the spice blend and sauté another minute. Add your veggies, beans, and whatever else you fancy and you're good to go!

INDIAN SEEDS BLEND:

2 TABLESPOONS EACH: BLACK MUSTARD SEEDS, CUMIN SEEDS, AND SESAME SEEDS

INDIAN SPICE BLEND:

1 TABLESPOON EACH: ASAFETIDA, RED CHILI FLAKES, AND DRIED TURMERIC

4 TABLESPOONS EACH: CUMIN POWDER AND CORIANDER POWDER

1 TEASPOON FENUGREEK

4 TEASPOONS AMCHUR POWDER (DRIED MANGO), OPTIONAL (SEE PAGE 251)

1. Mix the seeds together and store them in a glass (or otherwise airtight) container. They will keep indefinitely.
2. Mix the spices together until they are well combined. Store them in a glass (or otherwise airtight) container. They will keep for several months, or indefinitely.

MAKES ABOUT ⅓ CUP OF THE SEEDS MIX AND ABOUT ½ CUP OF THE SPICE BLEND

30 MINUTES OR UNDER! GF/SF/GREEN

Beaumonde

Thanks to Ruth (from Joy's Natural Foods) for this idea! We were chatting about white pepper one day (yes, I'm a nerd) when she suggested this seasoning. I had never heard of it before and quickly got busy developing a version of this classic, yet simple seasoning. I was hooked! It is so easy to make and tastes wonderful on all manner of vegetables, savory dishes, and potatoes. As it contains a large percentage of salt, be sure to add it to dishes that aren't already salty enough.

2 TEASPOONS DRIED CELERY SEED

4 TEASPOONS EACH: SEA SALT AND DRIED ONION GRANULES

¼ TEASPOON WHITE PEPPER

1. If you have a mortar and pestle, you can use it to crush the celery seed. Mix the crushed celery seed with the remaining ingredients. If you don't have a mortar and pestle, simply combine the whole celery seed with the remaining ingredients and blend in a food processor.
2. Store this in an airtight container out of direct sunlight. This will definitely keep indefinitely.

MAKES ABOUT ¼ CUP OF BEAUMONDE; 30 MINUTES OR UNDER! GF/SF/GREEN

Savory Mineral Sprinkle

This extremely healthful seasoning was inspired by herbalist Jennie Blechman. This is a very nutrient-rich, tasty mixture you can shake over just about anything. This recipe is totally salt-free, so keep that in mind when using it. Nettles are a very powerful, nutritious food that build energy and boost the immune system. Dulse is very high in iron, potassium, vitamins, and minerals. Finally, the nutritional yeast is a great source of B-vitamins. Shake the sprinkle and feel the twinkle!

3 TABLESPOONS DRIED NETTLE LEAVES

5 TABLESPOONS RAW SESAME SEEDS

2 TABLESPOONS NUTRITIONAL YEAST POWDER

I TEASPOON EACH: DRIED GARLIC GRANULES AND DRIED ONION GRANULES

2 TEASPOONS EACH: DULSE FLAKES AND DRIED DILL

½ TEASPOON GROUND BLACK PEPPER

I TABLESPOON CELERY SEED

⅛ TEASPOON GROUND CAYENNE

1. Whirl the nettles in a food processor until they become ground into small flakes.
2. Add the remaining ingredients and process *just* until everything is well combined and lightly ground. Don't allow the sesame seeds to break down too much, or you will have savory tahini on your hands! Store refrigerated in an airtight jar. This should keep for several months.

MAKES ½ CUP OF SEASONING; 30 MINUTES OR UNDER! GF/SF/GREEN

Creamy Fresh Herb Spread

This is a simple, delicious sandwich spread, especially fitting in the summer when there are lots of fresh herbs available. Of course, you can vary the herbs according to what you prefer. This highly flavorful spread is guaranteed to make any sandwich come to life…which may scare you.

½ CUP "VEGENAISE" VEGAN MAYONNAISE

2 TABLESPOONS MINCED *FRESH* BASIL

I TABLESPOON EACH (PACKED AND MINCED): *FRESH* CHIVES *AND FRESH* DILL

I TEASPOON DIJON MUSTARD

2 CLOVES GARLIC, MINCED OR PRESSED

OPTIONAL: SEA SALT AND BLACK PEPPER TO TASTE

Simply stir all of the ingredients together until well combined. Store refrigerated in an airtight container for up to a week.

MAKES ABOUT ¾ CUP SPREAD; 30 MINUTES OR UNDER! GF/BLUE

Summer Surprise Lemonade

This lemony, zingy drink is absolutely *the* thing on a hot day. However, you may consider this recipe as a starting point, as I've found people really vary on their lemonade preferences. If you prefer a sweeter lemonade, you may wish to add more sugar (or some agave nectar). This version is what I personally like to drink...because lemon is my native tongue.

1 ½ CUPS ICE CUBES
2 TABLESPOONS (PACKED OR LIGHTLY PACKED) *FRESH* MINT LEAVES, OPTIONAL
1 CUP FRESHLY SQUEEZED LEMON JUICE (SAVE THE LEMON SKINS IF THEY'RE ORGANIC)
½ CUP ORGANIC "WHITE" SUGAR (NOT POWDERED)
2 CUPS WATER, PREFERABLY FILTERED

1. Place the ice cubes in a bowl. Rub the mint leaves into the ice cubes to release the minty oils. Next, place the fresh mint and ice cubes in a pitcher.
2. Add the lemon juice, sugar, and water to the pitcher. If you have some organic lemon skins set aside, wash them and toss them in as well. Stir with a long wooden spoon to mix everything together very well.
3. Serve immediately (or allow this to "marinate" in the fridge if you prefer). If the mint starts to look sad at any point, it can be removed, replaced with fresh mint, or cheered up with a basil joke.

SERVES 3-4; 30 MINUTES OR UNDER! GF/SF/BLUE

PREFER ICE COLD TEA TO LEMONADE?

HERE'S AN EXTREMELY VITALIZING SUN TEA THAT I CALL "LIQUID RADIANCE TEA."

• 2 TABLESPOONS <u>EACH</u>: DRIED MINT, DRIED NETTLES, DRIED ALFALFA LEAF, *AND* DRIED HIBISCUS (OPTIONAL)
• 2 TEA BAGS OF GREEN TEA WITH MINT (DECAF)
• 2 TEA BAGS OF BLUEBERRY TEA

PLACE THE MINT, NETTLES, ALFALFA, AND HIBISCUS IN SECURE CLOTH TEA BAGS OR OTHER TEA-APPROPRIATE CONTAINERS. IF YOU CAN FIND A "TOBY TEABOY," THEY WORK GREAT! PLACE ALONG WITH THE TEA BAGS IN A GALLON SIZE GLASS CONTAINER AND FILL WITH WATER. ALLOW TO STEEP IN THE SUN FOR SEVERAL HOURS, THEN REFRIGERATE. THIS WILL KEEP FOR ABOUT 3 DAYS IN THE FRIDGE. AHHHH...REFRESHING, REVITALIZING, <u>AND</u> REJUVENATING!

Supercorn!

If this was a report in grade school, it would be covered in smiley faces, gold stars, and "excellent!" stickers. If this was a superhero, it would have a large, green popcorn puff inside a golden shield and possess the superpowers to nourish the bodies of children and adults while simultaneously satisfying their taste buds. Thanks to Jennie Blechman for the idea of roasting garlic right in the pan—absolute *genius*!

POPPING OIL:

1 TABLESPOON OIL
(OLIVE OR COCONUT)

POPCORN:

½ CUP POPCORN KERNELS

GENIUS:

8 SMALL, WHOLE
GARLIC CLOVES, UNPEELED

FLAVORAMA:

• 4 TABLESPOONS OIL (MELTED COCONUT OR OLIVE)
• 1 TABLESPOON DULSE FLAKES (SEE PAGE 251)
• ½ TEASPOON GARLIC GRANULES
• 1 ½ TEASPOONS DRIED DILL
• 2 TABLESPOONS NUTRITIONAL YEAST POWDER
• 1 TEASPOON EACH: ONION GRANULES, KELP
POWDER, *AND* LEMON-PEPPER
• ½ TEASPOON PLUS ⅛ TEASPOON SEA SALT

1. Place a heavy pot with a tight fitting lid over medium-high heat. Add the popping oil, one kernel of popcorn, and the whole garlic cloves.

2. When the kernel pops, add the remaining popcorn. To prevent it from burning, you will want to shake the pot frequently. This will distribute the oil and keep the popcorn kernels and garlic from sticking to the bottom of the pan. Be sure to hold onto the lid with hot pads while you shake it! Continue to cook until the popping slows down to 1-2 seconds in between pops. Remove from heat.

3. Empty the popped corn and garlic into a very large bowl. Drizzle evenly with the 4 tablespoons of oil and sprinkle with the remaining seasonings. I like to use a rubber spatula to stir everything up, so that all of the seasonings are properly distributed.

4. Eat the popcorn. When you come across a garlic clove in your endeavor, peel it and eat it along with a handful of popcorn. If you are sharing your popcorn with another person, you may want to keep a tally of how many garlic cloves you each have eaten. This may help you avoid a brawl over the last clove.

MAKES: A BIG BOWL OF FLAVOR; 30 MINUTES OR UNDER! GF/SF/Blue

Everything Nice Popcorn

Cinnamon, vanilla, and sugar. Do I *really* have to say anything else?

4 TEASPOONS OIL (COCONUT, SUNFLOWER, OR NON-VIRGIN OLIVE)
½ CUP POPCORN KERNELS
2 TABLESPOONS EACH: NON-HYDROGENATED MARGARINE, AGAVE NECTAR, *AND* ORGANIC SUGAR
¼ TEASPOON SEA SALT
1 TEASPOON EACH: GROUND CINNAMON *AND* VANILLA EXTRACT

1. Please follow steps 1 and 2 from the directions above (Supercorn), but leave out the bit about the garlic.

2. In a small pan, melt the margarine. Stir in the agave, sugar, salt, cinnamon, and vanilla and mix well.

3. Drizzle the sweetness over the popped corn, using a rubber spatula to mix everything together well. That's about all you need me for! Enjoy your bowl of delightful flavors—and I hope you like your movie.

SERVES ABOUT 4; 30 MINUTES OR UNDER! GF/Blue

Alethea's Apple Dip

This is a very simple recipe that I devised as a way to get my daughter to eat almond butter and apples on a regular basis. It makes for a quick, easy, nourishing snack.

¼ CUP BROWN RICE SYRUP

2 TABLESPOONS <u>EACH</u>: SMOOTH PEANUT BUTTER, ALMOND BUTTER, PURE MAPLE SYRUP, *AND* WATER

¼ TEASPOON GROUND CINNAMON

Stir all of the ingredients together until thoroughly combined. Serve as a dip for sliced apples—as you may have already guessed. This will store in an airtight container, refrigerated, for several weeks.

MAKES ABOUT ¾ CUP OF DIP; 30 MINUTES OR UNDER! GF/SF/BLUE

Fruit Be-Bops

I recently introduced this snack to a group of children as "fruit kebobs." After a few bites, everyone started to sing of their newfound love for "fruit *be-bops*!" Obviously, I think their name is much better. These only take about five minutes to prepare and are a very healthy, satisfying snack for children (or immature adults) of any age. Incidentally, this dish is a great way to get kids involved in cooking. They can help sift, stir, and place the fruit onto the skewers.

CHOCOLATE PEANUT BUTTER SAUCE:

1½ TABLESPOONS <u>EACH</u>: CAROB POWDER *AND* COCOA POWDER*

2 TABLESPOONS CREAMY PEANUT BUTTER

⅛ TEASPOON SEA SALT

3 TABLESPOONS PURE MAPLE SYRUP

2 TABLESPOONS NONDAIRY MILK

BE-BOPS:

1 RED APPLE, CORED AND CUT INTO 1-INCH CHUNKS

2 BANANAS, CUT INTO 1-INCH PIECES

½ LB. STRAWBERRIES, STEMS REMOVED

SPEAR ME (THE DETAILS):
• WOODEN SKEWERS (FOR KEBABS)**

1. To prevent lumps, begin by sifting the cocoa and carob powders. If you don't have a sifter, you can place them in a fine mesh strainer over a bowl. Push them through the strainer and into the bowl using the back of a spoon.
2. Mix the powders with the peanut butter, salt, maple syrup, and milk until very smooth.
3. Spear the fruit pieces onto the skewers in an attractive pattern. Serve with the sauce as a dip.

SERVES 4; 30 MINUTES OR UNDER! GF/SF/BLUE

*If desired, you can use <u>only</u> carob *or* cocoa. However, I find that combining the two lends a chocolate flavor, but with the additional nutritional benefits of carob.
**If your children are too young to handle skewers without injuring themselves (or the dog), you can substitute pretzel sticks, straws, or just serve the fruit unskewered.

Easy Apple-Cinnamon Compote

This light and healthy concoction is perfect as a topping for pancakes, waffles, French toast, or oatmeal. If you prefer a *richer* version of this whole scenario, you may add a bit of margarine and brown sugar.

2 RED DELICIOUS APPLES, DICED INTO ½-INCH PIECES (2⅔ CUPS DICED APPLE)

1 CUP UNSWEETENED APPLE JUICE

1 ½ TEASPOONS GROUND CINNAMON

4 TEASPOONS PURE MAPLE SYRUP

½ TEASPOON <u>EACH</u>: VANILLA EXTRACT *AND* FRESH LEMON JUICE

1. Place all ingredients (except for the lemon juice) in a pot set to medium-high heat. Bring to a boil.
2. Reduce the heat to medium-low and simmer for about 20 minutes, stirring occasionally, until the mixture has thickened and is somewhat syrupy. Stir in the lemon juice and combine well. Serve warm. This will keep in an airtight container, refrigerated, for a week or more.

MAKES ABOUT 2 CUPS OF COMPOTE; 30 MINUTES OR UNDER! GF/SF/GREEN

Quick and Delightful Zatar Wedges

This is a unique (and incredibly easy) sidekick to make that is even a hit with children! Zatar is a tangy, yummy blend of thyme, sumac, sesame seeds, and spices. If your local health food store doesn't carry it, you can find it in many ethnic markets or online (see page 253). It has a very long shelf life and makes a terrific addition to salads, the "Creamy Hummus" (page 79), and the "Fatoush Salad" (page 109).

TWO 8-INCH SPROUTED OR WHOLE GRAIN TORTILLAS OR PITA ROUNDS (OR GLUTEN-FREE TORTILLAS)

2 TEASPOONS OLIVE OIL (PREFERABLY EXTRA-VIRGIN)

3 TABLESPOONS ZATAR MIX (SEE PAGE 253)

ADDITIONAL 2 TEASPOONS OF OLIVE OIL (OR OIL IN A SPRAYER)

1. Preheat the oven to 400° F. Cut the tortillas into eight pieces each, as if you were cutting a pizza. You should end up with sixteen pie-shaped wedges.
2. Place the wedges on a large, lightly oiled cookie sheet. Brush them with the 2 teaspoons of oil so that each piece is lightly coated with oil. Sprinkle the zatar evenly over the wedges (if it seems like too much, it's just right). Spray or drizzle them (right over the zatar) with the remaining 2 teaspoons of oil.
3. Bake for 5-10 minutes, or until the tortilla portion of the wedges is lightly browned. Serve immediately.

SERVES ABOUT 4; 30 MINUTES OR UNDER! GF (WITH SUBSTITUTION)/SF/GREEN

Banana Muffins to Write Home About

Yes, you will be notifying your family after trying these healthy, yet freakishly delicious muffins. Please be sure to use fresh (not frozen and thawed) bananas in this recipe, as pre-frozen bananas can create excess moisture when baked.

FLEGG (FLAX EGG REPLACER):

2 TABLESPOONS GROUND FLAXSEED (FLAX MEAL)

3 TABLESPOONS BOILING WATER

STREUSEL TOPPING (OPTIONAL):

2 TABLESPOONS EACH: PACKED BROWN SUGAR *AND* FLOUR (WHOLE WHEAT PASTRY OR GLUTEN-FREE)

½ TEASPOON GROUND CINNAMON

1 TABLESPOON NON-HYDROGENATED MARGARINE

DRY INGREDIENTS:

½ CUP ROLLED OATS (OR QUINOA FLAKES IF YOU ARE GLUTEN INTOLERANT—SEE PAGE 44)

1¼ CUPS WHOLE WHEAT PASTRY FLOUR (OR GLUTEN-FREE ALL-PURPOSE FLOUR)

2½ TEASPOONS BAKING POWDER

½ TEASPOON SEA SALT

1½ TEASPOONS GROUND CINNAMON

¼ TEASPOON GROUND NUTMEG

⅔ CUP ORGANIC SUGAR OR SUCANAT

WET INGREDIENTS:

4 VERY, VERY RIPE BANANAS (RED ALERT! THIS IS EXTREMELY IMPORTANT—DO NOT USE VAGUELY RIPE BANANAS, OR THESE MUFFINS WILL LACK SWEETNESS.)

1 TEASPOON VANILLA EXTRACT

⅓ CUP OIL (SUNFLOWER, NON-VIRGIN OLIVE, OR SAFFLOWER)

2 TABLESPOONS NONDAIRY MILK

1. Preheat the oven to 350° F. Whisk the flaxseed and boiling water together in a small bowl. Allow the mixture to sit for 5-10 minutes, or until gooey.

2. If you will be using the optional topping, place the streusel ingredients in a small bowl and combine them well. If necessary, use your fingers to mix the ingredients together until the streusel is crumbly and thoroughly combined. Set aside.

3. Place the dry ingredients in a medium bowl and mix very well using a whisk or sifter. Set aside.

4. Smoosh the bananas very well in a large bowl. I use a potato masher for this, but a fork would also work. Add the rest of the wet ingredients to the bananas and combine well. Add the gooey flegg mixture to the wet banana mixture and stir until uniformly combined.

5. Add the dry mixture to the large bowl with the wet banana mixture in it. Stir them together until well combined, but don't over-mix.

6. Spray a dozen muffin cups lightly with oil (or place paper liners in each cup). Fill each muffin cup or liner with about ⅓ cup of the batter.

7. If streusel is in your immediate future, sprinkle some evenly on top of each muffin.

8. Bake for 25-30 minutes, or until nicely browned and a knife inserted in the center comes out clean. After a few minutes, take a knife and go around the edges of each muffin to loosen them. Remove to a cooling rack or plate. Notify your relatives (or not, if you don't like to share!).

MAKES 12 MUFFINS; GF (WITH SUBSTITUTIONS)/SF (WITHOUT STREUSEL)/BLUE

Lemon-Poppy Seed Muffins with Zesty Lemon Glaze

The most frequent thing I hear when serving these muffins is: "How can you *possibly* expect me to eat just one of these?" Luckily, these are much healthier than typical lemon poppy seed muffins due to the use of whole grains, flax, and animal-free ingredients.

FLEGG (FLAX EGG REPLACER):

2 TABLESPOONS GROUND FLAXSEED (FLAX MEAL)

3 TABLESPOONS BOILING WATER

DRY INGREDIENTS:

2 CUPS WHOLE WHEAT PASTRY FLOUR (OR ALL-PURPOSE GLUTEN-FREE FLOUR)

½ CUP ORGANIC "WHITE" SUGAR (NOT POWDERED)

½ TEASPOON SEA SALT

1 TEASPOON <u>EACH</u>: BAKING POWDER *AND* BAKING SODA

3 TABLESPOONS POPPY SEEDS

WET INGREDIENTS:

¾ CUP NONDAIRY MILK

¼ CUP <u>EACH</u>: *FRESH* LEMON JUICE, OIL (SUNFLOWER, SAFFLOWER, OR NON-VIRGIN OLIVE) *AND* PURE MAPLE SYRUP

1 HEAPING TABLESPOON MINCED OR GRATED ORGANIC LEMON ZEST

1 TEASPOON VANILLA EXTRACT

ZESTY LEMON GLAZE:

¼ CUP PLUS 2 TEASPOONS ORGANIC POWDERED SUGAR

½ TEASPOON MINCED OR CHOPPED ORGANIC LEMON ZEST

1 ½ TEASPOONS *FRESH* LEMON JUICE

⅛ TEASPOON VANILLA EXTRACT

1. Preheat the oven to 400° F. Whisk the flaxseed and boiling water together in a large bowl. Allow to sit for 5-10 minutes, or until gooey. Real gooey.
2. Mix the dry ingredients together in a medium bowl, using a whisk (or sifter) until thoroughly combined. Set aside.
3. When the flegg has become sufficiently gooey, add all of the wet ingredients to the flegg bowl. Stir the wet ingredients into the flegg mixture until well combined.
4. Next, add the dry mixture to the large bowl with the wet ingredients. Stir them together until well combined, but do not over-mix.
5. Spray a dozen muffin cups lightly with oil (or place paper liners in each cup). Pour the batter evenly into each muffin cup or liner.
6. Bake the muffins for 20-30 minutes, or until they are golden brown and a knife inserted in the center comes out clean.
7. After a few minutes, take a knife and go around the edges of each muffin to loosen them. Gently remove them from the muffin tin and place them on a cooling rack or plate.
8. To make the Zesty Lemon Glaze: Place the powdered sugar in a small bowl and sift or whisk it (if necessary) to remove any lumps. Add the zest, juice, and vanilla to the bowl and stir well to combine.
9. Once the muffins have cooled a bit, drizzle the glaze over them. Now, see if *you* can eat just one!

MAKES 12 MUFFINS; GF (WITH SUBSTITUTION)/SF/BLUE

Whole Multigrain Bread

I love that this bread is crunchy on the outside, soft on the inside, and still contains absolutely no refined flours! Although this recipe takes about five hours from start to finish, the actual hands-on time is minimal. Besides, there is just nothing like the smell of homemade bread baking in the oven. If you don't have all of the different grains (such as millet, quinoa, or amaranth) on hand, you may substitute one for another, or omit them completely if you prefer.

6 CUPS WHOLE WHEAT FLOUR (DO NOT USE WHOLE WHEAT PASTRY FLOUR)

¼ CUP VITAL WHEAT GLUTEN

3 CUPS HOT WATER (ABOUT 110° F.)

¼ CUP PURE MAPLE SYRUP

2 PACKETS BAKING YEAST (¼ OZ. EACH)

¼ CUP EACH: DRY MILLET *AND* DRY QUINOA

½ CUP EACH: ROLLED OATS *AND* DRY AMARANTH

1 TABLESPOON SEA SALT

2 TABLESPOONS FLAXSEED MEAL (GROUND FLAXSEEDS)

¼ CUP OIL (SUNFLOWER, SAFFLOWER, OR NON-VIRGIN OLIVE)

1. Mix the flour and gluten together well, either with a sifter or wire whisk. Set aside.
2. Pour the hot water into the largest bowl you have. Stir in the maple syrup. Drop in the yeast (do not stir) and allow it to sit undisturbed for 5 minutes (until foamy). You may hang a "do not disturb" sign on the bowl if you like.
3. Gradually add about three cups of the flour/gluten mixture to the water-yeast-maple syrup bowl. Using a large spoon, stir them together until well mixed. Place a cookie sheet (or waxed paper) over the bowl and then place a towel on top of that. This will prevent the dough from rising and sticking to the towel. Set aside in a warm place and allow the dough to rise for about an hour, or until double in size.
4. Next, add in the millet, quinoa, oats, amaranth, salt, flaxseed meal, and oil and stir well to combine.
5. Add in some more of the flour/gluten mixture, stirring with the spoon until it becomes too difficult. At this point, you can begin kneading in most of the remaining flour/gluten mixture. Add just enough so that you can knead the bread. The dough should be slightly sticky and a little difficult to work with. If you put in too much flour, you will end up with a dry, dense bread.
6. Sprinkle some of the flour/gluten mixture (or additional whole wheat flour) onto the counter and begin kneading the bread on top of the floured surface. Add more flour/gluten as needed, but allow the dough to remain fairly sticky. Knead for about 5 minutes, or until you can poke a finger into it and the dough springs back a bit.
7. Form the dough into a ball-type shape and put it into the big bowl. Next, cover it as you did before. Allow it to rise again in a warm place for an hour, or until doubled in size.
8. Punch down the dough and divide it into two or three loaves. Knead each one separately for about 2 or 3 minutes on the floured counter. Place each loaf on a lightly oiled cookie sheet (or in an oiled bread pan), giving them enough room to spread out. If you like, you can slash the tops with a knife or braid the bread—now is the time to get a little too cute. Let the loaves rise, uncovered, for an hour in a warm spot.
9. Preheat the oven to 350° F. Sprinkle or spray the top of each loaf with a little water and bake for 45 minutes to an hour, or until the bread is very nicely browned and sounds hollow when tapped.
10. Please do yourself a favor and eat some of the bread while it's fresh and hot, preferably with a little of your favorite non-hydrogenated margarine on it. *Deeee-lish!*

MAKES TWO OR THREE LOAVES OF BREAD (DEPENDING ON SIZE); SF/BLUE

Rosemary Herb Pizza Crust

Here is a delectable 100% whole grain pizza crust that is very easy to make. For a complete pizza recipe, please see page 177 for the "Spinach Artichoke Pizza with Rosemary." Enjoy!

1 TABLESPOON PURE MAPLE SYRUP

1 ½ CUPS WATER, HEATED TO ABOUT 110° F.

¼ OZ. BAKING YEAST

2 CUPS WHOLE WHEAT PASTRY FLOUR

1 ½ CUPS WHOLE WHEAT FLOUR

1 ¼ TEASPOONS SEA SALT

1 TEASPOON <u>EACH</u>: DRIED BASIL, DRIED THYME, DRIED ROSEMARY, DRIED OREGANO, *AND* GARLIC GRANULES

2 TABLESPOONS OLIVE OIL (OR SUNFLOWER OR SAFFLOWER OIL)

1. Place the maple syrup and water in a large bowl and stir to combine. Drop in the yeast (do not stir) and allow it to sit undisturbed for 5 minutes, until it is foamy.
2. Stir in all of the remaining items. Knead on a floured surface for about 5-10 minutes. Ideally, the dough should be a little annoyingly sticky, as that will yield a better crust. However, if the dough is way, *way* too wet (which can happen with certain kinds of coarse flours), just add in a little more flour.
3. Cover the bowl with your pizza pan. Allow the dough to rise in a warm spot, covered, for about 45 minutes to an hour, until it has doubled in size.
4. Divide the dough into two balls* that are equal in size.
5. Preheat the oven to 400° F. Lightly oil two pizza pans (or one if you're only making one pizza now) and set aside.
6. To shape your pizza crust, place the dough in the center of the pan and evenly push the dough toward the outer edges of the pan. Form the outer rim by pinching up about ½-inch of dough around the edge of the pan. Make sure there are no gaps in the crust anywhere. If there are, simply pinch the dough together to "patch" it. Prick the crust with a fork a few times to ensure that it will not poof up too much while it's baking.
7. Pre-bake the crust for about 10-15 minutes, or until lightly browned.
8. Top with pizza sauce, spreading it evenly over the crust using the back of a spoon. Add your desired toppings and bake for another 10-20 minutes, or until the toppings and crust are golden brown. Allow the pizza to cool slightly (yeah, right) and cut into individual pieces.

MAKES TWO PIZZA CRUSTS; SF/BLUE

*If you will only be making one pizza now, you can place the other ball of dough in an airtight plastic bag at this point. It can be refrigerated for several days or stored in the freezer for a month or more. Simply allow it to thaw at room temperature (or overnight in the fridge) before using.

Whole Grain & Flax Banana Bread

Here's a delicious, unusual, and moist banana bread that contains no refined flours, cholesterol, or animal products. Three cheers for guilt-free goodies!

WET INGREDIENTS:

3 MASHED BANANAS (USE VERY RIPE BANANAS)*

¼ CUP OIL (SUNFLOWER, SAFFLOWER, OR NON-VIRGIN OLIVE)

6 OZ. CONTAINER OF PLAIN OR VANILLA SOY YOGURT

I TEASPOON VANILLA EXTRACT

DRY INGREDIENTS:

I CUP WHOLE WHEAT PASTRY FLOUR (OR ALL-PURPOSE GLUTEN-FREE FLOUR)

½ CUP EACH: WHOLE WHEAT FLOUR (OR ALL-PURPOSE GLUTEN-FREE FLOUR) AND DRY CORNMEAL

½ CUP PLUS 3 TABLESPOONS ORGANIC SUGAR OR SUCANAT

I TEASPOON GROUND CINNAMON

½ TEASPOON EACH: BAKING SODA, BAKING POWDER, AND SEA SALT

¼ TEASPOON GROUND NUTMEG

2 TABLESPOONS GOLDEN FLAXSEEDS (WHOLE)

I TABLESPOON GROUND FLAXSEED (FLAXSEED MEAL)

2 TEASPOONS POPPY SEEDS (OPTIONAL)

1. Preheat the oven to 350° F. Combine the wet ingredients well in a large bowl.

2. Combine the dry ingredients well in a separate bowl using a sifter or wire whisk if necessary.

3. When the dry ingredients are thoroughly combined and lump-free, add them to the bowl with the wet ingredients. Stir them together with a spoon *just* until well mixed (don't over-mix).

4. Lightly oil a bread/loaf pan and pour the batter into it (using a rubber spatula to make sure you get all of the batter into the pan).

5. Bake for an hour, or until the bread is golden brown and a knife inserted in the center comes out clean. This is especially fabuloso served warm with a little non-hydrogenated margarine. Get out the pom-poms!

MAKES ABOUT TEN SLICES OF BREAD
GF (W/ SUBSTITUTIONS)/BLUE

*I don't recommend using bananas that have been frozen, as they can often create excess, funky moisture in the batter.

Spiced Lime Tortilla Chips

This is a very quick and easy way to score yourself some healthy, warm, yummy tortilla chips.

12 CORN TORTILLAS (YELLOW AND/OR BLUE CORN TORTILLAS)

FRESH JUICE OF ½ LIME

OIL FOR SPRAYING OR BRUSHING (OLIVE, MELTED COCONUT, OR SUNFLOWER)

SEASONED SALT TO TASTE

OPTIONAL TO TASTE: CAYENNE PEPPER AND DRIED ONION GRANULES

1. Preheat the oven to 375° F. Lightly oil two cookie sheets and set them aside. Stack six tortillas on a cutting board and cut them into fourths with a sharp knife. Repeat with the other six tortillas to form a total of 48 pieces (chips).
2. Place the chips in a single layer on the cookie sheets. Spray (or brush) the chips lightly with oil. Evenly scatter the lime juice over them and lightly sprinkle the tops with your desired seasonings.
3. Bake for 5 minutes. Remove the pans from the oven and flip all of the chips over with a spatula (or your fingers). Put them back in the oven for another 3-5 minutes, then check them again. If any are crisp and lightly browned, remove them now. You may need to taste a few at this point for security purposes.
4. If needed, pop them back in the oven for another 3-5 minutes. Be sure to check them often, as they can burn without any formal notice. These are best served hot and fresh, but will keep in an airtight container for a few days. However, be sure to wait until the chips are fully cooled before sealing them in a container.

MAKES 48 TORTILLA CHIPS; 30 MINUTES OR UNDER! GF/SF/GREEN

Pan-Toasted Croutons

These decadently delicious croutons make any salad or soup a show-stopper.
Plus, they take less than fifteen minutes, start to finish!

2 TABLESPOONS EXTRA-VIRGIN OLIVE OIL

4 CUPS CUBED CRUSTY SOURDOUGH BREAD (CUT OR TORN INTO BITE-SIZED CUBES)

¼ TEASPOON EACH: SEA SALT, DRIED GARLIC GRANULES, AND DRIED ONION GRANULES

¾ TEASPOON DRIED ROSEMARY LEAF

GROUND BLACK PEPPER, TO TASTE

1. In a very large pan or wok, heat the oil over medium-high heat. When the oil is hot, toss in the bread and all of the seasonings. Immediately stir the mixture very well (using a heat proof spatula if possible) so that the bread cubes are evenly coated with the oil and seasonings.
2. Stir-fry the bread cubes for about 5-10 minutes, stirring often, until they are evenly golden browned. These are best served immediately, but can be stored (once cooled) in an airtight container.

SERVES 6-8; 30 MINUTES OR UNDER! SF/PURPLE

Righteously Rich Hot Cocoa

Sweet, warming, nostalgic, and delicious. Who doesn't like a steaming hot cup of cocoa?
Dogs and babies, maybe. This version is all natural and full of antioxidants from the dark chocolate.
Did you know that dark chocolate is also an energy booster and even helps to lower blood pressure?
Of course, those are the *real* reasons I make this drink.

2 TABLESPOONS <u>EACH</u>: WATER *AND* COCOA POWDER

¼ CUP ORGANIC SUGAR OR SUCANAT

1 TEASPOON NON-HYDROGENATED MARGARINE

2 TEASPOONS VANILLA EXTRACT

1 ½ CUPS NONDAIRY MILK

DASH OF SEA SALT

OPTIONAL ADDITIONS:
•FOR MEXICAN HOT CHOCOLATE, ADD A PINCH OF CINNAMON AND GROUND CAYENNE. YEAH, BABY!

1. In a small-medium pot, stir or whisk the water, cocoa powder, and sugar together very well in order to make a paste and remove any lumps. Next, cook over medium heat, stirring often, for 2 or 3 minutes.
2. Whisk in the remaining ingredients (with a wire whisk or fork) until well combined. Continue to cook, stirring often, until the cocoa is hot. Pour into mugs and serve. Mmmmm….

SERVES 2; 30 MINUTES OR UNDER! GF/PURPLE

Peach Mango Kanten

If you are unfamiliar with kanten, it's a very nutritious, gelled concoction of agar-agar
(a seaweed) and fruit. However, don't let that stop you! Agar-agar is not only *extremely* nourishing,
it is also calorie-free and functions as a flavor enhancer. Thus, this light and simple combination
is also unusually bright in flavor!

1 ½ CUPS PEACH-MANGO JUICE (DO NOT SUBSTITUTE ORANGE OR OTHER ACIDIC JUICES)

2-3 TEASPOONS AGAR-AGAR (AGAR) FLAKES*

1 CUP FRESH OR FROZEN RASPBERRIES OR SLICED STRAWBERRIES

1. Place the juice and agar-agar flakes into a small pot and bring to a boil over high heat. Reduce the heat to low and simmer for about 3-5 minutes. Remove from heat and allow to cool slightly.
2. Stir in the berries. Place the mixture in an airtight container (or a decorative mold if you've used the full amount of agar). Allow the kanten to chill overnight (or for several hours) in the fridge before serving. Kanten will keep for up to a week refrigerated in an airtight container.

SERVES 4; GF/SF/GREEN

*If you desire a very firm—think "jell-o"—end result, use the full 3 teaspoons of agar-agar flakes.
However, don't feel like you have to put tiny green marshmallows in it if you do this.

Chapter Fifteen: Specialty Soups

In this chapter, I have only included the soups nearest and dearest to my heart. Many are like good medicine when your health needs a boost. Each one is also tasty enough to impress guests. Who doesn't like a little bowl of love?

Mulligatawny

When I first tried mulligatawny in an Indian restaurant, I needed a few moments alone. Needless to say, I got busy at home trying to duplicate its creamy, lemony, and totally intoxicating flavor. I like to serve this with some fresh bread and a salad for a satisfying but relatively light supper. One word of caution, however: Please do not be tempted to serve this as a non-blended soup. Pureeing this is an essential step in bringing the flavors together. *Yuuummmmm…*

1 ¼ CUPS DRY RED LENTILS

2 TEASPOONS CUMIN SEEDS

4 CUPS WATER, PREFERABLY FILTERED

8 LARGE CLOVES GARLIC, PEELED

¾ CUP EACH: FRESH CILANTRO (PACKED) *AND* FRESH LEMON JUICE

2 CUPS COCONUT MILK

½ TEASPOON GROUND ASAFETIDA POWDER

1 TABLESPOON SEA SALT (OR LESS IF YOU PREFER)

2 TABLESPOONS NON HYDROGENATED MARGARINE

1 TEASPOON GROUND BLACK PEPPER

FINAL TOUCHES: FRESH CILANTRO AND LEMON SLICES

1. In a large pot with a lid, bring the lentils, cumin seeds, and water to a boil over medium-high heat. Adjust the lid so that it is only partially covering the pot (to allow the steam to escape). Reduce the heat to low and simmer until the lentils are very soft, about 25-35 minutes.

2. Chop the garlic thoroughly in a food processor or good blender. Add the cooked lentil mixture from step one to the food processor (or blender) and blend until very smooth, using a rubber spatula to scrape down the sides if necessary.

3. Add the remaining ingredients (aside from the garnishes) to the food processor and blend until very smooth and creamy.

4. This next step is optional, as you may wish to serve the soup immediately after blending it in step three. However, if you do wish to warm the soup and marry the flavors a bit more, remove it to a medium-large pot (using the rubber spatula if needed). Cook over low heat for about 5 minutes, stirring occasionally.

5. Serve immediately. If desired, top with additional cilantro sprigs and lemon slices. Moan.

SERVES 8; GF/BLUE

Note: If you have any leftover soup, it will store refrigerated in an airtight container for several days. However, as it will thicken substantially after being refrigerated, you will most likely need to thin it with a little water or coconut milk upon reheating it.

Old Fashioned "Chicken" Noodle Soup

I've purposely made this a *very* simple soup as I love being able to toss this together in under ten minutes. However, if you don't mind spending a little more time, you can add a hearty element to this as well, such as seasoned tofu or seitan cubes. As is, this version is reminiscent of the noodle and broth soups I grew up on during cold and flu season. This comforting soup, however, is much healthier as it is animal-free and contains nourishing vegetables and fresh garlic. Get a blanket, a big bowl of this soup, and cozy up!

2 TABLESPOONS PLUS 1 TEASPOON "CHICKY BABY SEASONING" (RECIPE ON PAGE 194)

2½ CUPS WATER

½ CUP FIDEO* NOODLES OR OTHER SMALL PASTA SHAPES SUCH AS STARS OR LETTERS

2 TABLESPOONS <u>EACH</u>: FINELY DICED CARROTS *AND* FINELY DICED CELERY

2 MEDIUM-LARGE CLOVES GARLIC, MINCED OR PRESSED

1 TEASPOON OLIVE OIL (OPTIONAL)

OPTIONAL GARNISH: 1 TABLESPOON MINCED FRESH CHIVES

1. If you don't have the "Chicky Baby Seasoning" on hand already, please see the directions on page 194 and whip up a batch. You won't regret having this baby on hand, and it lasts indefinitely.
2. Next, bring the water to a boil over high heat and add the noodles. At this point, you have the option of throwing the carrots and celery in now or adding them later. It depends on whether you prefer your veggies cooked more or if you like them fresher and crisper.
3. Allow the noodles to cook until al dente (see the package instructions for the amount of time needed for your noodles of choice). For small noodles, this is usually well under 5 minutes.
4. Turn the heat down to medium-low and toss in the carrots and celery if you have not yet done so. Add the garlic, oil (if using), and Chicky Baby Seasoning. Cook for another minute or less, just to blend the flavors together. Serve topped with the fresh chives if desired. Get cozy and feel the mama love!

SERVES 2; 30 MINUTES OR UNDER! GF (WITH SUBSTITUTION)/SF/Blue

*If you cannot find fideo noodles, simply break angel hair pasta into ½-inch pieces or use any other kind of small pasta shape that speaks to you. Additionally, if you cannot eat gluten, you may substitute a gluten-free pasta or other cooked grain (such as rice or barley) for the noodles.

Potato-Leek Soup with Caramelized Shallots

This soup is perfect for special occasions or anytime you want something *really* impressive. It's more time consuming than the other recipes in this chapter, but well worth it. The mellow, deep flavor of the roasted garlic and caramelized shallots make this truly rich tasting. Additionally, leeks are a great energy booster and garlic is well known for its immune-boosting properties.

2 SMALL BULBS (WHOLE HEADS) GARLIC

¼ CUP OIL (EXTRA-VIRGIN OLIVE, OLIVE, SUNFLOWER, OR SAFFLOWER)

2 LEEKS, CLEANED WELL, TRIMMED, AND CHOPPED (WHITE AND GREEN PARTS)

ONE LARGE ONION, CHOPPED FINELY

1½ TEASPOONS DRIED CELERY SEED

5 CUPS PEELED AND DICED POTATOES (DO NOT USE UNPEELED POTATOES IN THIS DISH)

4½ CUPS WATER, PREFERABLY FILTERED

2 TABLESPOONS "CHICKY BABY SEASONING" (PAGE 194) OR OTHER VEGAN "CHICKEN" SEASONING

2 TEASPOONS DRIED, GROUND CORIANDER

SHALLOT WE?

2 TABLESPOONS OIL (OLIVE, SUNFLOWER, SAFFLOWER, OR EXTRA-VIRGIN OLIVE)

1½ CUPS VERY THINLY SLICED SHALLOTS

1 TEASPOON ORGANIC SUGAR OR SUCANAT

S & P:

2 TEASPOONS SEA SALT (OR LESS IF YOU PREFER)

FRESHLY GROUND PEPPER TO TASTE

OPTIONAL GARNISHES:
- "PAN-TOASTED CROUTONS" (PAGE 206)
- FRESH ROSEMARY SPRIGS (WHOLE OR CHOPPED)

1. Preheat the oven to 350° F. Spray or coat the garlic bulbs lightly with oil and wrap them in foil. Bake for one hour, or until the garlic is fully roasted (soft and mushy on the inside). Set aside.
2. Heat the ¼ cup of oil in a medium-large soup pot over medium heat. Sauté the leeks and onion in the oil for several minutes, stirring often, until they become softened.
3. Add the celery seed and sauté for a few more minutes, stirring, until the leeks and onion are nicely golden browned. Add the potatoes, water, "Chicky Baby Seasoning," and coriander. Stir well to combine. Reduce heat to medium-low and simmer, covered, until the potatoes are tender (I usually insert a fork in a potato chunk after 20 minutes to see if the potatoes are soft enough).
4. While the soup is cooking, you can caramelize the shallots. Place the 2 tablespoons of oil along with the shallots and sugar in a small skillet. Set the heat to medium. Sauté, stirring often, until the shallots are very nicely browned—this will take at least 10 minutes. When they are gorgeous, remove them from heat.
5. When the potatoes are soft, remove the soup from heat. Cut the tops off of the garlic bulbs and squeeze the cloves of garlic into the soup. Mix very well and add the salt and pepper.
6. Puree the soup in a blender or food processor until very smooth (you may need to do this in batches).
7. Ladle the creamy goodness into bowls. Top evenly with the caramelized shallots. If desired, garnish each serving with some of the croutons. Finally, scatter a little chopped rosemary leaf on top (or place a whole rosemary sprig in each bowl, simply as eye candy). Serve.

SERVES 4-6; GF/SF/BLUE

Red Lentil, Spinach, & Lemon Soup

My mom longs for this soup whenever she's feeling under the weather. She equates it with
Nature's perfect medicine! Luckily, it's also a snap to make and tastes phenomenal.
Lemon lovers, this is just what the good doctor ordered!

2 TABLESPOONS PLUS 2 TEASPOONS OIL (SUNFLOWER, COCONUT, OLIVE, OR SAFFLOWER)

MEDIUM-LARGE ONION, FINELY CHOPPED (1 ½ CUPS CHOPPED ONION)

6 CUPS WATER, PREFERABLY FILTERED

1 CUP PLUS 2 TABLESPOONS DRY RED LENTILS

ZEST OF 1 LARGE ORGANIC LEMON (ABOUT 2 TEASPOONS GRATED OR FINELY MINCED ZEST)

IT'S THYME FOR FRESHNESS:

2 TEASPOONS MINCED FRESH THYME LEAVES, OPTIONAL

¼ CUP PLUS 2 TABLESPOONS *FRESH* LEMON JUICE (START WITH ¼ CUP IF YOU'RE LEMON-SHY)

½ CUP NONDAIRY MILK, PLAIN AND UNSWEETENED

4 LARGE CLOVES GARLIC, MINCED OR PRESSED

2 CUPS (LIGHTLY PACKED) FRESH BABY SPINACH

1 TABLESPOON SEA SALT (OR LESS IF YOU PREFER)

FRESH GROUND PEPPER TO TASTE

GREEN GARNISH:

¼ CUP MINCED FRESH CHIVES (OR SCALLION TOPS)

1. In a large soup pot, heat the oil over medium-high heat. Add the onion and sauté for about 10 minutes, stirring often, until soft and lightly browned.
2. Add the water, red lentils, and lemon zest. Cover and bring to a boil. Reduce the heat to low and simmer until the lentils are *very* soft, about 30-40 minutes.
3. Turn off the heat and add the thyme, lemon juice, milk, garlic, spinach, salt, and pepper. Stir well and cover the soup pot with the lid. Allow the soup to sit, covered, until the spinach is wilted.
4. Stir well and serve garnished with the fresh chives (or scallions). Feel it!

SERVES 6; GF/SF/GREEN

> How did I live for all of those years without the magic of red lentils?
> Creamy, delicious, *ultra*-healthy red lentils changed my life. They're
> one of those foods that just proves that life is good!

Lemon-Ginger Miso Medicine

This soup idea came to me like a vision one day, so I can only say it is divinely inspired! It contains every good thing for supporting the immune system and yet still manages to taste wonderfully refreshing.

3 TABLESPOONS MELLOW WHITE MISO (DO NOT USE DARK MISO)

1 ½ CUPS PURIFIED WATER

2 TEASPOONS (OR MORE TO TASTE) GRATED FRESH GINGER

5 TEASPOONS *FRESH* LEMON JUICE

1 ¼ TEASPOONS TAMARI, SHOYU, OR SOY SAUCE

½ TEASPOON TOASTED (DARK) SESAME OIL

GARNISH:

1 ½ TEASPOONS TOASTED SESAME SEEDS (SEE PAGE 42)

2 TABLESPOONS FINELY CHOPPED CHIVES OR SCALLIONS (GREEN ONIONS)

1. In a medium soup pot, place the miso along with a tablespoon or so of the water. With a spoon, fork, or whisk, stir until smooth. Add in a bit more water and combine well again until all of the lumps are gone and you have a consistent texture.

2. Add the remaining water, ginger, lemon juice, tamari, and sesame oil. Set to medium-low heat. Cook very briefly (under 5 minutes), stirring often, *just* until the soup is nicely warmed. Don't overheat or allow it to boil.*

3. Serve immediately, topped with the sesame seeds and chives or scallions.

SERVES 2; 30 MINUTES OR UNDER! GF/GREEN

*Be sure not to boil miso soup at any point, as excess heat will destroy many of miso's nutritional properties.

HOW EXACTLY WILL THIS SOUP GIVE YOU THE SUPERPOWERS?

MISO ACTUALLY BINDS WITH TOXINS IN THE BODY AND ESCORTS THEM OUT. IT IS SO HIGHLY REGARDED IN THE EAST THAT MISO BROTH IS EVEN TAKEN AS A MORNING DRINK BY THE JAPANESE! IT'S ALSO EXTREMELY UPLIFTING TO THE IMMUNE SYSTEM AND HELPS DIGESTION. THE SUPERFOODS GINGER AND LEMON ARE CLEANSING, ALKALINIZING, AND IMMUNE-BOOSTING. I COULD GO ON AND ON, BUT I THINK I'LL LET YOU GET STARTED ON YOUR SOUP NOW.

Creamy Potato-Dill Soup with Pan-Toasted Croutons

This hearty soup is sure to satisfy just about anyone and everyone! The flavor is subtle and mellow, yet rich. This makes for a lovely and light meal paired with a tossed salad.

PAN-TOASTED CROUTONS:

1 TABLESPOON EXTRA-VIRGIN OLIVE OIL

2 CUPS CUBED CRUSTY SOURDOUGH (OR MULTIGRAIN) BREAD (CUT INTO BITE-SIZED CUBES)

1/8 TEASPOON EACH: SEA SALT, DRIED GARLIC GRANULES AND DRIED ONION GRANULES

3/4 TEASPOON DRIED DILL

GROUND BLACK PEPPER, TO TASTE

SOUP PART ONE:

3 CUPS PEELED AND CHOPPED POTATOES (DON'T USE UNPEELED POTATOES HERE)

2 CUPS WATER, PREFERABLY FILTERED

SOUP PART TWO:

1/2 CUP CHOPPED ONION

1 TABLESPOON OIL (COCONUT, OLIVE, SAFFLOWER, OR SUNFLOWER)

2 TABLESPOONS RICE FLOUR (OR WHOLE WHEAT PASTRY FLOUR)

1 CUP PLAIN NONDAIRY MILK, UNSWEETENED

FINAL CHAPTER OF SOUP:

2½ TABLESPOONS (PACKED) FRESH DILL, MINCED (ONE .66 OUNCE PACKAGE)

2 TABLESPOONS NON-HYDROGENATED MARGARINE

3 LARGE GARLIC CLOVES, MINCED OR PRESSED

1 TEASPOON EACH: DRIED ONION GRANULES AND BALSAMIC VINEGAR

1/2 TEASPOON GROUND BLACK PEPPER

1¼ TEASPOONS SEA SALT (OR LESS IF YOU PREFER)

2 TEASPOONS FRESH LEMON JUICE

1. First, we make the croutons: In a large skillet or wok, heat the 1 tablespoon of oil over medium-high heat. When the oil is hot, toss in the bread and crouton seasonings. Immediately stir very well so that the bread cubes are evenly coated with the oil and seasonings. Cook the bread cubes for about 5-10 minutes, stirring often, until they are evenly golden browned. Remove from the pan and set aside (uncovered).

2. In a large pot, boil the potatoes over medium-high heat in the 2 cups of water until they're soft (usually this takes at least 20 minutes). To test them, insert a fork in a potato chunk (they should be very soft). When the potatoes are tender, turn off the heat and mash them into the water to form a creamy base. Leave in a few chunks to remember them by, though.

3. In a separate pan, sauté the onion in the 1 tablespoon of oil over medium heat, stirring often, until the onion is golden brown and soft (about 5-10 minutes). Sprinkle the flour into the onion mixture and stir well. Add in about 2 tablespoons of the milk and stir again. *Slowly* add in more of the milk, stirring well with each bit, until the mixture is creamy and well combined. I usually end up using about ½ cup of the milk for this purpose. Next, add this mixture to the potatoes. Using a rubber spatula to scrape the pan will help you get all of the mixture out.

4. Add the remaining milk, dill, margarine, garlic, onion granules, vinegar, pepper, salt, and lemon juice. Stir very well to combine and cook over medium-low heat for another 3-5 minutes or so, just to blend the flavors. Top with the croutons and serve immediately.

SERVES ABOUT 5; GF/BLUE

Hearty Vegetarian Chili

This is filling, delicious, and extremely flavorful. This satisfying chili has also been a perennial favorite amongst my weight loss clients, as it feels like you're eating something quite rich when you are not. If you want a really authentic "meaty" texture, you may use the meatless crumbles. However, if you don't mind a slightly unusual twist, substitute the browned tempeh as it's even healthier.

2 TABLESPOONS OIL (OLIVE, COCONUT, SUNFLOWER, OR SAFFLOWER)

2 SMALL-MEDIUM ONIONS, CHOPPED

2 CUPS VEGAN BURGER CRUMBLES (SUCH AS BOCA BRAND) OR BROWNED TEMPEH*

2 CUPS LIQUID BROTH (VEGETABLE BROTH OR "VEGETARIAN 'CHICKEN' BROTH," P. 194)

2 CANS (15 OZ. EACH) RED KIDNEY OR PINTO BEANS, WITH JUICE (NOT DRAINED)

2 CANS (14.5 OZ. EACH) DICED TOMATOES, WITH JUICE (NOT DRAINED)

6 TABLESPOONS CHILI POWDER (USE A BLENDED CHILI POWDER MIX, NOT GROUND CHILIES)

¼ CUP TAMARI, SHOYU, OR SOY SAUCE

10 (YES, *TEN!*) MEDIUM CLOVES GARLIC, MINCED OR PRESSED

2 TABLESPOONS EACH: ORGANIC SUGAR (OR SUCANAT) *AND* BALSAMIC VINEGAR

2 TEASPOONS SEA SALT (OR LESS IF YOU PREFER)

1. Heat the oil in a large soup pot over medium-high heat. When the oil is hot, sauté the onions and crumbles (or browned tempeh*) in the oil until the onions begin to soften. If necessary, add a little of the broth to prevent sticking.
2. Add everything else (except for the salt) and stir well to combine.
3. Reduce the heat to medium-low and simmer, stirring often, until the mixture is thick and the desired consistency is attained. This should take about 30-45 minutes.
4. Stir in the sea salt and serve. Laugh silently to yourself if your guests begin to comment on the best beef chili they've ever eaten.

SERVES 8; GF/GREEN

*If you wish to substitute tempeh, first sauté 2 cups of crumbled tempeh in a little oil and tamari (or shoyu or soy sauce) for about 5-10 minutes (until lightly browned). Then, add as specified.

Immune Power Soup

This soup is health in a bowl! It contains *six* medicinal superfoods that are sure to deliver. Shiitake mushrooms and kale are top notch foods for building strength and boosting the immune system. Miso is a powerful detoxifier and cleanser. Garlic is antibacterial and anticarcinogenic, and also helps to detoxify the body. Ginger treats colds and eases congestion. Dulse is strengthening and an excellent source of minerals. Knowing all of that, you can feel quite *smug* about eating this soup. Incidentally, I find that I can even get children to eat this by leaving (or picking!) out the shiitakes and scallions.

POWER VEGGIES:

¼ CUP THINLY SLICED FRESH OR FROZEN SHIITAKE MUSHROOM CAPS

I LEAF OF KALE, DE-STEMMED AND SLICED INTO *VERY* THIN RIBBONS

I TEASPOON <u>EACH</u>: TOASTED (DARK) SESAME OIL *AND* TAMARI, SHOYU, OR SOY SAUCE

MISO HEALTHY:

I TABLESPOON DARK (OR RED) MISO

I CUP WATER, PREFERABLY FILTERED

DR. DELICIOUS:

I MEDIUM-LARGE CLOVE GARLIC, PRESSED OR MINCED

I TEASPOON GRATED GINGER (LEAVE THE PEEL ON IF ORGANIC), OR MORE TO TASTE

½ SCALLION (GREEN ONION), TRIMMED AND MINCED

½ TEASPOON DRIED DULSE FLAKES (OPTIONAL)

1. In a medium soup pot, sauté the shiitakes and kale in the oil and tamari for about 5 minutes over medium-low heat, stirring often. Remove from heat.

2. In a separate bowl, whisk a little of the water into the miso to create a smooth paste, being careful to stir out any lumps. A little at a time, whisk the remaining water into the miso, stirring well until very smooth.

3. Add the miso-water mixture to the soup pot and stir to combine. Add all of the remaining ingredients and stir well. Set to low heat and cook *just* until warmed through. Do not boil or overheat, as it can destroy many of the nutrients. Eat up and feel your batteries charge!

SERVES I ; 30 MINUTES OR UNDER! GF/GREEN

Chapter Sixteen: Oh, Sweetness! Delectable Desserts

Here are a few of my very favorite "tried and true" desserts. They contain absolutely no refined sugars, hydrogenated oils, or artificial ingredients. Plus, they can all be made using whole grains. I really love the fact that each of these desserts also proves that vegan food is just as decadent and satisfying as any other type of food—if not more so! Some of these desserts come together very quickly, while others are more time consuming. However, I think you'll find each one to be easy to prepare and well worth your efforts. Enjoy…it's sugar time, baby!

Chocolate Decadence Cake

This has gotten such comments as: "This is the best cake I've ever eaten—vegan or not!" and "This should be illegal!" I find it's easier to double a recipe than to cut it in half, so I have given this version which makes for one 9 x 9-inch cake. Please note that this cake isn't overly sweet by itself since it is meant to be paired with the frosting. However, the two *combined* are, in a word, sublime!

DRY INGREDIENTS:

1½ CUPS WHOLE WHEAT PASTRY FLOUR (OR GLUTEN-FREE ALL-PURPOSE FLOUR)

1 CUP ORGANIC "WHITE" SUGAR (NOT POWDERED)

3 TABLESPOONS COCOA POWDER (NOT DUTCH PROCESS COCOA), SIFTED IF LUMPY

1 LEVEL TEASPOON BAKING SODA

¼ TEASPOON SEA SALT

WET INGREDIENTS:

1 TEASPOON VANILLA EXTRACT

1 TABLESPOON APPLE CIDER VINEGAR

⅓ CUP OIL (SUNFLOWER, NON-VIRGIN OLIVE, MELTED COCONUT, OR SAFFLOWER)

1 CUP CHOCOLATE SOYMILK

FREAKY FROSTING:

5 TABLESPOONS (⅓ CUP) PLUS 1 TEASPOON NON-HYDROGENATED MARGARINE

2¼ CUPS PLUS 4 TEASPOONS ORGANIC POWDERED (CONFECTIONER'S) SUGAR

5 TABLESPOONS (⅓ CUP) PLUS 1 TEASPOON COCOA POWDER, SIFTED IF LUMPY

2 TEASPOONS VANILLA EXTRACT

⅛ TEASPOON SEA SALT

⅓ CUP CHOCOLATE SOYMILK

1. Preheat the oven to 350° F. Oil a 9 x 9-inch pan or a dozen muffin cups. Mix the dry ingredients and wet ingredients separately. Make sure each is lump-free and mixed very well.

2. Mix them together, but do not *over*-mix. Note that the batter will taste a bit odd at this point, but don't be alarmed—any hint of vinegar will magically disappear once the cake is baked!

3. Pour into your oiled baking pan or muffin cups and bake until a knife inserted in the center comes out clean. For cupcakes, this should take about 20 minutes. For cake, it will usually take 30 minutes or more.

4. Remove from the oven and allow your chocolate newborn to cool before you frost it.

5. To make the freakishly good frosting, whip the margarine in a large bowl (using electric beaters) until it becomes somewhat fluffy. Slowly add in the remaining ingredients one at a time, in the order given. Beat at high speed until very fluffy, using a rubber spatula to scrape down the sides of the bowl as needed. At this point, you will want to refrain from the temptation to shrink down to the size of a peanut and take a chocolate bath. *You may regret it later*. Next, refrigerate the frosting until the cake has cooled.

6. Frost your cake! Ideally, let the frosting warm to room temperature before serving the cake. Decorate with edible flowers, raspberries, strawberries, chocolate shavings, or anything else that makes you smile.

MAKES ONE 9 x 9-INCH CAKE; GF (WITH SUBSTITUTION)/PURPLE

To make a bundt cake: Double this recipe, bake it slightly longer, and thin the frosting with extra chocolate soymilk so that it "drizzles" properly. Alternatively, create a layer cake by doubling this recipe and baking two 9-inch round cakes. Place one on a plate and frost the top. Next, place the second cake on top of the frosting, then slather every visible surface with the remaining frosting.

Caramelized Banana Bliss Bombs

Who would be interested in a dessert that is all at once healthy, elegant, easy, quick, and downright scrumptious? Me. And hopefully *you*!

SPICED SAUCE:

ONE 12.3 OZ. CONTAINER OF SILKEN TOFU (FIRM)

½ CUP PURE MAPLE SYRUP

2 TABLESPOONS OIL (SUNFLOWER, MELTED COCONUT, NON-VIRGIN OLIVE, OR SAFFLOWER)

¼ TEASPOON <u>EACH</u>: GROUND CARDAMOM *AND* GROUND CINNAMON

⅛ TEASPOON SEA SALT

FLAIR:

1 ½ CUPS SLICED STRAWBERRIES

2 TABLESPOONS CRUSHED OR CHOPPED PECANS (RAW OR DRY TOASTED)

BANANIRVANA:

3 FIRM BANANAS (NOT OVERLY RIPE)

1 TABLESPOON SUCANAT OR PACKED BROWN SUGAR

1 TEASPOON VANILLA POWDER (OPTIONAL BUT DELICIOUS!)*

1 TABLESPOON NON-HYDROGENATED MARGARINE

1. In a blender, combine the tofu, maple syrup, oil, cardamom, cinnamon, and salt until very smooth and consistently creamy. Set aside (or refrigerate for up to a week).
2. Prepare the strawberries and pecans and set them aside.
3. Slice each banana in half lengthwise. Next, slice each banana half in half width-wise so that you end up with twelve banana segments that are each half of their original thickness and length.
4. Mix the sucanat and vanilla and lightly coat each banana segment evenly with the mixture. Alternately, you can throw caution to the wind and simply sprinkle the sugar and vanilla on each piece of banana.
5. Heat a very large skillet over medium-high heat. Add the margarine. When the margarine is melted, distribute it evenly over the pan.
6. Place the banana pieces in a single layer on the pan. Allow them to get nicely browned on the bottom (this should take well under 5 minutes). Gently flip them over with a heat proof spatula and allow them to brown on the other side. When both sides are gloriously browned and caramelized, turn off the heat.
7. *To serve*: Place the desired amount of sauce on a dessert plate. Top with three of the banana segments and garnish with some strawberries and pecans. Repeat for the remaining three portions. Serve immediately if you know what's good for you.

SERVES 4; 30 MINUTES OR UNDER! GF/BLUE

*Vanilla powder is available in many health food stores. It is white, powdery, and divine. If you can't find it, however, you may substitute an equal amount of vanilla extract.

> I ONCE MADE THIS FOR A COOKING CLASS WHICH INCLUDED A WOMAN WHO PROFESSED A VERY STRONG DISLIKE FOR TOFU. EVEN SHE LAUGHED WHEN SHE REALIZED THAT SHE WAS *LICKING* THE TOFU-BASED SAUCE OFF OF HER PLATE! NEEDLESS TO SAY, THIS WAS QUITE A HIT!

Fruit Mandala Tart with Apricot-Orange Glaze

Elegant, light, and thoroughly impressive! Serve this gorgeous dessert at the end of any meal for rave reviews. In other words, this is disturbingly *fabulous.*

COOKIE CRUST (WET):

¼ CUP NON-HYDROGENATED MARGARINE

½ CUP ORGANIC "WHITE" SUGAR (NOT POWDERED)

EGG REPLACER FOR ½ EGG*

¼ CUP NONDAIRY SOUR CREAM

¼ TEASPOON BAKING SODA

COOKIE CRUST (DRY):

1 ¼ CUPS WHOLE WHEAT PASTRY FLOUR (OR GLUTEN-FREE ALL-PURPOSE FLOUR)

¾ TEASPOON BAKING POWDER

¼ TEASPOON EACH: SEA SALT, GROUND GINGER, AND GROUND NUTMEG

ORANGE CREAM LAYER:

8 OZ. NONDAIRY CREAM CHEESE

2 TABLESPOONS EACH: PURE MAPLE SYRUP AND ORGANIC POWDERED SUGAR

1 TEASPOON EACH: VANILLA EXTRACT AND MINCED ORGANIC ORANGE ZEST

FRUIT LAYER:

1 CUP FRESH BLUEBERRIES

1 KIWI, PEELED AND SLICED

1 BANANA, PEELED AND SLICED

2 CUPS STRAWBERRIES, TRIMMED AND SLICED (SEE NOTE AT THE BOTTOM OF PAGE 221)

APRICOT-ORANGE GLAZE:

½ CUP APRICOT JAM

1 ½ TABLESPOONS EACH: FRESH ORANGE JUICE AND WATER

1. Kindly preheat the oven to 375° F. To make the crust: Cream the margarine in a large bowl using electric beaters. Add the sugar and beat it into the margarine until well combined.

2. *To replace the egg*: Please see the instructions on your egg replacer's box for exact measurements to equal the ½ egg. Place that amount of the egg replacer powder and water in a small bowl and whisk until fluffy, using a wire whisk or fork. Add this to the sugar-margarine bowl and combine everything together using the electric beaters. Set the empty egg replacer bowl aside for the next step.

3. In the bowl that the egg replacer was in, mix the sour cream with the baking soda. Next, add that to the main wet mixture. Cream with the beaters until well mixed.

4. In a separate bowl, sift or whisk the dry ingredients for the cookie crust together thoroughly. Add to the wet mixture and stir well to combine (using a large spoon).

5. Gently knead the dough on a lightly floured surface for a minute or so. Shape it into a smooth, round ball and place on a large sheet of waxed paper. Cover with another large sheet of waxed paper. Having your dough in between the waxed paper will make cleanup a snap and prevent sticking and tearing issues.

6. With a rolling pin, roll over the top sheet of waxed paper to flatten the dough. Continue to roll out the dough until it is the size and shape of your pizza pan. Next, gently remove the top sheet of waxed paper.

7. Place a lightly oiled pizza pan (oiled side down) on top of the dough and carefully turn the whole thing over so that the pan is on the counter with the dough on top of it. Gently remove the remaining sheet of waxed paper. Finally, trim around the outer edge of the dough if needed so that it looks like an even circle

(or pinch all around the border to create a decorative edge—if you're feelin' fancy).

8. Bake until golden brown, about 10-20 minutes. Allow to cool slightly, then *very gently* loosen the bottom with a spatula to prevent it from sticking to the pan. Forever.

9. Mix the cream cheese, maple syrup, powdered sugar, vanilla, and orange zest together until thoroughly combined. Next, evenly spread this mixture over the cooled crust.

10. Now it's time for fun with fruit! By beginning in the center, work outward in circles by placing the fruit in an artistic, beautiful pattern. This is the part where you really get creative! Don't worry if you have a little fruit left over—just pop it into the fridge and have yourself a fab fruit salad for breakfast.

11. After you've fruited up the entire surface, it's time for the glory glaze. To make the glaze, place the jam, juice, and water in a small pan and set over medium-low heat. Simmer, stirring often, for about 5 minutes. Next, pour it through a fine mesh strainer into a cup so that the pulp gets separated from the thin glaze. If necessary, use the back of a spoon to push the liquid through the strainer and into the cup.

12. While the glaze is still warm, brush the clear, pulp-free portion evenly over the fruit, using a pastry brush. Using a soft touch will ensure that the fruit stays in one place.

13. Finally, cut the tart into 8-10 slices and serve.

SERVES 8-10; GF (IF USING GLUTEN-FREE FLOUR)/BLUE

Want your strawberries to exemplify maximum cuteness?
First, cut off the stem. Next, place the strawberry, stem side down, on a chopping board and make your cuts from top to bottom. This way, your strawberry slices will all have pointed edges on them, creating the maximum visual appeal for this dish. In case you were wondering, the Latin name for these slices is *Strawberium Cuteness Maximus*.

Blueberry Streusel Cake with Lemon Icing

This super-yummy cake is easy to make, light, and also happens to be "*oh boy delicious*" according to several five-year-olds!

STREUSEL TOPPING:

¼ CUP <u>EACH</u>: NON-HYDROGENATED MARGARINE (MELTED) *AND* ORGANIC SUGAR (OR SUCANAT)

¾ CUP WHOLE WHEAT PASTRY FLOUR (OR GLUTEN-FREE ALL-PURPOSE FLOUR)

1 ⅛ TEASPOONS GROUND CINNAMON

½ TEASPOON BAKING POWDER

CAKE (DRY):

2 CUPS WHOLE WHEAT PASTRY FLOUR (OR GLUTEN-FREE ALL-PURPOSE FLOUR)

1 CUP ORGANIC "WHITE" SUGAR

2 TEASPOONS BAKING POWDER

1 ½ TABLESPOONS FINELY CHOPPED ORGANIC LEMON ZEST

½ TEASPOON SEA SALT

CAKE (WET):

¼ CUP OIL (SAFFLOWER, NON-VIRGIN OLIVE, OR SUNFLOWER)

2 TEASPOONS VANILLA EXTRACT

1 CUP NONDAIRY MILK

BERRY CRUCIAL: 2 CUPS FRESH OR FROZEN BLUEBERRIES

LOVELY LEMON ICING:

1 ¼ CUPS ORGANIC POWDERED SUGAR

1 TABLESPOON PLUS 2 TEASPOONS *FRESH* LEMON JUICE

½ TEASPOON PLUS ⅛ TEASPOON VANILLA EXTRACT

⅛ TEASPOON SEA SALT

1. In a small bowl, stir the streusel topping ingredients together very well until thoroughly combined and crumbly. Set aside.

2. Preheat the oven to 350° F. Combine all of the dry cake ingredients thoroughly, making sure to set any lumps straight.

3. Combine the wet cake ingredients very well in a separate bowl. Stir the wet mixture into the dry ingredients and combine well, but do not over-mix.

4. Gently stir in the blueberries. Lightly oil a 9.5 x 13.5-inch pan and spread the batter into it. Sprinkle the streusel evenly over the cake. Bake for one hour, or until a knife inserted in the center comes out clean. Allow the cake to cool slightly before icing it.

5. To make the icing, begin by removing any lumps from the sugar if necessary. You can do this with your fingers, a fork, or by pouring it through a strainer or sifter. Next, combine all of the icing ingredients together well, stirring with a spoon.

6. When the cake is slightly cooled, drizzle the icing evenly over the top. You can pretend you are Jackson Pollack if you like. Finally, cut the cake and get ready for a serious yum situation.

SERVES 12; GF (WITH SUBSTITUTION)/BLUE

Grandma's Apple Crisp

This dish brings me back to winter nights of childhood, savoring this homey creation next to a crackling fireplace. No, we didn't live in a little house on a prairie, but I felt like we did when we ate this! In our family, this was always served with a little milk poured over the top. However, it's also great plain or with some nondairy vanilla ice cream. Whichever way you end up, it's simple, easy, and delicious every time!

THRILLING FILLING:

4 CUPS CHOPPED APPLES (SKINS ON)

1 ½ TEASPOONS GROUND CINNAMON

PINCH OF SALT

¼ CUP WATER

1 TABLESPOON FRESH LEMON JUICE

CRUMBLE TOPPING:

- ¼ CUP MELTED NON-HYDROGENATED MARGARINE
- ¾ CUP FLOUR (WHOLE WHEAT PASTRY, WHITE, OR GLUTEN-FREE ALL-PURPOSE)
- ½ CUP ORGANIC "WHITE" SUGAR
- PINCH OF SALT

1. Preheat the oven to 350° F. If you're like me and don't have a microwave, this is a great time to put the margarine in the oven to melt (in a heat proof container).

2. Mix together the apples, cinnamon, salt, water, and lemon juice. Place this mixture in a lightly oiled 10 x 6-inch baking dish or a round pie pan. Next, mix the melted margarine with the flour, sugar, and salt until thoroughly combined. Crumble this evenly on top of the apples.

3. Bake for 45-50 minutes, or until the topping is nicely browned and "crisp." This is best served hot (or very warm). If you like, pour a little nondairy milk over the top. If you have any *Little House On the Prairie* reruns handy, this would be an ideal time to bust them out.

SERVES 6; GF (WITH SUBSTITUTION)/PURPLE

Ultra Light Blackberry Cobbler

Thanks to Dr. John and Mary McDougall for sharing their recipe for Blueberry Cobbler, which this was based on. I've always loved this dish because it's *crazy* easy, fat-free, high in fiber, and still manages to taste wonderful! However, as its texture is unique, this tastes much better when eaten soon after it's made. Like *that's* a problem.

⅔ CUP WHOLE WHEAT PASTRY FLOUR (OR ALL-PURPOSE GLUTEN-FREE FLOUR)

1 ½ TEASPOONS BAKING POWDER

⅛ TEASPOON SEA SALT

1 ½ TEASPOONS VANILLA EXTRACT

⅓ CUP PURE MAPLE SYRUP

⅔ CUP NONDAIRY MILK

LAST ADDITION:
- 2 CUPS BLACKBERRIES (FRESH OR FROZEN)

1. Preheat the oven to 350° F. Combine the flour, baking powder, and sea salt very well in a medium bowl. Stir in the vanilla, maple syrup, and milk until evenly combined.

2. Lightly oil a round pie pan. Pour the mixture into the pan, using a rubber spatula to remove all of the batter. Evenly sprinkle the blackberries over the top of the mixture. Bake for about 45 minutes, or until the cobbler is a gorgeous shade of brown. Allow to cool for 5 minutes or so, then serve immediately.

SERVES 4-6; GF (WITH SUBSTITUTION)/SF/GREEN

Luscious Lemon Bars with Ginger Shortbread Crust

If you can eat just one of these, feel free to skip the earlier chapters on dealing with food issues. Either that, or you've cut this into four servings. In other words...these bars are delicious, addictive, and a lemon lover's dream! Be warned, though—this dessert is for lemon lovers *only*! No "hint" of lemon here!

GINGER SHORTBREAD CRUST:

1 ½ CUPS FLOUR (WHOLE WHEAT PASTRY, WHITE, OR ALL-PURPOSE GLUTEN-FREE)

¼ CUP ORGANIC POWDERED (CONFECTIONER'S) SUGAR

1 TEASPOON GROUND GINGER

½ CUP MELTED NON-HYDROGENATED MARGARINE OR MELTED COCONUT OIL

FILLING PART ONE:

1 CUP ORGANIC "WHITE" SUGAR (NOT POWDERED)

2 TABLESPOONS (*PACKED*) FINELY MINCED ORGANIC LEMON ZEST

½ CUP *FRESH* LEMON JUICE

¼ TEASPOON SALT

FILLING PART TWO:

½ CUP PLAIN AND UNSWEETENED APPLESAUCE

½ TABLESPOON BAKING POWDER

½ TEASPOON DRY EGG REPLACER POWDER (SUCH AS ENER-G)

1 TABLESPOON ARROWROOT (OR CORNSTARCH)

GARNISHES:
• POWDERED SUGAR
• FINELY CHOPPED LEMON ZEST

1. Preheat the oven to 350° F. Combine the flour, powdered sugar, and ginger in a medium bowl until uniform. Stir in the margarine *just* until combined (do not over-mix). If the dough is too dry, you can add in a little more melted margarine or oil. At this point, you may wish to refrigerate the dough (in airtight plastic) until it is chilled for a more traditional shortbread.

2. Press the dough into a well oiled 8 x 11.5-inch baking dish, making a raised rim of ½-inch around the sides. Press the dough firmly and evenly with your hands to ensure a uniform, non-crumbly crust.

3. Bake for 5-10 minutes. Be careful not to overcook the crust, as you will baking it much longer after the filling is inside. Better to undercook than overcook at this point!

4. Mix part one of the filling ingredients (sugar, lemon zest, lemon juice, and salt) together well.

5. Combine part two of the filling items in a separate bowl and stir well to mix. Pour into the lemon-sugar mixture and stir well to combine. Pour the filling evenly over the crust.

6. Bake for about 30-40 minutes, or until the crust is nicely browned. Again, with this dessert, it's better to undercook than overcook. Even if the all of the filling doesn't look done yet, it's fine to remove it from the oven if the crust is brown and much of the filling looks firm. The filling and center will firm up more upon cooling, especially if you can refrigerate it for several hours or overnight. Consider this an opportunity to be strong!

7. After the lemon bars cool, put some powdered sugar in a fine-mesh strainer and tap it all over the top to create a fine, powdery effect. Next, for maximum level cuteness, sprinkle some additional lemon zest over the top. These will keep in an airtight container, refrigerated, for several days.

MAKES ONE 8 X 11.5-INCH PAN OF LEMON BARS; GF/SF (WITH SUBSTITUTIONS)/PURPLE

Mommy's Chocolate Chip Cookies

These kid-friendly—heck, human-friendly— treats are delicious, quick, and easy. At age three, my daughter took great pride in knowing that most baked goods require the dry and wet ingredients to be mixed separately, hence the "dry bowl" and "wet bowl."

Dry Bowl:

1 cup flour (whole wheat pastry, white, or all-purpose gluten-free)

1 teaspoon baking powder

¼ teaspoon sea salt

⅔ cup organic sugar

Wet Bowl:

¼ cup melted non-hydrogenated margarine (or coconut oil if you cannot eat soy)

2 tablespoons nondairy milk

2 teaspoons vanilla extract

Essential Ingredient:

• ½ cup semi-sweet nondairy chocolate chips

1. Preheat the oven to 350° F. Mix the dry ingredients together thoroughly. In a separate bowl, combine the wet items together very well.

2. Mix the wet and dry ingredients together and stir in the chocolate chips. Don't worry if the chips don't "stick" yet and seem a little too wild and free. They will fall in line soon.

3. Lightly oil two cookie sheets. Drop tablespoonfuls of the batter onto the cookie sheets, leaving enough room for them to spread out slightly. If the consistency is a bit crumbly, just pack the dough and chips together, using a spoon (or your fingers).

4. Bake for around 10 minutes, or until the cookies just begin to brown lightly. If you overcook them, they will be very crisp. The cookies will firm up a bit after they cool, so you can take them out before they actually look ready.

5. Don't wait too long to lift these sugar babies off the pans or they may become a permanent part of your cookie sheets. Gently remove the cookies with a spatula and place them on a cooling rack. However, if you don't have a cooling rack, just place them on a plate. If you don't have a plate, just put them on the counter. Enjoy! These are especially soft and delicious when warm.

Makes about two dozen cookies

30 minutes or under! GF/SF (with substitutions)/Purple

Blackberry Peach Goodness

This dessert is a perennial winner as it's both delicious *and* light—fancy that! I used to make this regularly for my weight loss clients and they just loved it. It seemed that not feeling deprived of desserts was a key element in making them want to stick with their healthy new diets. Of course, if you aren't concerned about calories, you can double the topping amount. Either way, it's delicious and fresh tasting!

GOOEY GOODNESS FILLING:

10 OZ. FRESH OR FROZEN BLACKBERRIES

4 CUPS CHOPPED FRESH, RIPE PEACHES

3 TABLESPOONS ORGANIC SUGAR OR SUCANAT (OR MORE IF USING FRUIT THAT'S LESS THAN SWEET)

1 TABLESPOON ARROWROOT (OR CORNSTARCH)

2 TABLESPOONS FRESH LEMON JUICE

TOO TASTY TOPPING:

½ CUP ROLLED OATS*

⅓ CUP WHOLE WHEAT PASTRY FLOUR*

3 TABLESPOONS ORGANIC "WHITE" SUGAR (NOT POWDERED)

1 TEASPOON GROUND CINNAMON

½ TEASPOON GROUND NUTMEG

⅛ TEASPOON SALT

3 TABLESPOONS OIL (SUNFLOWER, NON-VIRGIN OLIVE, OR MELTED COCONUT)

1. Preheat the oven to 375° F. Lightly oil a round pie pan and set it aside.
2. Gently combine the filling ingredients in a large bowl. Place them evenly in the pie pan.
3. In a medium bowl, combine the dry topping ingredients (oats, flour, "white" sugar, cinnamon, nutmeg, and salt). Stir very well to combine.
4. Drizzle the oil into the dry topping mixture and stir well until thoroughly combined. Sprinkle evenly over the berry-peach mixture.
5. Bake for about 40 minutes, or until it resembles a gooey fruit nirvana with a golden brown topping. Cool slightly and serve *immediately*. This is no laughing matter.

SERVES ABOUT 6; GF (WITH SUBSTITUTIONS)/SF/BLUE

*For a gluten-free version, substitute an all-purpose gluten-free flour for the whole wheat pastry flour. You may also substitute quinoa flakes or gluten-free oats for the rolled oats. See page 44 for more details.

Cocoa-Mint Mousse Nests

These are such a hit! Plus, they're not only scrumptious and pretty, they are also quite light. However, if you find that these are just *too* fabulous and attractive to eat, they may instead be spray-coated with a clear varnish and used as kitchen decorations.

MOUSSE:
1 2.5 OZ. PACK OF SILKEN TOFU (FIRM)

¼ CUP COCOA POWDER

½ CUP PURE MAPLE SYRUP

2 TEASPOONS <u>EACH</u>: VANILLA EXTRACT AND NON-HYDROGENATED MARGARINE

¼ TEASPOON MINT EXTRACT

⅛ TEASPOON SEA SALT

NESTS:
4 LARGE (OR 8 SMALL)* SHEETS OF PHYLLO DOUGH, THAWED (SEE PAGE 42 FOR PHYLLO TIPS)

2-4 TABLESPOONS MELTED NON-HYDROGENATED MARGARINE**

CHOCOLATE SWIRLS:
•¼ CUP NONDAIRY CHOCOLATE CHIPS (SEMI-SWEET)

•1 TEASPOON NON-HYDROGENATED MARGARINE

GARNISHES:
•ORGANIC POWDERED SUGAR

•1 2 FRESH MINT SPRIGS

1. In a food processor, blend the tofu until very smooth. Add the rest of the mousse ingredients and process until creamy. Be sure there are no chunks of tofu remaining. You will want to use a rubber spatula to scrape down the sides occasionally to achieve this stunning result. Set aside.

2. Spray a muffin tin (12 cups) lightly with oil and set aside.

3. Preheat the oven to 400° F. Gently unfold your thawed phyllo and lay it on the counter. Take out four (or eight)* sheets of the phyllo dough and set them aside.

4. Gently refold the remaining phyllo dough and wrap it tightly in plastic. Rewrap again in another airtight plastic bag and place it in the refrigerator.

5. Cut the phyllo sheets into squares that are about four inches in size.

6. Layer the phyllo into the muffin cups one piece at a time, brushing each piece lightly with margarine (or spraying with oil)** as you go. Each muffin cup should contain several pieces of phyllo, layered one on top of another to form a phyllo "cup" that will hold your mousse.

7. Bake the phyllo cups until golden brown (about 5 minutes). Watch them closely, as they can burn easily. Remove from the oven and allow them to cool slightly. Place the phyllo cups on dessert plates and spoon the mousse evenly into the nests.

8. Melt the chocolate chips and margarine in a very small pan over the lowest heat possible (or in a double boiler), stirring constantly until *just* melted. Spoon into a pastry tool (or a plastic bag with a small hole cut out of the corner). Squeeze gently to make swirls on top of each portion of mousse. Dust the tops lightly with some organic powdered sugar and garnish with a mint sprig. Serve and soak up the praise!

MAKES 1 2 "NESTS"/BLUE

*If your 1 lb. package of phyllo contains 20 (larger) sheets, you will use 4 of them. If your 1 lb. package of phyllo contains 40 (smaller) sheets, you will need 8 of them.

**You may spray the phyllo with oil, rather than brush it with margarine (as it's quicker and lower in fat this way). Of course, the more "buttery" and time consuming approach yields a more intense, rich flavor.

Oatmeal Raisin Cookies w/ Vanilla Icing

Try not to eat any of the icing before it gets onto the cookies. Just *try*.

COOKIES:

¼ CUP NON-HYDROGENATED MARGARINE

⅓ CUP EACH: OIL (COCONUT, SUNFLOWER, OR NON-VIRGIN OLIVE) *AND* NONDAIRY MILK

I CUP ORGANIC "WHITE" SUGAR (NOT POWDERED)

I TEASPOON VANILLA EXTRACT

I ¼ TEASPOONS GROUND CINNAMON

I ¼ CUPS WHOLE WHEAT PASTRY FLOUR*

½ TEASPOON SEA SALT

I ½ CUPS ROLLED OATS (NOT INSTANT)*

½ TEASPOON EACH: BAKING SODA *AND* BAKING POWDER

¼ CUP RAISINS (OR CHOCOLATE CHIPS IF YOU'RE A REBEL)

VANILLA ICING:
- I TABLESPOON NON-HYDROGENATED MARGARINE
- ¾ CUP ORGANIC POWDERED (CONFECTIONER'S) SUGAR
- ¾ TEASPOON VANILLA EXTRACT
- I TABLESPOON NONDAIRY MILK
- PINCH OF SEA SALT

1. Preheat the oven to 350° F.
2. In a medium bowl, cream (with electric beaters or by hand) the margarine and oil until well blended.
3. Add in the milk, "white" sugar, and vanilla. Stir until well combined.
4. In a separate bowl, mix the cinnamon, flour, salt, oats, baking soda, and baking powder together and combine well. Add to the wet mixture and mix everything together with a spoon. Stir in the raisins (or chocolate chips, Jimmy).
5. Drop by spoonfuls onto oiled cookie sheets. Leave a little room in between each one just in case your yoga cookies feel like stretching. Bake until golden browned, about 10 minutes.
6. Remove to a cooling rack (or plate), being careful to leave the cookies intact.
7. To make the icing, melt the margarine. Next, sift or whisk the powdered sugar to remove any lumps. Combine all of the icing ingredients very well in a small bowl, using a fork or wire whisk. Drizzle artistically (or randomly—whichever you prefer) over the cookies and serve. Sweet *baby*!

MAKES ABOUT 3 DOZEN COOKIES; 30 MINUTES OR UNDER! GF (WITH SUBSTITUTIONS)/PURPLE

*If you are gluten intolerant, you may substitute all-purpose gluten-free flour for the whole wheat pastry flour and quinoa flakes (or gluten-free oats) for the rolled oats. See page 44 for more information.

Lemon Lover's Cupcakes w/ Lemon Zest Buttercream Frosting

For someone who adores lemon (me, for example), this dessert is sugar paradise!
Be sure to use standard (not Meyer) *fresh* lemons, and don't skimp on the zest. Please also
note that this recipe works best as cupcakes (rather than as a standard cake). Enjoy!

CUPCAKES, DRY INGREDIENTS:

1 ½ CUPS FLOUR (WHOLE WHEAT PASTRY, UNBLEACHED WHITE, OR GLUTEN-FREE ALL-PURPOSE)

1 CUP ORGANIC "WHITE" SUGAR (NOT POWDERED)

1 TEASPOON BAKING SODA

¼ TEASPOON EACH: BAKING POWDER *AND* SEA SALT

CUPCAKES, WET INGREDIENTS:

½ CUP PLUS 5 TEASPOONS *FRESH* LEMON JUICE

2 TABLESPOONS (TIGHTLY PACKED) ORGANIC LEMON ZEST (FINELY MINCED OR GRATED)

⅓ CUP OIL (SUNFLOWER, NON-VIRGIN OLIVE, OR SAFFLOWER)

½ CUP NONDAIRY MILK

2 TEASPOONS EACH: APPLE CIDER VINEGAR *AND* VANILLA EXTRACT

LEMON ZEST BUTTERCREAM FROSTING:

¼ CUP (4 TABLESPOONS) NON-HYDROGENATED MARGARINE

1 ½ CUPS ORGANIC POWDERED (CONFECTIONER'S) SUGAR

1 TABLESPOON EACH: NONDAIRY MILK *AND* MINCED ORGANIC LEMON ZEST (TIGHTLY PACKED)

4 TEASPOONS *FRESH* LEMON JUICE

1 TEASPOON VANILLA EXTRACT

OPTIONAL GARNISHES: LEMON SLICES, EDIBLE FLOWERS, AND/OR LEMON ZEST STRIPS

1. Preheat the oven to 350° F. Lightly oil a dozen muffin cups (or use paper liners). Stir or sift the dry cupcake ingredients together very well. In a separate bowl, mix the wet cupcake ingredients together well.
2. Gently mix the two together, stirring *just* until well blended (do not over-mix). Please note that if you taste the batter at this point, it may seem a bit vinegary. However, the vinegar is in fact your friend and will taste different once baked. Pour the batter evenly into the muffin cups.
3. Bake for about 20 minutes. You will know they're done when you can insert a knife in the center of one of the cupcakes and it comes out clean. Next, set them aside to cool.
4. To make the frosting, place the margarine in a medium-large bowl and, using electric beaters, whip until fluffy. Slowly add the other frosting ingredients in the order given, whipping them with the beaters until very well mixed. Scrape down the sides of the bowl with a rubber spatula as needed. What you want here is a smooth, fluffy, puffy lemon cloud that you have to resist diving into. When your frosting has achieved a state of glorious perfection, cover and refrigerate it until you are ready to frost the cupcakes.
5. When the cupcakes have cooled enough to avoid melting the frosting, you can freely slather it on using a rubber spatula or butter knife. Top with the garnishes of your choice (if using) and serve.

MAKES ABOUT 12-14 CUPCAKES; GF (WITH SUBSTITUTION)/PURPLE

> TAKE CARE TO GRATE ONLY THE YELLOW PEEL OF THE LEMON,
> AS THE WHITE PORTION UNDER THE SKIN IS QUITE BITTER.

Caramel Corn

Rent a good movie, make a batch of this, and you'll have the perfect couch potato party on your hands! Using three types of sweeteners lends a depth of flavor and mellow richness that's mysteriously addictive.

½ CUP POPCORN KERNELS

1 TABLESPOON OIL (COCONUT, SUNFLOWER, SAFFLOWER, OR NON-VIRGIN OLIVE)

CARAMEL:

3 TABLESPOONS EACH: NON-HYDROGENATED MARGARINE *AND* BROWN RICE SYRUP

4 TABLESPOONS ORGANIC "WHITE" SUGAR (NOT POWDERED)

5 TABLESPOONS PURE MAPLE SYRUP

½ TEASPOON SEA SALT (OR LESS IF YOU PREFER)

OPTIONAL CRUNCHLINGS:

⅓ CUP DRY-ROASTED PEANUTS (OR ALMONDS)

1. If you have an air popper, you can omit the oil and just pop away. Otherwise, to make your popcorn on the stove, start with a medium-large pot (that has a tight fitting lid). Place the oil and one kernel of corn inside the covered pot and set the heat to medium-high. When the kernel pops, add the rest of the popcorn. Shake the pot often while the kernels are popping to prevent them from burning. When the kernels slow to about 1-2 seconds in between pops, turn the heat off.
2. Place the caramel ingredients in a medium skillet over medium-high heat. Bring to a boil. Turn the heat down to low and simmer, stirring, for about 5 minutes.
3. Place your popped corn in a huge bowl or on top of waxed paper. If desired, toss in the nuts. Pour the caramel on top and stir gently (yet thoroughly) to mix.
4. Put on your movie and potato down!

MAKES ABOUT 4 SERVINGS; 30 MINUTES OR UNDER! GF/PURPLE

Handy Dandy Tip:
Soak your bowl and caramel pan (and anything else with caramel on it) for several minutes before attempting to wash them. This will dissolve the hardened caramel with ease and keep you from going to the "dark place."

Apple Puffs with Vanilla Bean Caramel Sauce

Hoping to get a marriage proposal or a raise, but short on time? Yes, these are *that* good. No one will ever guess how easily you threw this together either, especially when you use words like "vanilla bean."

6 LARGE (OR 12 SMALL)* SHEETS OF PHYLLO DOUGH, THAWED (SEE PAGE 42 FOR TIPS)

OIL FOR SPRAYING (NON-VIRGIN OLIVE, SUNFLOWER, OR SAFFLOWER)

FILLING SO GOOD:

2 APPLES, VERY THINLY SLICED (UNPEELED IF ORGANIC)

2 TEASPOONS GROUND CINNAMON

2 TABLESPOONS ORGANIC SUGAR OR SUCANAT

1/8 TEASPOON SEA SALT

1 TEASPOON FRESH LEMON JUICE

VANILLA BEAN CARAMEL SAUCE:

6-INCH SEGMENT OF A VANILLA BEAN

6 TABLESPOONS EACH: PURE MAPLE SYRUP *AND* NON-HYDROGENATED MARGARINE

3 TABLESPOONS BROWN RICE SYRUP

4 TABLESPOONS ORGANIC "WHITE" SUGAR (NOT POWDERED)

3/8 TEASPOON SEA SALT (SCANT 1/2 TEASPOON)

1. Mix the items for the filling together in a medium bowl and set aside.
2. Spray or lightly coat a cookie sheet with oil and set it aside.
3. Preheat the oven to 350° F. Gently unwrap the phyllo dough. Remove six (or twelve)* sheets and lay them flat on a clean, dry surface. If desired, cover them with a slightly damp towel. Re-wrap the remaining phyllo in airtight plastic and place back in the fridge.
4. Remove one large (or two small)* sheet(s) of phyllo and place on a clean, dry surface (covering the other phyllo with the towel again). If you are using two small sheets, just place one on top of the other. Spray or brush the phyllo with a little oil. Fold it into thirds (the long way) so that it resembles a tall, skinny rectangle. As you go, you will want to spray or brush each portion of dry (unoiled) phyllo, so that all the exposed portions of phyllo have been lightly coated with oil.
5. Place about one-sixth of the apple mixture at the base of the phyllo rectangle. Fold the bottom of the phyllo up and over the mixture. Continue to fold up, forming it into a triangle as you go. Once you have an apple-filled triangle, place it on the cookie sheet and give it one last hurrah of oil.
6. Repeat step five with the remaining phyllo and apple mixture. If you like, dust the triangle puffs with a little ground cinnamon. If you want *total* cuteness, you can sprinkle the cinnamon on top in a stripe pattern (or make swirls with the cinnamon using your finger or a small brush).
7. Place the puffs in the oven and bake them until they're golden brown (about 15-25 minutes). Remove.
8. To create the sauce, make a lengthwise cut all the way down the vanilla bean with a sharp knife and open it like a pod. Scrape out all of the gooey insides with a table knife (or the back of your fingernail) and place in a small pot. Add the remaining caramel sauce ingredients to the pot and set to medium-low heat, stirring very well to combine. When the sauce comes to a boil, turn the heat down to the lowest setting your stove can muster up. Then allow it to simmer gently for another 3-5 minutes, stirring often.
9. Top the apple puffs with the sauce. Dust with a little powdered sugar and serve immediately. Say yes.

SERVES 6; BLUE

*If your 1 lb. package of phyllo contains 20 (large) sheets, you will use 6 of them. If it contains 40 (small) sheets, you will need 12 of them.

Chocolate Bliss Pie

This pie, in a word, is *smashfantabulous*! Please don't look that up…I think it only exists in the same dimension as this pie. If you serve this to guests, you'll *completely* impress them. You will also shock them when you reveal that the main ingredient is tofu!

CRUST*:

1 ¼ CUPS GRAHAM CRACKER CRUMBS (SWIRL GRAHAM CRACKERS IN A FOOD PROCESSOR UNTIL FINE)

2 TABLESPOONS ORGANIC SUGAR

¼ CUP NON-HYDROGENATED MARGARINE, MELTED

FILLING:

2 PACKAGES (12.3 OZ. EACH) ASEPTIC PACK SILKEN TOFU, EXTRA-FIRM

1 CUP ORGANIC POWDERED (CONFECTIONER'S) SUGAR

½ CUP EACH: COCOA POWDER *AND* PURE MAPLE SYRUP

2 TABLESPOONS NON-HYDROGENATED MARGARINE, MELTED

1 TABLESPOON VANILLA EXTRACT

1 TEASPOON TAMARI, SHOYU, OR SOY SAUCE (NOT A MISPRINT!)

⅛ TEASPOON SEA SALT

CHOCO-LUSCIOUS TOPPING:

⅓ CUP NONDAIRY SEMI-SWEET CHOCOLATE CHIPS

1 TEASPOON NON-HYDROGENATED MARGARINE

1. Preheat the oven to 350° F. To prepare the crust, mix the graham cracker crumbs and sugar together in a medium bowl. Stir in the ¼ cup of melted margarine and combine well. Pour the mixture into a round pie pan. You will want the sides of the crust to almost come up to the top of the pan, so allocate your mixture accordingly. The secret to a firm graham cracker crust is to take your time, pressing all parts of the crust well with the palms of your hands, so that it stays together and doesn't crumble. Pay special attention to the place where the base of the crust meets the sides. Bake for 10-15 minutes, or until aromatic and lightly browned. Turn off the oven and set the crust aside to cool.

2. Next, blend the tofu in a food processor (or really good blender). Scrape down the inside of the processor with a rubber spatula as you go to make sure that no chunks of tofu remain. Add the other filling ingredients one at a time. Blend *very* well, as you want a consistently creamy filling (with no tofu chunk souvenirs).

3. When the crust is cool, pour the filling into it and smooth out the top of the pie. *Not* with your tongue.

4. Next, melt the chocolate chips and margarine in a very small pan over the lowest heat possible (or in a double boiler), stirring constantly until *just* melted. Spoon into a pastry tool (or a plastic bag with a small hole cut out of the corner). Squeeze gently to make swirls (or any sort of fun design) all over the top of your pie. Refrigerate your chocolate masterpiece, gently covered with plastic wrap, for several hours (or, ideally, overnight). Excessive chocolate madness awaits you…*enjoy*.

SERVES 8; GF (WITH SUBSTITUTION)/PURPLE

*If you cannot eat gluten, you may substitute a gluten-free pie crust for the graham cracker crust.

Fresh Pumpkin Pie

This tastes quite unlike typical pumpkin pies made with canned pumpkin, eggs, and evaporated milk. This pie is actually *healthy*! I feel it's worth the extra effort to use fresh pumpkins because of the bright flavor they give. Being lucky enough to live near an organic pumpkin patch, I pick out a pie pumpkin every fall just for this. And, yes, you will want to specifically use a "pie" pumpkin if you can. Be sure to roast the seeds while you bake the pie—not only delicious, they're also a wonderful source of zinc (which many people swear by for preventing and curing colds). What great planning, Mother Nature!

ONE SMALL PIE PUMPKIN (OR 2 CUPS COOKED, MASHED PUMPKIN)

ONE 9-INCH WHOLE GRAIN (OR GLUTEN-FREE) PIE CRUST

12.3 OZ. ASEPTIC PACK OF SILKEN TOFU, EXTRA-FIRM

3-5 TEASPOONS PUMPKIN PIE SPICE (USE 3 TEASPOONS FOR A MILD CHILD AND UP TO 5 FOR SERIOUS JIVE)

¾ CUP PURE MAPLE SYRUP

¼ CUP ORGANIC "WHITE" SUGAR (NOT POWDERED)

¼ TEASPOON SEA SALT

1. Preheat the oven to 400° F. Cut the pumpkin in half. Scoop out the seeds* and remove all of the stringy pulp from the inside of the pumpkin, using a large metal spoon. Place the pumpkin (cut sides down) in a large baking pan. Pour enough water over the pumpkin so that there is about ½-inch of water in the pan. Bake for 45-60 minutes, or until the pumpkin flesh is soft and tender when you prick it with a fork. Remove the pumpkin and allow it to cool slightly.
2. Place the pie crust in the oven and bake for about 5 minutes. Remove the crust, but leave the oven on.
3. When the pumpkin has cooled slightly, scoop out two cups of the flesh and place in a food processor (or cooperative blender). Any unused portion of the pumpkin will freeze very nicely for a future use.
4. Blend the tofu along with the pumpkin in the processor until very smooth and no chunks remain. Then, blend in the remaining ingredients until completely smooth and creamy.
5. Pour the filling into the prebaked pie shell. Bake for about 45 minutes, or until nicely browned.
6. Allow to cool in the refrigerator for several hours or overnight. Serve plain or with nondairy vanilla ice cream (or nondairy whipped topping).

MAKES ONE 9-INCH PIE (SERVES 8); GF (WITH SUBSTITUTION)/BLUE

*To roast pumpkin seeds:

While scooping out the seeds, place them in a strainer. Remove the stringy pulp and rinse the seeds (in the strainer) under cold water. Toss the drained seeds with a little oil and seasoned salt and lay them flat on a baking sheet. Roast at 400° F., turning every 10 minutes, until they are golden brown (about 30 minutes total). Once cooled, they will store in an airtight container at room temperature for several days.

I FIND THAT THE EXTRA STEP OF USING FRESH PUMPKIN IS OFFSET BY THE EASE OF USING A PRE-MADE PIE CRUST. FORTUNATELY, THERE ARE LOTS OF DELICIOUS, NATURAL CRUSTS ON THE MARKET (IN THE FREEZER SECTION OF HEALTH FOOD STORES). OF COURSE, IF YOU HAVE THE TIME, YOU CAN MAKE THIS EVEN BETTER BY SUBSTITUTING A HOMEMADE CRUST.

Old Fashioned Frosted Sugar Cookies

Making these cookies was one of the things I liked best about Christmas as a child. It was endless fun to decorate them with all sorts of colors and candies. Now that there are natural food colorings on the market, I've revisited these delightful cookies. What a deliciously creative way to spend the afternoon!

SUGAR COOKIES (WET):

1 CUP (2 STICKS) NON-HYDROGENATED MARGARINE

2 CUPS ORGANIC "WHITE" SUGAR (NOT POWDERED)

EGG REPLACER EQUIVALENT FOR 2 EGGS (I USE ENER-G)

1 CUP NONDAIRY SOUR CREAM

1 TEASPOON BAKING SODA

SUGAR COOKIES (DRY):

5 CUPS WHOLE WHEAT PASTRY FLOUR (OR GLUTEN-FREE ALL-PURPOSE FLOUR)

1 TABLESPOON BAKING POWDER

1 TEASPOON EACH: SEA SALT AND GROUND NUTMEG

FUN FROSTING:

½ CUP EACH: NON-HYDROGENATED MARGARINE AND NONDAIRY MILK (OR MORE IF NEEDED)

4 CUPS ORGANIC POWDERED (CONFECTIONER'S) SUGAR

4 TEASPOONS VANILLA EXTRACT

¼ TEASPOON SEA SALT

NATURAL FOOD COLORINGS (FOUND IN HEALTH FOOD STORES)

ALSO HANDY FOR THIS RECIPE:

NATURALLY COLORED SPRINKLES (FOUND IN HEALTH FOOD STORES)

ROLLING PIN AND COOKIE CUTTERS

1. To make the cookies: Cream the 1 cup of margarine in a large bowl with electric beaters. Add the sugar and beat it into the margarine until well combined.

2. Whisk the egg replacer mixture (egg replacer powder with the required amount of water) in a small bowl until fluffy, using a wire whisk or fork. The amount you will need varies by brand, so check the box for exact instructions. Add this to the sugar-margarine bowl and combine well using the electric beaters. Set the empty egg replacer bowl aside for the next step.

3. Using the bowl that the egg replacer was in, mix the sour cream with the baking soda. Add that to the main wet mixture and cream with the beaters until well mixed.

4. Sift or whisk the dry ingredients together. Add to the wet mixture and stir well to combine with a spoon.

5. Preheat the oven to 350° F. Knead the dough on a lightly floured surface for about a minute.

6. With a rolling pin, roll the dough out to about ¼-inch thickness, keeping it on the floured area to prevent sticking. Using your cookie cutters, make fun (and/or serious) shapes in the dough. Carefully place the cookies on an ungreased cookie sheet and bake until lightly browned, about 5-10 minutes. Remove gently and allow to cool, preferably on a cooling rack.

7. Repeat step six until all of the dough is used up, dusting the counter with more flour as needed.

8. Continue to allow all (o.k., *most*) of the cookies to cool. Next, with electric beaters, whip together the ½ cup margarine and 4 cups powdered sugar in a medium sized bowl. Add the remaining frosting ingredients and blend until smooth. At this point, our family's tradition is to divide the frosting into several small bowls. We then stir a different color into each bowl, using drops of the natural food coloring. Don't forget to keep a plain bowl so that you have some white frosting as well. Have a blast decorating your cookies!

MAKES: FAR TOO MANY COOKIES (LUCKILY, THEY MAKE GREAT GIFTS!); GF (W/ SUBSTITUTION)/PURPLE

Raspberry Season Pie

My good friend Jo loves raspberries so much that they make her lips quiver (think "cat looking at mouse"). When she first tried this pie, you can imagine the scene! Although this is fairly sweet, it's still nutritious due to its abundance of high fiber, vitamin-rich raspberries. *Ah, summer.*

CRUST*:

1 ¼ CUPS GRAHAM CRACKER CRUMBS (SWIRL GRAHAM CRACKERS IN A FOOD PROCESSOR UNTIL FINE)

2 TABLESPOONS ORGANIC "WHITE" SUGAR (NOT POWDERED)

¼ CUP NON-HYDROGENATED MARGARINE, MELTED

RASPBERRY LOVE:

2 CUPS FRESH RASPBERRIES

½ CUP PLUS 2 TABLESPOONS ORGANIC "WHITE" SUGAR (NOT POWDERED)

2 TABLESPOONS *FRESH* LEMON JUICE

½ TEASPOON VANILLA EXTRACT

5 TEASPOONS ARROWROOT (OR CORNSTARCH)

LONE ITEM: 1 CUP FRESH RASPBERRIES

1. Preheat the oven to 350° F. To prepare the crust, mix the graham cracker crumbs and 2 tablespoons of sugar together in a medium bowl. Stir in the melted margarine and combine well. Pour the mixture into a round pie pan. You will want the sides of the crust to almost come up to the top of the pan, so allocate your mixture accordingly. The secret to a firm graham cracker crust is to take your time, pressing all parts of the crust well with the palms of your hands so that it stays together and doesn't crumble. Pay special attention to the portion where the base meets the sides. Bake for 10-15 minutes, or until lightly browned. Set aside to cool.

2. In a medium pot, cook the two cups of raspberries with the remaining sugar over medium heat, stirring often, for about 5 minutes. Next, stir in the lemon juice and vanilla. Finally, sprinkle in the arrowroot a little bit at a time, whisking the mixture continuously to avoid lumps. Keep whisking it until it's thickened. This should only take a minute or two. Make sure not to overcook, however, as the mixture will thicken up even more when it cools.

3. Allow the filling to cool in the pan for about 15 minutes, stirring it often to release the steam.

4. Gently place the one cup of fresh raspberries evenly into the pie shell.

5. Pour the raspberry love filling into the pie crust (over the fresh raspberries). If necessary, use a rubber spatula to spread it out so that it evenly covers the fresh raspberries.

6. Cover the pie gently with plastic wrap (or waxed paper) and refrigerate it for several hours or overnight. Serve plain or with some nondairy ice cream or whip.

MAKES ONE 9-INCH PIE; GF/SF (WITH SUBSTITUTIONS)/BLUE

*You may substitute a frozen, pre-made gluten-free or soy-free crust if needed. Simply pre-bake it as you would with the graham cracker crust and proceed with the recipe.

♥*Tip*: You can use this formula for strawberry (or other berry) pie as well. Be sure to adjust the sugar content if needed, as berries can vary greatly in sweetness. Whatever you choose, it's perfect anytime you have lots of sweet-tart berries on hand and want a taste of summer!

Carrot Spice Cake with Creamy Lemon Frosting

This is rich, spicy, and totally delish. It's also free from refined flours, artificial ingredients, cholesterol, animal products, and hydrogenated oils. You can actually feel *good* about eating this decadent treat!

CARROT MIXTURE:

1 CUP <u>EACH</u>: GRATED CARROTS *AND* PURE MAPLE SYRUP

1 ½ TEASPOONS GROUND CINNAMON

½ TEASPOON <u>EACH</u>: GROUND NUTMEG, GROUND GINGER, *AND* GROUND ALLSPICE

½ CUP <u>EACH</u>: WATER, RAISINS, *AND* ORANGE JUICE (THE FRESHER THE BETTER)

ADDITIONS:

2 CUPS WHOLE WHEAT PASTRY FLOUR (OR GLUTEN-FREE ALL-PURPOSE FLOUR)

2 TEASPOONS BAKING SODA

⅛ TEASPOON SEA SALT

½ CUP OIL (SUNFLOWER, SAFFLOWER, NON-VIRGIN OLIVE, OR COCONUT)

CREAMY LEMON FROSTING:

ONE 8 OZ. CONTAINER NONDAIRY CREAM CHEESE

¼ CUP NON-HYDROGENATED MARGARINE

1 TABLESPOON VANILLA EXTRACT

ZEST OF TWO LARGE ORGANIC LEMONS (MINCED OR GRATED)

⅛ TEASPOON SEA SALT

1 TABLESPOON *FRESH* LEMON JUICE

2 ½ CUPS ORGANIC POWDERED (CONFECTIONER'S) SUGAR

> **GARNISH**: THE ZEST OF ONE LARGE LEMON (MINCED OR CHOPPED)

1. Combine the ingredients for the carrot mixture in a large bowl and stir well. You can now choose one of the following methods to marry the flavors: You can allow the items to soak overnight in the fridge in a covered container. Alternatively, you can place the items in a saucepan and bring them to a boil over high heat. Reduce the heat to low and simmer for five minutes. Remove from heat and cool to room temperature.

2. Preheat the oven to 350° F. Place the flour, baking soda, and salt in a large bowl and whisk or sift until well combined.

3. Stir the oil into the carrot mixture and combine well. Pour the wet mixture into the bowl with the dry ingredients and stir until everything is well combined. However, do not over-mix.

4. Lightly oil an 11.5 x 8-inch cake pan. Pour the batter into the pan, using a rubber spatula to make sure you get all of the goodness into the cake pan. Bake for about 45 minutes, or until a knife inserted into the center comes out clean. Remove from the oven and allow the cake to cool slightly before frosting it.

5. To make the frosting, place the cream cheese and margarine in a medium-large bowl and whip with electric beaters until well combined—but don't over-mix or your frosting might lose its consistency. You may also want to have a rubber spatula on hand to scrape down the sides of the bowl, as this will ensure a consistent frosting. Add the remaining items for the frosting and whip *just* until well combined. Refrigerate the frosting until the cake has cooled.

6. When the cake is cool enough not to melt the frosting, slather on the good stuff using a rubber spatula or butter knife. Scatter the lemon zest on top and serve. *Oh yes*. Yes, yes, yes!

MAKES ONE 11.5 x 8-INCH CAKE; GF (WITH SUBSTITUTION)/PURPLE

Light and Delicious Peach-Cinnamon Bake

No one will ever guess how low in fat and calories this is! It is pure, down-home delicious goodness. Do try to use ripe and organic peaches, however, as they make all the difference.

TENDER TOP CRUST:

¾ CUP WHOLE WHEAT PASTRY FLOUR (OR GLUTEN-FREE ALL-PURPOSE FLOUR)

1 ⅛ TEASPOONS BAKING POWDER

⅛ TEASPOON SEA SALT

2 TABLESPOONS EACH: OIL (SUNFLOWER, NON-VIRGIN OLIVE, OR COCONUT) AND PURE MAPLE SYRUP

1 TABLESPOON NONDAIRY MILK

PEACHY GOOD INNARDS:

5½ CUPS CHOPPED RIPE PEACHES

3-4 TABLESPOONS ARROWROOT (OR CORNSTARCH)

1 TEASPOON GROUND CINNAMON

½ TEASPOON GROUND NUTMEG

¼ TEASPOON SEA SALT

¼ CUP PLUS 2 TABLESPOONS PURE MAPLE SYRUP

2¼ TEASPOONS FRESH LEMON JUICE

1. Preheat the oven to 400° F.

2. Next, begin the top crust. First, mix the flour, baking powder, and salt in a medium sized bowl.

3. Separately, in a small bowl, mix the oil, 2 tablespoons maple syrup, and milk. Stir it into the flour mixture *just* until well combined (do not over-mix). Using a gentle, light touch will ensure that your crust doesn't become tough. Place the dough in an airtight container or plastic bag and refrigerate it until step six. Don't worry if the dough seems overly wet and rebellious—refrigeration will reform it.

4. Place the peaches in a large, covered baking dish. Sprinkle in the 3 tablespoons of arrowroot, along with the cinnamon, nutmeg, and salt. Stir gently to combine.

5. Pour the maple syrup and lemon juice into the peach concoction and gently mix everything together. Cover and bake for about 10-15 minutes. Remove and stir. If the mixture looks too runny, you can sprinkle in the additional tablespoon of arrowroot. Gently stir and bake for another 10-20 minutes, or until thickened. Remove from heat, but leave the oven on.

6. Take the dough out of the fridge and form it into a ball. Next, place it on waxed paper. Place another piece of waxed paper on top of the dough. Go over the top of the wax paper with a rolling pin to make the dough into a circle the size of a pie pan.

7. Place the peach mixture into a lightly oiled pie pan. Next, gently remove the top sheet of waxed paper from the crust. Carefully flip the crust over and onto the peach mixture. Gently remove the second sheet of waxed paper. Tuck the crust into the sides and/or make a decorative rim around the edge (using your fingers, a fork, or a pastry tool).

8. Bake for an additional 10 minutes, or until the crust is lightly browned. Remove and allow to cool for 5-10 minutes before serving...if that's even possible, given the smell you're dealing with right now.

SERVES 6 (MAKES ONE STANDARD SIZED PIE); GF (WITH SUBSTITUTION)/SF/BLUE

Chocolate Dipped Treasures

This is just the thing for when you want a very quick, relatively light dessert. Yet, it's the absolute *essence* of simple elegance! This recipe is more of a suggestion than an exact science, as it's fun to vary the items you dip into the chocolate. So, if you've got a lot of booty in your treasure chest, double the dip, matey!

WAXED PAPER

TREASURE CHEST OPTIONS:

FRESH STRAWBERRIES

BANANA CHUNKS OR SLICES

WHOLE RAW ALMONDS

DRIED MANGO SLICES (OH, YEAH) OR DRIED APRICOTS

GINGER: DRIED, CRYSTALLIZED GINGER OR PAPER THIN SLICES OF FRESH GINGER

GINGERSNAP COOKIES OR GRAHAM CRACKERS

ORANGE SEGMENTS

ORGANIC CITRUS PEEL (ORANGE, LEMON, OR LIME), JULIENNE CUT OR ZESTED IN STRIPS

PRETZELS

ROSEHIPS (DRIED)

FRESH MINT LEAVES

CHILI PEPPERS (YOU KNOW WHO YOU ARE)

DRIED CRANBERRIES, DRIED BLUEBERRIES, OR RAISINS

FIGS (DRIED OR FRESH)

CHOCOLATE DIP:

½ CUP NONDAIRY SEMI-SWEET CHOCOLATE CHIPS

2 TEASPOONS EACH: NON-HYDROGENATED MARGARINE AND NONDAIRY MILK

I TEASPOON VANILLA EXTRACT, OPTIONAL

1. Prepare the items you wish to dip, trimming and washing them if necessary. Set them aside.
2. Cover plates (or a cookie sheet) with a layer of the waxed paper. Set aside.
3. Next, melt the chocolate chips and margarine in a very small pan over the lowest heat possible (or in a double boiler), stirring constantly until *just* melted. Immediately remove from heat and stir in the milk and vanilla.
4. Next, dip your treasures into the chocolate and place them on the waxed paper. In order to accomplish this sweet task, your options are to either dunk the items partially into the chocolate *or* spread the chocolate on with a knife. Continue to dip until all of the chocolate sauce is gone.
5. Place the plates (or cookie sheet) of dipped goodies in the fridge until the chocolate hardens—usually at least 30 minutes. If you want (need?!) lightning fast results, you can pop them into the freezer instead. They can then harden in 5 or 10 minutes, depending on your freezer. Serve immediately, or refrigerate in an airtight container for several days.

SERVES 4; 30 MINUTES OR UNDER! (IF USING FREEZER SET METHOD) GF/BLUE

Tip: If your chocolate sauce is too thick, simply thin it with just a little more nondairy milk. Also, for Mexican Chocolate, a little cayenne and cinnamon can be added to the sauce.

Apple Cinnamon Raisin "Pie"

Cinnamon lovers, this treat is for you! I have called this a "pie" because it only contains one crust. However, this makes it so light and healthy that you can feel fabulous about digging on in!

TOP CRUST:

¾ CUP WHOLE WHEAT PASTRY FLOUR (OR GLUTEN-FREE ALL-PURPOSE FLOUR)

1⅛ TEASPOONS BAKING POWDER

⅛ TEASPOON SEA SALT

2 TABLESPOONS EACH: OIL (SUNFLOWER, NON-VIRGIN OLIVE, OR COCONUT) AND PURE MAPLE SYRUP

1 TABLESPOON NONDAIRY MILK

FILLING:

5 CUPS (PACKED) THINLY SLICED APPLES, PEELS LEFT ON IF ORGANIC

½ CUP RAISINS

3 TABLESPOONS ARROWROOT (OR CORNSTARCH)

1 TABLESPOON GROUND CINNAMON (OR LESS IF YOU AREN'T A CINNAMON NUT)

½ TEASPOON GROUND NUTMEG

⅛ TEASPOON ALLSPICE (OPTIONAL)

¼ TEASPOON SEA SALT

¼ CUP PLUS 2 TABLESPOONS PURE MAPLE SYRUP

2¼ TEASPOONS FRESH LEMON JUICE

1. Preheat the oven to 400° F.

2. Next, begin the top crust. First, mix the flour, baking powder, and salt in a medium sized bowl.

3. Separately, in a small bowl, mix the oil, 2 tablespoons maple syrup, and milk. Stir it into the flour mixture *just* until well combined (do not over-mix). Using a gentle, light touch will ensure that your crust does not become tough. Place the dough in an airtight container or plastic bag and refrigerate it until step six. Don't worry if the dough seems overly wet—refrigerating it will firm it up.

4. Place the apples and raisins in a large, covered baking dish. Sprinkle in the arrowroot, along with the cinnamon, nutmeg, allspice, and salt. Stir well to combine.

5. Pour the maple syrup and lemon juice into the apple concoction and mix well. Cover and bake for about 10-15 minutes. Remove and stir. Bake for another 10-20 minutes, or until the mixture is thickened and the apples are tender. Remove from heat, but leave the oven on.

6. Take the dough out of the fridge and form it into a ball. Next, place it on waxed paper. Place another piece of waxed paper on top of the dough. Go over the top of the wax paper with a rolling pin to make the dough into a circle the size of a pie pan.

7. Place the apple mixture into a lightly oiled pie pan. Next, gently remove the top sheet of waxed paper from the crust. Carefully flip the crust over and onto the apple mixture. Gently remove the second sheet of waxed paper. Tuck the crust into the sides and/or make a decorative rim around the edge (using your fingers, a fork, or a pastry tool). Bake for an additional 10 minutes, or until the crust is lightly browned. Remove and cool for 5-10 minutes before serving. Nibble the deliciousness.

SERVES 6 (MAKES ONE STANDARD SIZED PIE); GF (WITH SUBSTITUTION)/SF/BLUE

Chocolate Peanut Butter Mini-Cups

Oh, sweet baby, are these good. They can also be put together in under 30 minutes!
Once you try these, you may never go back to the store bought kind.

8 TINY MINI-MUFFIN PAPER LINERS OR "CANDY CUPS" (ABOUT 1-INCH IN DIAMETER)

PEANUT BUTTER FILLING:

2 TABLESPOONS NATURAL CREAMY PEANUT BUTTER, AT ROOM TEMPERATURE

¼ TEASPOON SEA SALT

4 TEASPOONS PURE MAPLE SYRUP

2 TEASPOONS ORGANIC POWDERED (CONFECTIONER'S) SUGAR

CHOCOLATE:

½ CUP NONDAIRY SEMI-SWEET CHOCOLATE CHIPS

2 TEASPOONS NON-HYDROGENATED MARGARINE

1 TEASPOON VANILLA EXTRACT

1. Stir the peanut butter, sea salt, maple syrup, and powdered sugar together until very well combined. Set aside.
2. Set your muffin liners on a plate (or inside of a plastic container) so that they're ready for action.
3. Next, melt the chocolate chips and margarine in a very small pan over the lowest heat imaginable (or in a double boiler), stirring constantly until *just* melted. Remove from heat immediately and stir in the vanilla.
4. Using a table knife (or other utensil that makes sense), scoop out a little of the chocolate mixture and swirl it around the insides of a muffin liner, making sure it finds its way into the crevices of the paper. Try to make the sides relatively thick, as it will help the cups hold together better. Don't worry if some of the chocolate finds its way onto the base of the liner. It's all good...*real* good. Repeat with the other seven liners and place in the freezer for 5 minutes, or until the chocolate is mostly hardened.
5. Remove them from the freezer. Using your chosen utensil, scoop out a little more chocolate to make a base in the bottom of the muffin cups. Be sure to connect the bottom with the sides so that there are no gaps. Pop into the freezer again for 5 minutes, or until the chocolate base is mostly hardened.
6. Next, place some of the peanut butter filling into the center of each cup. Distribute it evenly and you should have just the right amount for each cup. You're almost done!
7. The remaining chocolate should still be soft enough to work with, but if it's not, reheat on low again *just* until it melts. Next, with the knife, gently spread the remaining chocolate on top of the peanut butter filling. Again, try to connect the fresh portion of the chocolate to the hardened portion (sides), so that the end result is totally connected. We're all connected, and now your chocolate is too.
8. Freeze again for 5 minutes, or until they're firm enough to eat. Finally, get ready for some lip smackin' snacking! These will store refrigerated in an airtight container for up to ten days. *I think.* Actually, that's just an educated guess. I don't know anyone (including myself) that would still have these around after a week!

MAKES 8 MINI-CUPS; 30 MINUTES OR UNDER! GF/BLUE (UNLESS YOU EAT TOO MANY!)

Orange-Spiced Baklava

Most people would never guess how easy it is to prepare a luscious tray of baklava. Do you still not believe me? Then try this delectable recipe and prepare for a yummy surprise! I've purposely kept the orange flavor subtle, but you may increase the orange zest if you prefer a stronger orange kick.

½ LB. PHYLLO DOUGH, THAWED (SEE PAGE 42)

6-8 TABLESPOONS NON-HYDROGENATED MARGARINE

SAUCE OF BLISS:

½ CUP EACH: WATER AND AGAVE NECTAR

¼ CUP ORGANIC "WHITE" SUGAR

2 WHOLE CINNAMON STICKS

3 WHOLE CARDAMOM PODS

3 WHOLE CLOVES

½ TEASPOON EACH: VANILLA EXTRACT, MINCED ORANGE ZEST, AND FRESH LEMON JUICE

1/16 TEASPOON SEA SALT (A DASH, IN OTHER WORDS!)

FILLING:
- ½ CUP (2.25 OZ.) WALNUTS
- I TEASPOON GROUND CINNAMON
- I TABLESPOON ORGANIC SUGAR
- ⅛ TEASPOON SEA SALT

1. Place all of the sauce ingredients in a small pan, stir well, and bring to a boil over medium heat. Reduce the heat to low and simmer gently (uncovered) for 15 minutes, stirring occasionally. Set aside. Once cooled, remove the cinnamon sticks, cardamom pods, and cloves.

2. *To prepare the filling*: Chop the walnuts in a food processor until very coarsely ground. Alternatively, you can place them in a sealed plastic bag and smoosh them with a rolling pin or mallet. Mix with the cinnamon, sugar, and salt and set aside.

3. Preheat the oven to 350° F. Melt the margarine. Get ready to rock.

4. Divide the ½ lb. of phyllo into two portions. Set one of the portions aside, covered with a lightly damp towel. Using a pastry brush, coat the bottom and sides of a 9 x 9-inch pan with some of the melted margarine. Place one sheet of phyllo (from the uncovered stack) on the bottom of the pan and brush it lightly with margarine. If your phyllo doesn't fit the size of the pan, simply cut it or overlap it a bit—you can even things out as you go. Continue layering one piece of phyllo at a time, brushing each piece lightly with margarine, until you have used up the first portion of the phyllo. Top evenly with the nut mixture.

5. Uncover the second portion of the phyllo and use it up in the same manner as you did before. Keep placing single layers of phyllo on top of each other, brushing each lightly with margarine.

6. When you've used up the last of the phyllo, bring on the knife. You're about to cut the phyllo into individual pieces....*very carefully*. Begin by cutting diagonal lines (with a 1½-inch space in between each cut) across the whole pan. If it helps, you can hold onto the top layer of phyllo with your other hand as you make your cuts all the way through to the bottom of the pan. Next, make cuts (again with a 1½-inch space in between) that are horizontal across the pan. Short story long, you want diamond-shaped baklava.

7. Next, pour about half of the sauce evenly over the top of the phyllo.

8. Bake for about 20-30 minutes, or until very nicely golden browned. Once the phyllo just starts to brown (after about 15 minutes), you will want to check it often, as it can burn easily.

9. Remove from the oven. Pour the remaining sauce evenly over the top of the baklava. This may seem like a lot of sauce, but the longer the baklava sits, the less saucy and sweet it becomes. Enjoy your gleeful feelings of accomplishment...and the insanely delicious eats.

MAKES ONE 9 x 9-INCH PAN OF BAKLAVA (ABOUT 15 PIECES); PURPLE

Quick, Light, and Outta Sight Turnovers

As the name implies, these babies are a snap to make and unusually light. To be totally true to the title of this recipe, you can make these without the vanilla icing. However, for another three minutes of work (and a few extra calories), it gives them added pizzazz and a richer flavor. Personally, I like having both options. Sometimes I want a healthy fix for my sweet tooth and other times I need a quick, snazzy dessert to serve guests. Incidentally, this also works well with other berries. Simply substitute raspberries, strawberries, or blackberries for the blueberries (and use their corresponding jam for the blueberry jam). Once you get the hang of using phyllo, you'll feel confident about pulling this dessert off in no time!

8 SHEETS OF PHYLLO (9 x 13-INCHES EACH), THAWED (SEE PAGE 42 FOR PHYLLO TIPS)

SPRAY OIL (OR A SMALL AMOUNT OF OIL AND A PASTRY BRUSH)

FILLING:

1 CUP BLUEBERRIES, THAWED IF FROZEN

6 TABLESPOONS BLUEBERRY JAM (OR FRUIT SPREAD)

2½ TEASPOONS ARROWROOT (OR CORNSTARCH)

¼ TEASPOON VANILLA EXTRACT

VANILLA ICING (OPTIONAL):

1 TEASPOON NON-HYDROGENATED MARGARINE

¼ CUP ORGANIC POWDERED (CONFECTIONER'S) SUGAR, SIFTED IF LUMPY

¼ TEASPOON VANILLA EXTRACT

1 TEASPOON NONDAIRY MILK

GARNISH:

1 TABLESPOON ORGANIC POWDERED (CONFECTIONER'S) SUGAR

1. Preheat the oven to 350° F. Lightly oil a small cookie sheet (or baking pan) and set aside.
2. In a medium sized bowl, combine the filling items together until well mixed. Set aside.
3. Lay two sheets of phyllo (one on top of the other) on a clean, dry counter top. Fold in half lengthwise to form a 4½ x 13-inch rectangle. Place ¼ of the berry filling at the base of the phyllo rectangle. Fold the bottom of the phyllo up and over the mixture. Continue to fold up, forming it into a triangle as you go. If the filling seems a little gooey, don't despair. It will firm up in the oven. Besides, a little gooey fruit oozing out of your delish turnover? Worse things in life. Place your triangular bundle of joy on the oiled baking pan and spray or lightly brush with oil.
4. Continue this process to make the three other turnovers, spraying or brushing them lightly with oil as well. Place them in the oven for 10-20 minutes, or until golden browned.
5. If you'll be making the icing, do the deal while the turnovers are baking. Simply melt the margarine, then add the other ingredients, stirring well with a spoon until uniformly mixed.
6. When the turnovers are golden brown, remove them from the oven. Allow to cool for 5 minutes. Drizzle the icing (if using) over them and dust with some of the powdered sugar. Serve immediately.

SERVES 4; 30 MINUTES OR UNDER! SF (WITHOUT ICING)/BLUE

Flippin' Fresh Key Lime Pie

Recently, a friend told me that he's never had a truly satisfying slice of vegan key lime pie. Of course, I immediately decided that this was a serious problem in need of a remedy! After many failed attempts, I finally became inspired to create an uncooked filling. Although this makes it a bit pudding-like, it's worth it. Being *unusually* fresh tasting and tangy, this dessert also manages to be high in fiber, potassium, and many vitamins! I have given two options for the crust, as it's delicious both ways.

GINGERSNAP PIE CRUST OPTION:

¼ CUP NON-HYDROGENATED MARGARINE

¾ CUP UNDERLINE EACH: GRAHAM CRACKER CRUMBS *AND* GINGERSNAP CRUMBS (SWIRL GRAHAM CRACKERS AND GINGERSNAPS IN A FOOD PROCESSOR UNTIL FINELY GROUND)

¼ TEASPOON GROUND DRIED GINGER (OPTIONAL)

I TABLESPOON ORGANIC SUGAR OR SUCANAT

LIME TIME:

2 CUPS MASHED AVOCADO (TRUST ME)

2 TABLESPOONS (*PACKED*) MINCED ORGANIC LIME ZEST

2 CUPS ORGANIC POWDERED (CONFECTIONER'S) SUGAR

I CUP *FRESH* LIME JUICE (YES, ONE CUP)

¼ TEASPOON SEA SALT

I TEASPOON VANILLA EXTRACT

RAW PIE CRUST OPTION:

• 2½ CUPS RAW ALMONDS

• ¼ TEASPOON SEA SALT

• ¼ CUP RAISINS (TIGHTLY PACKED AND UNSOAKED)

• ½ CUP PITTED DATES (TIGHTLY PACKED AND UNSOAKED)

OPTIONAL GARNISH:

• I TEASPOON EACH (CHOPPED): ORANGE ZEST, LIME ZEST, *AND* LEMON ZEST

1. *If using the gingersnap crust*, preheat the oven to 350° F. Melt the margarine. Mix the graham cracker crumbs and gingersnap crumbs together in a bowl. Add the ginger and sugar and combine well. Stir in the melted margarine and combine thoroughly. Pour into a round pie pan. You'll want the sides of the crust to come up almost to the top of the pan, so allocate your mixture accordingly. The secret to a firm crust is to take your time, pressing all parts of the crust well with the palms of your hands, so that it stays together and doesn't crumble. Also, pay special attention to the place where the sides meet the bottom. Bake for about 10 minutes, or until aromatic and lightly browned. Skip (or hop) to step three.

2. *If using the raw pie crust*, place the almonds, salt, raisins, and dates in a food processor. Blend very well, but *just* until the mixture resembles coarse crumbs and is beginning to stick together. You still want to retain a crumbly consistency, so don't over-blend. Transfer the mixture to a round pie pan and press to form a crust. For details and tips on making the crust, see step one. And, yes, you may have too much mixture for the pie crust, but it makes amazing raw cookies! Just form into balls, roll in coconut (or not), and refrigerate. Cover the crust with plastic wrap and place in the freezer until the filling is ready.

3. In a food processor, blend the avocado until it is perfectly smooth and no lumps remain. Scrape down the sides as needed with a rubber spatula. Blend in the lime zest, powdered sugar, lime juice, salt, and vanilla until very smooth and uniformly creamy. Pour into the chosen crust and smooth out the top.

4. Cover the pie and allow it to chill out in the refrigerator for several hours (or overnight), until it has firmed up a bit. Sprinkle gleefully with the zests (if using) and serve. Lime lovers unite!

MAKES ONE PIE (SERVES 8); SF/GF (IF USING THE RAW CRUST)/BLUE

Just in case you're curious, the powdered sugar is the ingredient that prevents this pie from being a totally raw food item (when using the raw crust). Because I felt that *lots* of lime juice was key (pun intended) to the bright flavor, adding a raw, liquid sweetener made it far too runny. Also, a raw granulated sugar runs the risk of being "grainy." Hence, the flippin' powdered sugar.

Coconut Rice w/ Mango, Mint, and Crystallized Ginger

This is a Thai-inspired dessert that's quick, simple, subtle, and rich—and it's real purty to boot.

⅔ CUP WHITE SUSHI RICE

2 CUPS COCONUT MILK

3 TABLESPOONS ORGANIC "WHITE" SUGAR

SCANT ⅛ TEASPOON SEA SALT

- ¾ CUP DICED FRESH MANGO (PEELED)
- 2 TEASPOONS (*PACKED*) FRESH MINT, MINCED
- 1 TABLESPOON MINCED CRYSTALLIZED GINGER
- ½ TEASPOON UNTOASTED BLACK SESAME SEEDS

1. In a medium pot (with a tight fitting lid), place the rice and coconut milk. Stir well. Cover and bring to a boil over medium heat. Reduce the heat to low and simmer, covered, for 20-25 minutes (or until the rice is tender and most of the liquid has been absorbed). Stir in the sugar and salt.

2. Place the rice in four bowls and arrange the mango around the rice. Sprinkle with the mint, ginger, and sesame seeds and Thai one on.

SERVES ABOUT 4; 30 MINUTES OR UNDER! GF/SF/PURPLE

Glorious Chocolate Truffles

Glorious, divine, scrumptious, and guilt-free, these truffles will make you giddy...and quite popular!

CASHEW-VANILLA CREAM:

½ CUP EACH: RAW CASHEWS *AND* NONDAIRY MILK (SOY, RICE, ALMOND, OR COCONUT)

2 TEASPOONS VANILLA EXTRACT

⅛ TEASPOON SEA SALT

CHOCOLATENESS:

10 OZ. BAG (1 ¾ CUPS) NONDAIRY SEMI-SWEET CHOCOLATE CHIPS

2 TABLESPOONS NON-HYDROGENATED MARGARINE

OPTIONAL MIX-INS: CHOPPED PEANUTS, CHOPPED CRYSTALLIZED GINGER, CRUSHED PEPPERMINT CANDY, CACAO NIBS, MINCED ORANGE OR LIME ZEST (ORGANIC), OR FAIRY DUST

OPTIONAL HOLY ROLLERS: ORGANIC POWDERED SUGAR, COCOA POWDER, CACAO NIBS, CRUSHED PEPPERMINT CANDY, CHOPPED PEANUTS, OR CHOPPED PECANS

1. In a food processor or blender, puree the cashews, milk, vanilla, and salt until *completely* creamy and emulsified. Set aside.

2. In a double boiler (or small pot set to the lowest heat imaginable), heat the chocolate chips and margarine, stirring often, *just* until melted. Do not overcook!

3. Stir the cashew-vanilla cream into the melted chocolate until well mixed. If you wish to add any of the optional mix-ins, stir them in now. If you like, you can make a few different mixtures for variety. Set your mixture(s) aside in the fridge or freezer until thick enough to work with. In the freezer, this usually takes about 30 minutes and in the fridge it usually takes 1½ hours or longer.

4. When it's firm enough to work with, let it come in from the cold. Remove about one tablespoon of the mixture and roll it into a ball. If desired, roll it in some of the optional holy roller items. Have some fun with different coatings here—get crazy! But not too crazy. Set aside on waxed paper or on a plate.

5. Repeat about 29 times, or until there is no longer any chocolate left in a non-spherical state. Place the chocolate truffles in the fridge until you're ready to beckon them. Have fun daring people to eat just one.

MAKES ABOUT 30 TRUFFLES; GF/PURPLE

Chapter Seventeen: Menu Suggestions

In this chapter, I have given you some sample menus for a variety of different situations. Of course, you may customize these suggestions in any way that suits you and your family. I hope these ideas serve as inspiration for you to have fun creating fabulous, healthy meals in *your* kitchen!

Fabulous Meals that are SURE to Impress

These menus are flat-out *perfect* for those times when you need to astonish unsuspecting guests with your fabulousness.

THAI STYLE DINNER:
> Fresh Thai Spring Rolls (served with The Peanut Sauce) (72)
> Thai Tofu & Tropical Fruit Salad (107)
> Thai Emerald Noodles (165)
> Flippin' Fresh Key Lime Pie (243) *or* Caramelized Banana Bliss Bombs (219)

INDIAN FEAST #1:
> Indian Papadams (84)
> Lemon-Cilantro Pakoras (82)
> Cilantro Chutney Elixir (125) and/or Tamarind-Date Chutney (126)
> Indian Kuchumber Salad (108)
> Aloo Gobi Chole (163)
> Seasoned Indian Basmati Rice (102)
> Cocoa-Mint Mousse Nests (not Indian, but a great flavor complement, 227)

INDIAN FEAST #2:
> Mulligatawny (209)
> Indian Phyllo "Samosas" (86)
> Spicy Onion Chutney (126) and/or Tamarind-Date Chutney (126)
> Cilantro Chutney Elixir (optional, 125)
> Indian Kuchumber Salad (108)
> Saag "Paneer" with plain cooked basmati rice (161)
> Chocolate Dipped Treasures (not Indian, but a great ending, 238)

JAPANESE STYLE DINNER:
> Nori Rolls with Creamy Ginger-Wasabi and Lemon-Lime Soy Sauce (76)
> Tossed salad with Ginger Magic Dressing (121)
> Soba Noodles with Tempura Vegetables and Ginger-Daikon Sauce (158)
> Apple Puffs with Vanilla Bean Caramel Sauce (not authentic Japanese, yeah yeah, 231)

JAPANESE AND ECLECTIC ASIAN DINNER:
> Tempura Asparagus Nori Rolls (77) *or* Vegetable Tempura with Ginger-Daikon Sauce (68)
> Edamame Miso Dip with Black Sesame Crackers (66)
> Sesame Tofu with Fresh Basil and Thai Sweet Chili Sauce (164)
> Fruit Mandala Tart with Apricot-Orange Glaze (220)

GREEK STYLE DINNER:

Fatoush Salad (109) *or* Greek Salad (106)
Red Lentil, Spinach, and Lemon Soup (212)
Dolmadas (85)
Fresh Greek Delight (135)
Orange-Spiced Baklava (241)

ITALIAN STYLE DINNER #1:

Green Bread (69)
Baby Greens with Arugula, Apples, and Caramelized Pecans (111)
Asparagus, Portabella, and Kalamata Triangle Puffs (optional, 83)
Tomato, Basil, and Roasted Pine Nut Penne (167)
Luscious Lemon Bars with Ginger Shortbread Crust (224)

ITALIAN STYLE DINNER #2 (SPRING FEAST!):

Sourdough Bruschetta (66)
Spinach-Strawberry Salad (104)
Lemon Asparagus Linguine (168)
Fruit Mandala Tart with Apricot-Orange Glaze (220)

ITALIAN STYLE DINNER #3:

Potato-Leek Soup with Caramelized Shallots (211)
Italian Bread Salad with Tangy Basil Vinaigrette (114)
Shiitake & Tempeh Puffs with Rosemary (170)
Lemon Lover's Cupcakes with Lemon Zest Buttercream Frosting (229)

ITALIAN STYLE DINNER #4:

Olive Oil with Crispy Garlic and Rosemary (80)
Crusty sourdough or multigrain bread (recipe not in this book—give your local bakery some love)
Three Citrus Asparagus (69)
Rosemary Mushroom Strudel (70)
Luscious Lasagna (173)
Chocolate Bliss Pie (232) *or* Chocolate Decadence Cake (218)

MEXICAN STYLE DINNER:

Mexican Fiesta Rice (96)
Perfect Pinto Beans (95)
Avocado and Grapefruit Salad with Chili-Roasted Almonds (110)
Mexican Polenta Bake (162)
Chocolate Bliss Pie (232) *or* Chocolate Dipped Treasures (238)

RAW FOODS FEAST:

Spinach-Strawberry Salad (104) (using raw almonds in place of toasted)
Zucchini Chips to Dry For (188)
Moroccan Barley-Spinach Toss (184)
Triple Omega Wrap with Basil & Tomatoes (183)
Blackberry Peach Cobbler (188) *or* Divine Mango Pie (183)

SERIOUS BREAKFAST/BRUNCH SPREAD:

Tropical Smoothies (51)
Lemon-Rosemary Home Fries (56)
Love Bug Parfaits (53)
Yellow Tofu (optional, 64)
Blueberry Waffles with Blueberry Citrus Sauce (59)

Eclectic Mid-Eastern Meal:

Quick and Delightful Zatar Wedges (200)
Creamy Hummus (79)
Dolmadas (85)
Fatoush Salad (109)
Ful Mudhamas (90)
Orange-Spiced Baklava (241)

Autumn Celebration Meal:

(This one could also be called "*How to Impress Omnivores on Thanksgiving!*")

Baby Greens with Arugula, Apples, and Caramelized Pecans (111)
Garlic Mashers (99) with Scrumptious Shiitake Gravy (122)
Potato-Leek Soup with Caramelized Shallots (optional, 211)
Oven Roasted Cauliflower with Rosemary and Garlic (100)
Shiitake & Tempeh Puffs with Rosemary (170)
Apple Pie Acorn Squash (93)
Grandma's Apple Crisp (223)
Chocolate Bliss Pie (232)

Super Light Meals that Still Rock!

Here are some ideas for lighter, quicker meals. However, although they're ultra-healthy and very easy to prepare, they are all still delicious!

Any of these desserts can be added to the "Super Light" meals:

Quick, Light, and Outta Sight Turnovers (242)
Blackberry Peach Goodness (226)
Apple Cinnamon Raisin "Pie" (239)
Ultra Light Blackberry Cobbler (223)
Light and Delicious Peach-Cinnamon Bake (237)

Indian Inspired Light Meal:

Indian Phyllo "Samosas" (86) with Cilantro Chutney Elixir (125)
Tossed salad with Light Balsamic Dressing (129)
Fat-Free Red Lentils & Spinach with Tamarind (154) *or* Moong Dal (138)

Mexican Style Light Meal #1:

Black Bean, Cilantro, and Apricot Salad (115)
Spinach Quesadilla (143)

Mexican Style Light Meal #2:

Perfect Pintos (95)
Mexican Fiesta Rice (96)
Mexican Polenta Bake (162)
Tossed green salad with Light Balsamic Dressing (129)

ELEGANT AND LIGHT BREAKFAST:
>   Virtuous Vanilla Shake (48)
>   Raspberry Lemon Zest Pancakes (59)

SOUTHERN STYLE LIGHT MEAL:
>   Kid's Kale (92)
>   Creamy Polenta (94)
>   Black-eyed Peas with Kale (You just can't ever have too much kale!) (139)

ASIAN STYLE LIGHT MEAL #1:
>   Vietnamese Spring Rolls (75)
>   Chili-Ginger Cabbage (113)
>   Lo Fat Lo Mein (148)

ASIAN STYLE LIGHT MEAL #2:
>   Delectable Lowfat "Egg Rolls" (67)
>   Skinny Dinny (149)

MOROCCAN INSPIRED LIGHT MEAL:
>   Spinach, Orange, and Toasted Almond Salad (109)
>   Moroccan Quinoa (88)
>   Perfect Pintos (95)

SUPER IMMUNE-BOOSTER LIGHT MEAL #1:
>   Kid's Kale (92)
>   Immune Power Soup (216)
>   Shiitake, Walnut, and Dried Cranberry Salad (113)
>   *Optional*: cooked amaranth or quinoa (recipe not in this book)

SUPER IMMUNE-BOOSTER LIGHT MEAL #2:
>   Lemon-Ginger Miso Medicine (213)
>   Zesty Kale with Cranberries (89)
>   Vitality Noodles (152)

VITAMIN C (AND IRON) IMMUNE-BOOSTER LIGHT MEAL:
>   Cooked black beans (recipe not in this book)
>   *To top the black beans*: 9½ Minute Green Chili Sauce (131)
>   Cilantro-Lime Rice (89)
>   Spinach, Orange, and Toasted Almond Salad (109)

HOME-STYLE LIGHT MEAL:
>   Oven "Fries" (92)
>   Tossed salad with Cleansing Miso-Lime Dressing (128)
>   Deluxe Almond-Veggie Burgers (136)

☼ TIP: BE SURE TO CHECK OUT THE INDEX FOR OTHER MENU IDEAS! THERE, YOU CAN LOOK UP JAPANESE, THAI, MEXICAN, MOROCCAN, ITALIAN, RAW, GREEK, AND INDIAN FOODS FOR MORE IDEAS ON PUTTING SPECIAL—OR EVERYDAY—MEALS TOGETHER. IN THE INDEX, YOU'LL FIND EACH CUISINE LISTED WITH THE CORRESPONDING RECIPES UNDERNEATH. FOR EXAMPLE, ALL OF THE ITALIAN RECIPES WILL BE LOCATED UNDER "ITALIAN FOOD(S)." FROM THERE, YOU CAN MIX AND MATCH TO YOUR HEALTHY HEART'S CONTENT!

Kids are Eaters Too!

Here are some menus that will actually get children *excited* about eating healthy meals! I kid you not—I've seen it firsthand and it's a beautiful thing. Also, if you can get them involved in meal preparation, they'll be more likely to try new foods. Stirring, pouring, sifting, and measuring are all great ways for kids to feel included. Spending time together in the kitchen creates lasting memories and is a natural, fun way to do some bonding. Have fun...and good luck!

Kid Friendly Home-Style Meal:
Kid's Kale (92) *or* Krazy Kale Chips (91)
Creamy Polenta (94)
Perfect Pintos (95)
Grandma's Apple Crisp (223)

Kid Friendly Italian Meal:
Green Bread (69)
Spinach-Strawberry Salad (104)
Lemon Asparagus Linguine (168)
Lemon Lover's Cupcakes with Lemon Zest Buttercream Frosting (229)

Kid Friendly Eclectic Meal:
Baby Greens with Arugula, Apples, and Caramelized Pecans (111)
Garlic Mashers (99)
Black-eyed Peas with Kale (139)
Chocolate Peanut Butter Mini-Cups (240)

Kid Friendly Super Simple Meal:
Zen Rice with Seaweed Gomasio (99)
Baby greens with Quick 4-ingredient Raspberry Dressing (dressing, 111)
Old Fashioned "Chicken" Noodle Soup (210)

Kid Friendly Asian Meal #1:
Nori Rolls with Lemon-Lime Soy Sauce (76)
Asian Asparagus Wraps (78)
Immune Power Soup (216)
Quick, Light, and Outta Sight Turnovers (242)

Kid Friendly Asian Meal #2:
Kid's Favorite Veggie Fried Rice (98)
Tossed salad with Ginger Magic Dressing (121)
Sesame Tofu with Basil (hold the chili sauce for kiddos, 164)
Mommy's Chocolate Chip Cookies (225)

Kid Friendly Mexican Meal:
Mexican Fiesta Rice (hold the chilies, 96)
Tossed Salad with Light Balsamic Dressing (129)
Tasty Lowfat Tostadas (147)
Righteously Rich Hot Cocoa (207)

Kid Friendly Immune-Booster Meal:
Kid's Kale (92)
Immune Power Soup (216) *or* Lemon-Ginger Miso Medicine (213)
Garlic Mashers (99)
Princess Salad (106)

KID FRIENDLY SNACKS AND MINI-MEALS:

Banana Muffins to Write Home About (201)

Lemon-Poppy Seed Muffins with Zesty Lemon Glaze (202)

Princess Salad (106)

Fruit Be-Bops (199)

Deluxe Almond-Veggie Burgers (especially when cut into fun shapes, 136)

Apples with Alethea's Apple Dip (199)

Supercorn! (198) and Everything Nice Popcorn (198)

Whole Multigrain Bread (203)

Whole Grain and Flax Banana Bread (205)

All Shakes and Smoothies (please see the breakfast chapter, 46-64)

Kiddie Power Drink (54)

Carrot-Orange Juice (55)

Carrot-Apple-Ginger Juice (light on the ginger, 55)

Pancakes and Waffles (please see the breakfast chapter, 46-64)

Grandma's Favorite French Toast (especially nutritious with sprouted grain bread, 62)

Love Bug Parfaits (53)

Yellow Tofu (64)

Krazy Kale Chips (91)

Creamy Hummus (79)

Spinach Quesadilla (143)

Kid's Choice Guacamole (101)

Illegal Pizza (150)

Oven "Fries" (92)

Standard Seasoned Tofu or Tempeh Cubes (105)

Zucchini Chips to Dry For (188)

Peach Mango Kanten (207)

Creamy Polenta (94)

...And, of course, just about any of the desserts! (183, 188, 217-244)

RANDOM KIDDO TIPS THAT ACTUALLY WORK!

♥I'VE READ THAT CHILDREN NEED TO TRY SOMETHING TEN TIMES BEFORE THEY DEVELOP A TASTE FOR IT! SO, DON'T GIVE UP IF YOUR CHILD DOESN'T LIKE SOMETHING AT FIRST.

♥*OUR RULE IS:* YOU HAVE TO TRY AT LEAST ONE TASTE OF SOMETHING BEFORE YOU DECLARE YOU DON'T LIKE IT. OFTEN, AFTER THE HESITANT FIRST BITE, IT'S A HIT!

♥MOST CHILDREN LIKE AT LEAST A HANDFUL OF DIFFERENT FRUITS AND VEGGIES. KEEP TRYING NEW ONES, TOO—YOU'D BE SURPRISED HOW MANY CHILDREN ADORE SEAWEED AND CILANTRO, FOR EXAMPLE! GETTING THEM USED TO EATING FRUITS AND VEGGIES EACH DAY WILL HELP THEM TREMENDOUSLY TO FORM GOOD HABITS THAT WILL LAST A LIFETIME.

♥GETTING KIDS INVOLVED IN THE KITCHEN MAKES THEM MORE WILLING TO TRY NEW FOODS.

♥IF YOU MODEL HEALTHY EATING FOR YOUR CHILDREN, THEY'LL BE VERY LIKELY TO FOLLOW SUIT. IT'S GOOD MOTIVATION, ANYWAY, FOR US GROWN-UPS TO BE HEALTHIER!

Chapter Eighteen: A Glossary of Unusual Items and Terms

♦**Agar-Agar (agar):** This sea vegetable makes for a fabulous thickening agent when cooked. It's high in fiber and minerals and can be found in health food stores.

♦**Agave nectar:** This natural sweetener is made from the agave plant and is a delicious replacement for honey. It also boasts a lower glycemic index than many other sweeteners. It is available in health food stores and supermarkets.

♦**Amaranth:** This "supergrain" is ridiculously nutritious and was the revered food of the Aztecs. I highly recommend trying it, as it's easy to prepare and mild, yet nutty tasting. You can purchase amaranth in most health food stores.

♦**Amchur:** This is dried mango powder, commonly used in Indian food. It gives a sour component, so if you cannot find it, simply substitute a bit of lemon juice. It is most commonly found in Indian markets, including online Indian markets.

♦**Arrowroot:** This is a healthy, natural replacement for cornstarch. I like to buy it in a one pound bag (or in bulk), as it's *muuuuch* less expensive this way. Please see page 39 for more riveting details on this thickening secret agent.

♦**Asafetida:** This is also called "hing" and is used in Indian foods throughout this cookbook. It has a very distinct aroma and must be cooked to fully release its gorgeous flavor. It is available in most health food stores and in Indian markets. If nothing else, you can order it from an online Indian market.

♦**Bean thread noodles:** These are clear and shiny when cooked and are made from mung bean starch. They're available in Asian groceries or the Asian section of grocery stores. Please note that the size of bean thread "nests" varies by brand, so try to approximate the number of *ounces* called for in each recipe as best you can.

♦**Brown rice syrup:** This divine, thick syrup is made solely from brown rice! It's less sweet than other sweeteners and lends a mellow, rich flavor.

♦**Coconut oil:** This fat, once shunned by health-minded individuals, has now gained popularity. It seems that coconut oil may have been unfairly linked along with other saturated fats to an increase in cholesterol levels. It is, however, over fifty percent medium-chain fatty acids (the kind that are not stored as fat). The body instead metabolizes these kinds of fats into energy. Unrefined coconut oil also does not contain trans-fatty acids like hydrogenated oils do. It can be used successfully for a multitude of cooking and baking applications, even those requiring high heat.

♦**Dulse:** This is a sea vegetable that's very high in iron and minerals. I prefer the flaked form of dulse, although it is also available in strips. You can usually find dulse in any self-respecting health food store.

♦**Edamame:** These are also called "green soybeans." They are easily digestible, very high in fiber, and quite nutritious. I like to purchase the <u>shelled</u> edamame from the freezer section of health food stores (or supermarkets). Although normally served steamed, I find that they are perfectly delightful thawed and uncooked.

♦**Flax meal:** Also called ground flax, this is a great way to get your Omega-3s

(AS WELL AS LOTS OF FIBER), ALL WHILE EATING A MUFFIN! FLAX MEAL MAKES A GREAT EGG REPLACER WHEN COMBINED WITH BOILING WATER. IT'S ALSO A GREAT WAY TO BOOST THE NUTRITION AND FIBER LEVELS OF A SMOOTHIE, SHAKE, OR BREAD PRODUCT.

♦HEMP PROTEIN POWDER: AVAILABLE IN MOST HEALTH FOOD STORES, THIS SUPERFOOD IS THE ONLY PROTEIN POWDER I UNABASHEDLY RECOMMEND AS IT DOES NOT CONTAIN <u>ANY</u> JUNK! IT'S VERY HIGH IN FIBER, ESSENTIAL FATTY ACIDS, AND TURNS A SIMPLE SHAKE INTO A SATISFYING MEAL.

♦KALAMATA OLIVES: THIS VERY FLAVORFUL VARIETY OF OLIVE IS THE ONE I PREFER, WHICH MAY BECOME APPARENT AS YOU LEAF THROUGH THE RECIPE SECTION! KALAMATAS CAN BE FOUND IN MOST HEALTH FOOD STORES, SUPERMARKETS, AND ITALIAN GROCERIES. YUM!

♦KELP: THIS SEA VEGETABLE IS VERY HIGH IN MINERALS AND VITAMINS. I USE THE POWDERED FORM OF KELP, WHICH IS AVAILABLE IN MOST HEALTH FOOD STORES.

♦KOMBU: A DRIED SEAWEED THAT IS USUALLY PURCHASED IN "STRIP" FORM, KOMBU IS AVAILABLE PRE-PACKAGED IN MOST HEALTH FOOD STORES. IT IS A WONDERFUL FLAVOR ENHANCER AND ADDS MANY MINERALS AND NUTRIENTS TO ANYTHING IT'S COOKED WITH. IT ALSO GREATLY ASSISTS DIGESTION AND REDUCES THE LIKELIHOOD OF GAS WHEN ADDED TO A POT OF GRAINS, BEANS, OR SOUPS. IN OTHER WORDS, YOU CAN EXPECT KOMBU TO BE A TRIED AND TRUE FRIEND WHEN IT COMES TO EATING BEANS! TO USE, SIMPLY BREAK OFF A 2-INCH PIECE AND COOK IT ALONG WITH YOUR DISH (REMOVE THE KOMBU BEFORE SERVING).

♦MEXICAN OREGANO: THIS IS A TYPE OF OREGANO THAT IS CONDUCIVE TO, YOU GUESSED IT, MEXICAN FOODS. IF YOU CANNOT FIND IT, SIMPLY SUBSTITUTE REGULAR OREGANO. I WON'T TELL.

♦NON-HYDROGENATED MARGARINE: I PREFER THE "EARTH BALANCE" MARGARINE, AS IT TASTES GREAT AND DOES NOT CONTAIN ANY HYDROGENATED FATS. FOR ALL OF THE RECIPES IN THIS BOOK, I HAVE USED THE REGULAR (FULL FAT, NOT WHIPPED) TYPE OF EARTH BALANCE MARGARINE, WHICH IS AVAILABLE IN TUBS OR STICKS. HOWEVER, WHEN SIMPLY BUTTERING TOAST, ETC., I PREFER THE WHIPPED VERSION OF EARTH BALANCE AS IT'S LOWER IN FAT AND EASILY SPREADABLE.

♦NORI: THIS SEA VEGETABLE IS AVAILABLE PACKAGED IN SQUARE SHEETS IN MOST SUPERMARKETS, HEALTH FOOD STORES, AND ASIAN MARKETS. IT IS THE BASE FOR NORI ROLLS AND SUSHI. AS WITH ANY SEA VEGETABLE, NORI IS HIGH IN MINERALS AND VITAMINS. NORI SHEETS ARE AVAILABLE EITHER RAW OR TOASTED—EITHER TYPE IS FINE FOR ANY RECIPE IN THIS BOOK.

♦NUTRITIONAL YEAST: THIS POPULAR "SEASONING" IS GROWN ON MINERAL-RICH MOLASSES AND IS OFTEN USED AS A SAVORY, CHEESY FLAVOR ELEMENT. BE CAREFUL TO BUY A HIGH QUALITY BRAND, HOWEVER, AND DO NOT MISTAKE BREWER'S YEAST FOR NUTRITIONAL YEAST, AS THEY ARE VERY DIFFERENT. I USE THE VEGETARIAN SUPPORT FORMULA (RED STAR BRAND), AS IT'S HIGH IN MANY B-VITAMINS, INCLUDING VITAMIN B-12. IN ALL OF MY RECIPES, I HAVE USED THE POWDERED FORM. IF YOU USE NUTRITIONAL YEAST FLAKES INSTEAD, YOU MAY NEED TO ADD SLIGHTLY MORE AS THEY'RE LESS COMPACT WHEN MEASURED.

♦ORGANIC "WHITE" SUGAR: WHEN A RECIPE CALLS FOR THIS, IT MEANS THAT ONLY FINELY GRANULATED SUGAR SHOULD BE USED, AS SUCANAT OR BROWN SUGAR WOULD BE TOO "HEAVY" FOR THAT PARTICULAR DISH. ORGANIC "WHITE" SUGAR IS BASICALLY THE UNREFINED, ORGANIC VERSION OF PLAIN WHITE SUGAR. IT HAS A VERY LIGHT TAN COLOR AND IS AVAILABLE IN ANY HEALTH FOOD STORE AND IN MOST SUPERMARKETS.

♦PHYLLO (FILO): THIS IS A VERY THIN PASTRY THAT MAKES QUICK WORK OF MANY SEEMINGLY COMPLICATED DISHES. IT IS AVAILABLE IN THE FROZEN SECTION OF ANY SUPERMARKET. OTHER VARIETIES OF PHYLLO INCLUDE WHOLE WHEAT PHYLLO AND SPELT PHYLLO, AVAILABLE IN THE FROZEN SECTION OF SOME HEALTH FOOD STORES. PLEASE SEE PAGE 42 FOR PHYLLO TIPS.

♦QUINOA: Pronounced keen-wah, this is a high-energy grain-like food that is very rich in vitamins, calcium, protein, and fiber. It is quick and easy to prepare, and lends itself to a variety of dishes. It should be rinsed, however, before it's cooked to remove any bitter taste. Quinoa is available in health food stores and supermarkets.

♦RICE FLOUR: Although brown rice flour is preferable, white rice flour can also be used. However, do not substitute rice flour for whole wheat flour, pastry flour, white flour, or all-purpose gluten-free flour as it doesn't always work.

♦SEASONED SALT: There are organic brands on the market such as "Simply Organic" that I prefer for this type of seasoning. If you can't find this brand, however, another may be substituted as long as it does not contain MSG. Lawry's brand is available in most supermarkets and has an MSG-free variety.

♦SILKEN TOFU: This type of tofu is available on the shelf of most supermarkets and health food stores in aseptic packaging. It is softer and creamier in consistency, which makes it perfect for desserts or salad dressings. It will store at room temperature (unopened) for several months. For more tofu tips, see pages 42-43.

♦SUCANAT: This is a natural sweetener that contains both sugar cane and molasses. It is a "heavier" and more coarse type of sugar, so it is only used in recipes that aren't in need of a delicate sweetener. It lends a rich molasses flavor to the foods that it's added to. It can be found in most supermarkets and in any health food store.

♦TAHINI: This is also called sesame paste and is made from ground sesame seeds. Tahini is available raw or roasted. I generally prefer the raw, as it contains more of the fresh nutrients. Be sure to use a high quality tahini, as many commercial brands can taste bitter. High quality, organic tahini is available in health food stores and many supermarkets.

♦TAMARIND: This sour fruit is a delightful addition to Indian (and other) dishes. You can find "wet" tamarind in the refrigerated section of any Indian market and in many other ethnic markets as well. Here in Colorado, I buy mine from an Italian grocery!

♦TEMPEH: This fermented soy product is high in fiber and extremely nutritious. It should be marinated and cooked before serving to truly bring out its uniquely delicious flavor. There are many varieties of tempeh, but my personal favorite is the five-grain. Tempeh is available in the refrigerated or frozen section of any health food store and in many supermarkets.

♦TOASTED SESAME OIL: This is a very flavorful oil made from toasted sesame seeds. It cannot be replaced by regular sesame oil (or other oils), as the flavor is totally unique. Toasted sesame oil can be found in health food stores or in the Asian foods section of grocery stores.

♦WHOLE WHEAT PASTRY FLOUR: This flour is what makes it possible to create "traditional" tasting foods while still retaining whole-grain nutrition. In other words, your muffins will taste like they've been made with white flour, but will have all the fiber and nutrients of whole wheat! This magic flour is available in health food stores and supermarkets. For more information on whole wheat pastry flour, see page 40.

♦ZATAR: This delightful seasoning blend is made from thyme, sumac, and other spices. It is available in many health food stores or online. I have found the "Sahtein" zatar (by Jerusalem Foods) to be quite delicious and also to have a very long shelf life.

Green and Blue Just for You!

I have personally found it very handy to have a reference list of "green" and "blue" recipes, especially when I'm doing the Two-Week Ultimate Radiant Health Plan (page 26). If you find it handy too, then the next few pages should make you smile. For those of you who haven't read the book like a novel thus far, you may wish to refer to page 45 for a green and blue recipe refresher course.

GREEN RECIPES:

"GREEN" BREAKFASTS:
•Frozen Bananas, 47
•Mango Ginger-Mint Power Smoothie, 47
•Virtuous Vanilla Shake, 48
•Four Goodness Shake, 48
•Triple Green Purple Power Shake, 50
•Super Antioxidant Smoothie, 50
•Berry Good Morning Shake, 51
•Tropical Smoothie, 51
•Indian Spiced Supergrain Cereal, 52
•Juice of Empowerment, 54
•Kiddie Power Drink, 54
•Carrot-Orange Juice, 55
•Carrot-Apple-Ginger Juice, 55
•Magical Multigrain Pancake Mix, 57
•Sweet Banana Pancakes, 58
•Apple Cinnamon Flapjacks, 58
•Raspberry Lemon Zest Pancakes, 59
•Earth's Healthiest Waffles, 60
•Grandma's Favorite French Toast, 62

"GREEN" STARTERS:
•Sourdough Bruschetta (if made using
  whole or sprouted grain bread), 66
•Delectable Lowfat "Egg Rolls," 67
•Three Citrus Asparagus, 69
•Fresh Thai Spring Rolls, 72
•Southwest Spring Rolls, 73
•Mango-Cucumber Spring Rolls, 74
•Vietnamese Spring Rolls, 75
•Nori Rolls with Lemon-Lime Soy Sauce
  (hold the Creamy Ginger-Wasabi), 76
•Dolmadas, 85

"GREEN" DESSERT:
•Ultra Light Blackberry Cobbler (if made
  using whole grain flour), 223

"GREEN" SIMPLE SIDES:
•Moroccan Quinoa, 88
•Zesty Kale with Cranberries, 89
•Cilantro-Lime Rice, 89
•Ful Mudhamas, 90
•Cucumber-Dill Toss, 90
•Anna's Zucchini, 91
•Krazy Kale Chips, 91
•Kid's Kale, 92
•Perfect Pinto Beans, 95
•Yummy Fat-Free Refried Beans, 96
•Zen Rice with Seaweed Gomasio, 99
•Oven Roasted Cauliflower with Rosemary and
  Garlic, 100
•Quick and Healthy Herbed Garlic Bread, 102
•Seasoned Indian (brown) Basmati Rice, 102

"GREEN" SALADS:
•Spinach-Strawberry Salad, 104
•Baby Greens with Light Ginger-Miso Dressing, 104
•Princess Salad, 106
•Indian Kuchumber Salad, 108
•Spinach, Orange, & Toasted Almond Salad, 109
•Chili-Ginger Cabbage, 113
•Shiitake, Walnut, & Dried Cranberry Salad, 113
•Japanese Salad with Ginger Magic Dressing, 115
•Black Bean, Cilantro, and Apricot Salad, 115

"GREEN" RAW FOODS:
•Divine Mango Pie, 183
•Moroccan Barley-Spinach Toss, 184
•Nori Rawls with Sprouted Barley, 185-186
•Main Dish Salad with Tahini-Lemon Dressing, 186
•Almond Milk, 187
•Almond-Banana Power Morning Shake, 187
•Zucchini Chips to Dry For, 188
•Raw Radiance Superballs, 190
•Sprouting/Sprouts, 191-192

"GREEN" SAUCES & DRESSINGS:

"GREEN" THIS, THAT,

AND BREAD:

"GREEN" ENTRÉES:

"GREEN" SOUPS:

Other "Green" Food Ideas:

- Fruits and vegetables are the *essence* of "green," especially when eaten fresh, organic, and raw!
- Lowfat popcorn is a great "green" treat! Pop the kernels in a minimum (up to 1 tablespoon) of coconut oil and sprinkle lightly with sea salt and/or nutritional yeast. For a flavor kick, sprinkle a little hot sauce and garlic on there too!
- Cooked or sprouted whole grains, lightly seasoned, make a nourishing and filling side or main dish. We make a staple out of cooked quinoa with a light drizzle of olive oil and/or lemon juice and sea salt.
- Cooked whole grains, beans, or whole grain pasta can be topped with any of the "green" sauces or dressings.
- Potatoes have an unfair bad rap! They are a "green" whole food, and can be baked and served with fresh chives and a light drizzle of olive oil. I also like to slice a cooked, cooled baked potato and fry it in a teaspoon of coconut or olive oil for quick, "un-fried" potatoes.
- High fiber cereals with nondairy milk are quick, easy, and light.
- You can *bake* just about any veggie (seasoned lightly with spices, oil, and/or vinegar) for a delicious, healthy snack. Broccoli, kale, cauliflower, carrots, beets, you name it—they all work great!
- Toss some chickpeas with a little oil and the seasonings of your choice and bake until crisp.
- Pan-fry tempeh strips and veggies in tamari, sliced garlic, and a teaspoon of coconut oil until browned. Wrap in a whole grain tortilla with lettuce, onions, ketchup, pickles, and mustard. Yummy!

BLUE RECIPES:

Weekly Journal Planner

Here's an inspirational planner that can be used to keep you focused and on target. Each week, you can photocopy it, fill it out, and post it somewhere that it can't be ignored. Be sure to give yourself lots of positive reinforcement (including tallying your wins under "I Did It!") when you fulfill your goals!

IN THE BEGINNING:

•General notes on my state of inner and outer wellness at the beginning of this week:

•Priorities this week (see pages 18-19): _____
•Starting weight: _____

GOALS FOR THIS WEEK:

(REMEMBER TO KEEP THEM 100% REALISTIC AND DOABLE AS THIS IS THE FOUNDATION YOU'LL BE BUILDING ON FOR LIFE—YOU CAN ALWAYS EXCEED THESE MINIMUMS!):

♥This week I will use this affirmation (see pages 24-25): _____
at the following times: _____

♥This week I will meditate (see pages 20-22) at the following time(s): _____

♥I really will exercise a total of _____ minutes this week, for an average of _____ minutes per day.

♥I will be grateful for _____ things every day (see page 20 for gratitude tips—you'll thank me later).

♥I will reflect on my day _____ time(s) this week (see page 25).

♥I will look in the mirror and force myself to see how beautiful and lovable I am _____ times this week. I will say "I love myself" as I look at my fabulous reflection (see pages 22-23).

♥I will use my amazing, powerful imagination to visualize myself, my daily habits, and my life as I ideally wish them to be _____ time(s) this week (see pages 17-18). And I'll have fun doing it!

♥I will eat _____ veggies each day and _____ fruit(s) each day! My other food-related goals are to: _____
_____ this week.

I DID IT!

•Monday, I fulfilled _____ goals!   •Friday, I fulfilled _____ goals!
•Tuesday, I fulfilled _____ goals!   •Saturday, I fulfilled _____ goals!
•Wednesday, I fulfilled _____ goals!   •Sunday, I fulfilled _____ goals!
•Thursday, I fulfilled _____ goals!

Weekly Menu and Shopping Planner

Here is a menu planning and shopping guide that can be photocopied—or simply used as a tool to create your own masterful plan. For more on the subject of menu planning, please see pages 36-38.

MEAL PLANNING DAY: _____

COOKING DAY(S): _____

ITEMS ON HAND TO USE UP A.S.A.P (BEFORE THEY GO BAD!):

BREAKFASTS: _____
- *example*: lemon water and fresh fruit   •
- •   •
- •   •
- •   •

LUNCHES: _____
- •   •
- •   •
- •   •
- •   •

QUICK DINNERS OR MINI-MEALS THAT CAN BE MADE IN A HURRY: _____
- •   •
- •   •
- •   •
- •   •

COMPLETE DINNERS: _____
- •   •
- •   •
- •   •
- •   •

DESSERT OF THE WEEK: _____
- •

Shopping Guide

"I will stay focused and totally in control while at the supermarket!" Say this like you mean it.

SHOPPING DAY: _____

GROCERIES FOR THE WEEK:

Recommendations and Resources

BOOKS:

- *THE NEW WHOLE FOODS ENCYCLOPEDIA* (BY REBECCA WOOD): I CANNOT, CANNOT RECOMMEND THIS BOOK ENOUGH! IT IS MY FOOD "BIBLE" AND CONTAINS A WEALTH OF INFORMATION.
- *LOCAL WILD LIFE* BY KATRINA BLAIR (WWW.TURTLELAKEREFUGE.ORG)
- *RAW FOOD MADE EASY FOR 1 OR 2 PEOPLE* (BY JENNIFER CORNBLEET)
- *THE McDOUGALL PLAN* (OR ANYTHING ELSE BY DR. JOHN McDOUGALL)
- *THE AMERICAN VEGETARIAN COOKBOOK* (AND OTHER WORKS BY MARILYN DIAMOND)

RESTAURANTS THAT ARE A CUT ABOVE:

- *CHICAGO DINER* (CHICAGO, ILLINOIS): SOME OF THE YUMMIEST VEGAN FOOD I'VE EVER HAD!
- *McFOSTER'S NATURAL KIND* (OMAHA, NEBRASKA): VERY VEGAN FRIENDLY
- *ELIA'S* (SOUTH BEND, INDIANA): WARM SERVICE & VEGAN FRIENDLY FOODS
- *UDUPI CAFÉ* (INDIANAPOLIS, INDIANA): DELICIOUS VEGETARIAN INDIAN CUISINE
- *MILLENNIUM RESTAURANT* (SAN FRANCISCO, CALIFORNIA): GOURMET VEGAN CUISINE
- *WATERCOURSE* (DENVER, COLORADO): ANYTHING ON THE MENU CAN BE MADE VEGAN...YUM!
- *SUNFLOWER VEGETARIAN RESTAURANT* (VIENNA, VIRGINIA): MOSTLY VEGAN & VERY YUMMY

PACKAGED FOODS I LOVE:

- *EZEKIEL 4:9 SPROUTED GRAIN BREADS AND TORTILLAS* (FOOD FOR LIFE BRAND): THIS FLOURLESS BREAD IS JUST ABOUT AS HEALTHY AS IT GETS! MY PERSONAL FAVORITE IS THE SESAME. IT'S AVAILABLE IN THE FROZEN SECTION OF HEALTH FOOD STORES (AND MANY SUPERMARKETS).
- *MARY'S GONE CRACKERS "STICKS AND TWIGS"* ARE A YUMMY WHOLE FOOD SNACK FOR ON-THE-GO.
- *ARTEMISIA BOTANICALS PRODUCTS*: I AM SO LUCKY TO KNOW THIS FABULOUS HERBALIST! SHE MAKES THE MOST DIVINE TEAS, GREEN POWDER, HERB TINCTURES, MEDICINES, AND BODY CARE PRODUCTS I'VE EVER USED. YOU CAN REACH HER AT ARTEMISIABOTANICALS@HOTMAIL.COM.
- *GT'S SYNERGY KOMBUCHA*: I'M OFFICIALLY ADDICTED. TRY THE GUAVA, GRAPE, AND SUPERFRUITS.
- *TURTLE LAKE REFUGE RAW FOODS*: SO GOOD! WWW.TURTLELAKEREFUGE.ORG
- *EARTH BALANCE NON-HYDROGENATED MARGARINE*: SEE PAGE 252 FOR MORE INFORMATION.
- *NANCY'S SOY YOGURT*: THIS IS THE ONLY NONDAIRY YOGURT ON THE MARKET THAT I UNABASHEDLY RECOMMEND. IT'S FRESH, NOURISHING, AND JUST "FEELS" HEALTHY!
- *WOODSTOCK FARMS FROZEN SLICED SHIITAKE MUSHROOMS*: THEY TASTE WONDERFULLY FRESH, SO I CAN ONLY IMAGINE THAT THEY'RE USING VERY HIGH QUALITY MUSHROOMS.
- *EDEN BRAND FOODS*: IF I WERE TO USE A PACKAGED SOYMILK, EDEN WOULD BE MY CHOICE. THEIR QUALITY FOODS ALWAYS IMPRESS ME AS BEING MADE WITH A HIGHER AWARENESS AND CARE.

KITCHEN ITEMS:

- *SANLINX "SOYAPOWER" NONDAIRY MILK MAKER*: AVAILABLE ONLINE, THIS FABULOUS SMALL APPLIANCE PAYS FOR ITSELF IN NO TIME. IT ALSO ENSURES THE FRESHEST, LEAST PROCESSED MILK POSSIBLE, WITHOUT ADDED SWEETENERS OR PRESERVATIVES.
- *PAMPERED CHEF GARLIC PRESS*: SO WELL DESIGNED, IT MAKES PRESSING GARLIC A SNAP!
- *CUISINART* BRAND FOOD PROCESSORS

Index

A handy reference section for you and yours—in an exciting and innovative alphabetical format!

E

The Blank Slate

By popular demand, here are a few blank pages to make your own notes, write down inspiring thoughts and ideas, or draw pictures of the author with blackened teeth and elf ears.

www.radianthealth-innerwealth.com

May you uncover your own natural, beautiful state of radiant health and inner wealth that is yours for the taking!

Thank you!